# how2become

# 300 FPAS Situational Judgement Test Questions

**www.How2Become.com**

As part of this product you have also received FREE access to online tests that will help you to pass Situational Judgement Tests

To gain access, simply go to:

# www.MyPsychometricTests.co.uk

Get more products for passing any test at:

# www.How2Become.com

Orders: Please contact How2Become Ltd, Suite 14, 50 Churchill Square Business Centre, Kings Hill, Kent ME19 4YU.

You can order through Amazon.co.uk under ISBN: 9781912370054, via the website www.How2Become.com or through Gardners.com.

ISBN: 9781912370054

First published in 2018 by How2Become Ltd.

Typeset by Katie Noakes for How2Become Ltd.

## Disclaimer

# CONTENTS

Introduction                                              7

Practice Questions Section 1                             11

Answers to Practice Questions Section 1                 107

Practice Questions Section 2                            201

Answers to Practice Questions Section 2                 303

# INTRODUCTION

Hello, and welcome to *300 FPAS Situational Judgement Test Questions*. In this book, we will give you all of the information that you need on how to pass the FPAS Situational Judgement Test section. Before we start testing you, let's run through some basic information on what FPAS is, and what the test involves.

## FPAS

FPAS stands for Foundation Programme Application System. This is an online system used within the UK, to help final year medical students apply for training positions. The FPAS is run by the UK Foundation Programme Office. To gain a place with the Foundation Programme, you will first need to complete an application form, which is done online. In this form, you will need to answer a number of mandatory application form sections. There are 10 sections in total, in which you will need to fill in details about your personal information, qualifications, education, references and preferences.

Assuming you meet the required entry standards, you will then be eligible to sit the Situational Judgement Test.

## FPAS SITUATIONAL JUDGEMENT TEST

Situational judgement is a common form of assessment. It is used by many employers these days, to ascertain whether a potential employee is the right fit for their organisation. Situational judgement tests will evaluate your decision making, and allow potential employers to see whether your code of ethics and values match up with theirs. The majority of situational judgement tests do not have right or wrong answers, and simply come down to how an employer assesses the answers of the candidate against their own behavioural/organisational expectations. However, the FPAS SJT does have right and wrong answers, along with a specific mark scheme.

The FPAS Situational Judgement Test (FPAS SJT) will provide you with medical based scenarios. These questions will focus around testing your medical principles and ethics, and focus on qualities such professionalism, bedside manner, teamwork and your ability to cope whilst under pressure. You will not need a sustained level of clinical knowledge to complete these questions.

In order to find out what date the test will be run on, for the year that you are applying, you should speak directly to your medical school, or contact the UK Foundation Progamme themselves. They will also be able to provide you with advice on how to book your test.

## FPAS SJT QUESTIONS

In total, there are 70 questions in the examination, and you will be given 2 hours and 20 minutes to complete the exam. The test is scored out of 50.00, and the majority of candidates will score between 20.01 and 50.00.

The exam is split into two sections:

**Section 1.** In this section, you will be provided with a medical scenario, and 5 answer options.

Your job is to rank these answer options, with 1 being the most appropriate and 5 being the least appropriate. There is a total score of 20 available for each question, with each correct ranking being scored 4 points, and 3 if you score one answer lower by one (for example, if you put option A as 2, when it should have been 1). The further off you are on each option, the lower you will score. This is one of the things that makes the test so challenging. If you rank one answer option wrong, then you'll get another one wrong too, and therefore one wrong answer can snowball and greatly impact the rest of your marks for that question.

Section 1 accounts for approximately two-thirds of the entire test.

**Section 2.** In this section, the questions are slightly different. Once again you will be given a medical scenario, but now you will be given 8 answer options. Your job is to choose the best 3 answers. There is a total of 12 marks per question here, with each correct answer being worth 4 marks.

How to Answer

In this section, we'll give you some basic tips on things to consider when answering the questions, which should helpfully make your life much easier.

The central aim of the FPAS SJT is to establish whether you have the decision making skills to work within a hospital, and whether your ethics and principles are in line with what would be expected. When ranking the answers from 1-5, you'll need to take into account a range of factors, including medical ethics, professionalism and consent. Each question will present you with different things to assess and consider, before coming to a decision. For this reason, it can be hard to establish a precise system for weighing up the value of answer options. In some questions, you might be presented with 4 awful options and just 1 good option, and you'll then need to assess which of the bad options is 'the least bad'. Similarly, you might be given 4 great options and 1 terrible option – again you would need to assess which of the good options is the best. Sometimes, placing the top and bottom answer is easy, but ordering the answers in the middle can prove to be quite tricky. With this in mind, here are some guidelines on how to go about breaking down difficult scenarios:

1. Is the patient safe, or will this harm them? Patient safety should always be your number one priority. If you are making a decision that will impact upon a patient, then you should make the decision with the intention of benefitting their care. If you feel that one of the answer options will harm or negatively impact the patient, then this should go (at the very least) near the bottom of your answer order. There will be a number of questions focusing around topics such as confidentiality, and respecting patient decisions.

2. Try and think about the wider implications of each decision. For example, if you have a patient thrown out by security, then how is this going to impact them, how is it going to impact the hospital, and how is it going to impact you?

3. Think about how your decision could impact the behaviour and feelings of your colleagues, if appropriate. Could this upset those around you? Could it have a negative impact on them? It's important that you can demonstrate good teamwork, and be a supportive outlet for your colleagues.

4. Consider your level of expertise when working as a junior doctor. Are you qualified to make this decision, or would it be better to consult someone more senior? The assessors want to

be able to see that you have the wisdom and foresight to understand your own limitations, and not to try and take on tasks that you aren't prepared or ready for. Try and be pragmatic. Think about whether the action that the answer option is demanding is realistic and possible at that time.

When answering the second part of the test, you should take a similar approach. In this test, you won't need to rank the options, but you will still need to provide the three best responses – and the above framework should help you to do this.

It's extremely important, when taking the FPAS SJT, that you answer the questions based on established medical ethics, and the guidelines laid out by the General Medical Council (GMC). You can read all about these principles at the following link:

**http://www.foundationprogramme.nhs.uk/pages/resource-bank/fp-afp**

Along with this, you are also expected to have some knowledge of medical law, and essential criteria that you would use when making decisions, such as the mental health act and the mental capacity act. Again, the above link should provide you with sustained information about all of these factors.

Now that we've given you a full introduction to the FPAS SJT, let's get started with some practice questions! This book is divided into two parts, with 150 questions based on section 1 of the test, and 150 questions based on section 2. You can check your answers after each section, and match them up against our explanations.

# PRACTICE QUESTIONS
# SECTION 1

In the below questions, you will be given a scenario, and then asked to rank the answer options from 1-5 – with 1 being the most appropriate and 5 being the least appropriate. There are 150 questions in total, and you can find the answers to these at the end of the section.

> **Q1.** You are a Foundation Year 1 (FY1), working on the ward round. You have spent the past half an hour dealing with a sick patient. When you arrive at your next patient – who is 80 years old and suffering from cancer – he starts to shout at you:
>
> *'Where the hell have you have been? I'm hungry!'*
>
> *'I'm sorry sir, I was dealing with another patient.'*
>
> *'That's not good enough. Can you fetch a senior doctor please? I don't think you should be working on this ward anymore. Hopefully you'll get the sack.'*

**Take a look at the responses below, and then rank them from most appropriate to least appropriate.**

A. Apologise to the patient, and go fetch a senior doctor to deal with the situation.

B. Wheel the patient to the exit doors, and wish him good luck. Rudeness will result in immediate discharge.

C. Leave the patient and go find a senior nurse. She will be able to offer you advice.

D. Explain to the patient that although you can appreciate his concerns, he is not the only person on the ward. Assure him that he now has your attention.

E.  Go fetch a senior doctor.

| 1 | 2 | 3 | 4 | 5 |
|---|---|---|---|---|
| D | A | C | E | B |

> **Q2.** You are an FY2, working in the paediatric ward. A seven year-old boy has come into the ward, complaining of severe back pain. His mother is present too. The boy proceeds to tell you that he has been experiencing back pain ever since his mother pushed him down the stairs. His mother is incredulous at this. She grabs the boy by his arm, and starts shaking him, demanding that he tell the truth.
>
> *'I am telling the truth, you pushed me!'*
>
> *'Stop telling lies! You know what happens to liars…'*
>
> *'I'm not a liar.'*
>
> *'Well then…you're a snitch! Just you wait until we get home.'*

**Take a look at the responses below, and then rank them from most appropriate to least appropriate.**

A. Tell the boy to stop lying.

B. Ask the mother to leave the room, so that you can conduct a full physical examination of the boy, checking for signs of abuse.

C. Call social services. The mother has essentially admitted to her guilt.

D. Ask the boy to leave the room with a nurse, so that you can further question the mother.

E. Prescribe the boy some painkillers for his back pain, and then discharge him. There is no substantial evidence for abuse here.

| 1 | 2 | 3 | 4 | 5 |
|---|---|---|---|---|
| B | D | C | E | A |

**Q3.** You are working in the paediatric ward. Just before you are due to start your shift, one of the senior doctors approaches you. He asks you to tie your hair back, and take out your earrings, in line with the hospital uniform policy. After reading the uniform policy only yesterday, you are aware that there is a hair-tie policy, but there is nothing in the rules about earrings.

**Take a look at the responses below, and then rank them from most appropriate to least appropriate.**

A. Tell the doctor that although you are happy to tie your hair back, you won't be taking out your earrings.

B. File an internal complaint against the doctor. Sexism in the workplace is not acceptable.

C. Explain to the doctor that there is nothing in the rules about wearing earrings. Refuse to tie your hair back, as a result of his mistake.

D. Apologise to the doctor. Tie your hair back, and take out your earrings.

E. Apologise to the doctor. Tie your hair back, but query him about the earrings.

| 1 | 2 | 3 | 4 | 5 |
|---|---|---|---|---|
| E | A | D | C | B |

**Q4.** You are an FY1, working in your local hospital. Over the past few days, you have been treating a patient with severe damage to his right leg. The patient claims that he fell out of a window. Throughout the treatment, the man's girlfriend has maintained a constant vigil by his bedside. When his girlfriend leaves the room to grab some coffee, the patient confesses to you that he is having an affair, and that he fell out of the window when his mistress's husband came home early. His girlfriend does not know about this.

Later on, whilst the patient is sleeping, the man's girlfriend confesses to you that she has never been so happy, and that she is planning on giving up her job to move away with him.

**Take a look at the responses below, and then rank them from most appropriate to least appropriate.**

A. Immediately tell the man's girlfriend that he is cheating on her. You have a moral responsibility.

B. Smile and nod. Tell the woman that hopefully her boyfriend will be patched up soon.

C. Ask the woman not to discuss personal matters with you.

D. Wake the man up and announce that he has something to tell his girlfriend.

E. When the patient wakes up, inform him that although you are bound by confidentiality, he should consider telling his girlfriend the truth.

| 1 | 2 | 3 | 4 | 5 |
|---|---|---|---|---|
| B | E | C | D | A |

**Q5.** It's Thursday, and you are working on the ward round. At the end of the session, a senior colleague pulls you to one side, and starts to berate you. He claims that you are a pathetic excuse for a doctor, and that you will never be a leader. He tells you that if you don't start improving, he'll go to those in charge and demand you are thrown out.

You feel as if you have done really well today, and are shocked by this.

**Take a look at the responses below, and then rank them from most appropriate to least appropriate.**

A. Ask your colleague what exactly you have done wrong. Tell him that you are really surprised by the criticism.

B. Tell your colleague that he needs to calm down and treat you with more respect, if he wants you to take him seriously.

C. Break down and cry. Hopefully he'll feel sorry for you.

D. Calmly but firmly tell your colleague that you do not need to put up with such abuse, and that he can come and speak to you when he has calmed down.

E. Ask your colleague for guidance on what you've done wrong, but make it clear that this is not an appropriate way for him to address you in future.

| 1 | 2 | 3 | 4 | 5 |
|---|---|---|---|---|
| E | A | D | B | C |

(handwritten: 1 E ✓, 2 A ✗D, 3 D ✗A, 4 B ✓, 5 C ✓)

---

**Q6.** It's Friday night, and you are working late at the hospital. One of your patients is just about to go in for surgery, and you are having a last-minute consultation with your friend – who will be working on the surgical team for the operation. Whilst you converse with him, it becomes apparent to you that your friend has been drinking alcohol. When you question him over this, he assures you that it will be fine, and heads off to prep for surgery.

**Take a look at the responses below, and then rank them from most appropriate to least appropriate.**

A. Go straight to the head of surgery's office, and inform him about your friend. Hopefully he'll be fired – you never liked him much anyway.

B. Go straight to the lead surgeon for the operation, and inform him about your friend's condition.

C. Trust in your friend's ability. A little bit of alcohol never hurt anyone.

D. Follow after your friend and try to persuade him to pull out of the operation.

E. Tell your friend that if he isn't honest with the lead surgeon about the fact he's been drinking, you will tell the surgeon yourself.

| 1 | 2 | 3 | 4 | 5 |
|---|---|---|---|---|
| D | E | B | A | C |

(handwritten: 1 D ✗ B, 2 E ✓, 3 B ✗D, 4 A ✓, 5 C ✓)

---

**Q7.** It's the end of the week, and a patient who has been under your care is getting discharged. The patient in question has been in the hospital for over a month now, and it's been a rough ride. Luckily, the patient in question has pulled through, and they are now completely healthy. As they are leaving, the patient pulls you to one side and offers you a box of chocolates, as a thank you for your hard work. The hospital that you work at has a strict policy of not receiving gifts from patients.

**Take a look at the responses below, and then rank them from most appropriate to least appropriate.**

A. Accept the chocolates. Nobody is going to know.

B. Thank the patient for their gift, but politely decline. Explain to them that you were just doing your job.

C. Ask the patient to share the chocolates with you over a dinner date.

D. Ask one of the senior doctors about whether you can keep the chocolates.

E. Tell the patient that for your hard work, you expected a better gift.

| 1 | 2 | 3 | 4 | 5 |
|---|---|---|---|---|
| B | D | A | C | E |
| | | | X E | X C |

> **Q8.** You have been working at your current hospital for a period of 3 weeks. Unfortunately, you have been having some issues with one of the senior doctors. The individual in question keeps making mean spirited remarks towards you, and is extremely condescending. You feel that he is making the hospital quite difficult to work in. You have asked him to stop, he has simply continued.

**Take a look at the responses below, and then rank them from most appropriate to least appropriate.**

A. Go straight to senior management and file a complaint. They are the best placed people to deal with this.

B. Confide in another doctor, and ask them what you should do.

C. Take physical retaliation against your colleague. If he won't listen to verbal warnings, then there's only one solution.

D. Quit. There are plenty of other jobs, in other hospitals. You don't need to put up with this.

E. Tell your colleague that if he doesn't stop then you are going to report him to senior management.

| 1 | 2 | 3 | 4 | 5 |
|---|---|---|---|---|
| E | B | A | D | C |
| X A | X E | X B | | |

> **Q9.** You are an FY2 student in an emergency care department. Over the past year, the hospital has taken on a number of junior doctors. One day, a group of the doctors approaches you. They are led by a man named Chris:
>
> **Chris:** 'We're fed up, mate. The training at this hospital is appalling. I've barely learned anything since I started here.'
>
> **Greg:** 'Everything about this place stinks. From the way the senior staff treat their patients, to the bogs on floor two. Low standards.'
>
> **Kerry:** 'Last week one of the surgical team was watching the football on his phone in the middle of an operation. It's unacceptable!'

**Take a look at the responses below, and then rank them from most appropriate to least appropriate.**

A. 'If you don't like it, there's the door. I'm sure there's plenty of hospitals who would love to take on a bunch of ungrateful trainees...'

B. 'Thank you for letting me know your concerns. If you would like, I can accompany you to a senior doctor's office, so that we can discuss this further.'

C. 'I'm sorry to hear that you are unhappy. If it helps, I am happy to offer one-to-one tuition, to get you all get up to speed with things...I charge £30 per hour.'

D. 'That's terrible to hear. I will bring these issues to the concern of a senior member of staff immediately. Please be assured that we will deal with this as a matter of priority.'

E. 'Okay, thank you for bringing this to my attention. My advice is to list all of these issues down, and then we can bring it to the attention of a senior member of staff.'

| 1 | 2 | 3 | 4 | 5 |
|---|---|---|---|---|
| E | B | D | C | A |

18/20

Q10. You are a medical student at university. One day, as you are preparing for your exams, your friend Melanie approaches you:

**Melanie:** 'Can you keep a secret?'

**You:** 'Sure! What's up?'

**Melanie:** 'I've got hold of the answers for the Medical Law exam...here, take a look! We can copy them down and then use them in the real thing.'

**Take a look at the responses below, and then rank them from most appropriate to least appropriate.**

A. Take a pen and quickly jot down the answers. This will save you a whole lot of time revising.

B. Tell Melanie that cheating is unethical, and that you'll play no part in this.

C. Tell Melanie that there's no guarantee those are the actual answers, and therefore she could be wasting her time.

D. Announce loudly to everyone in the library that Melanie is cheating.

E. Go straight to the head of the course, and report Melanie for her behaviour.

| 1 | 2 | 3 | 4 | 5 |
|---|---|---|---|---|
| C | B | E | D | A |

**Q11.** You are taking part in medical ward rounds. The final patient in the session is a 70 year-old woman. In order to deal with her condition, the consultant leading the round – Marvin, prescribes the woman a course of antibiotics. You immediately notice that the dosage the consultant has prescribed, is far too much. So does another intern, named Karen.

**Karen:** 'Oi, Marvin. Are you sure that's correct?'

**Marvin:** 'Excuse me?'

**Karen:** 'The dosage you've prescribed is far too high. With her symptoms, you could actually kill her.'

**Marvin:** 'Please keep your opinions to yourself, Karen. I am the lead consultant here for a reason, I know what I'm doing.'

**Karen:** 'More like the lead idiot. You are putting the patient at risk.'

**Take a look at the responses below, and then rank them from most appropriate to least appropriate.**

A. Speak up. Tell Marvin that Karen is actually correct, and query the dosage yourself.

B. Say nothing. This is not your argument to get involved in.

C. Tell Karen that she should be more respectful towards Marvin, but query the dosage yourself.

D. Change the dosage yourself, without telling Marvin.

E. Wait until rounds have finished, and then approach Marvin in private, to query the dosage.

| 1 | 2 | 3 | 4 | 5 |
|---|---|---|---|---|
| C | A | E | D | B |

**Q12.** You are working in the hospital's morning 'walk-in' session, with a trainee named Joel. A girl enters the room. She informs you that she is 15 years old, and that she fears she might be pregnant. After conducting a routine pregnancy test, the following conversation takes place:

**You:** 'Well, I can tell you that you aren't pregnant.'

**Patient:** 'Oh thank god, what a relief!'

**You:** 'I'm glad you are happy with that.'

**Patient:** 'Very! Please could you prescribe me with some contraceptive medication?'

**Joel:** 'Legally, we can't. You are underage.'

PRACTICE QUESTIONS SECTION 1 19

Take a look at the responses below, and then rank them from most appropriate to least appropriate.

A. Inform Joel that he is incorrect. Tell the girl that you are happy to prescribe her with contraceptive pills, but that first you need to ask her a few routine questions about her relationship.

B. Perform a citizen's arrest. The girl has broken the law by having underage sex – she must be detained.

C. Prescribe her the pills.

D. Go and find a senior manager, to see what they think you should do.

E. Prescribe the girl with the pills, and give her your work/office contact number, so that she has someone to talk to about future sexual health issues.

| 1 | 2 | 3 | 4 | 5 |
|---|---|---|---|---|
| A | E | C | D | B |

Q13. You are working in the paediatric ward. One of your patients is a 6 year-old boy, who has been admitted with severe headaches. Earlier today, you sent the boy for an MRI scan, and are now waiting for the results. As you come back into the ward following your lunchbreak, the boy's mother approaches you. She is extremely unhappy:

'Where the hell are those MRI results?'

'I'm sorry Madam, we are still waiting for them to come through. We'll know by tomorrow at the latest.'

'That's not good enough! My son could be dead by then. I want the results NOW!'

Take a look at the responses below, and then rank them from most appropriate to least appropriate.

A. Inform the woman that there is nothing you can do to speed up the results, but that you will bring them to the family as soon as you hear anything.

B. Call security, and ask them to throw the woman and her son out of the hospital.

C. Sympathise with the woman, and tell her that you will do your very best to bring her the results as soon as possible.

D. Ask the woman to take a seat, and try to calm down. Once she's calmed down, explain to her that rudeness won't make the scan go any faster.

E. Inform the woman that as a result of her rudeness, it will now be even longer before she receives the scan results.

C, D, A, E, B

| 1 | 2 | 3 | 4 | 5 |
|---|---|---|---|---|
|   |   |   |   |   |

Q14. You are working on the night shift at the hospital. One of your patients is a 40 year old man – named David. David is suffering from stomach cancer, and he is in crippling pain. David has no immediate friends or family, and has had no visitors whilst in the hospital. Although David's chances of survival are slim, he has not yet been diagnosed as terminal.

When you go to check on David, he requests that you triple his medication, in a bid to end his life. He tells you that he doesn't want to carry on dealing with such pain. He claims that nobody will miss him, and that the kindest thing you could do is to help him die.

**Take a look at the responses below, and then rank them from most appropriate to least appropriate.**

A. Agree to help David die. Triple the dosage.

B. Ask David to try and explain to you why he feels this way.

C. Book David an appointment with the palliative care team, for the next morning.

D. Tell David that you cannot help him to die, but that you'll try and find a doctor who might be more willing to do so.

E. Tell David that you cannot do this for him. Try to encourage him towards fighting the illness.

| 1 | 2 | 3 | 4 | 5 |
|---|---|---|---|---|
| B | E | C | D | A |

Q15. You are working on the geriatric ward of the hospital. A patient approaches you, and complains about one of the nurses in the ward. He says that the nurse in question was extremely rough in dealing with him, had cold hands, and failed to provide him with his medication. He demands to know what you are going to do about it.

**Take a look at the responses below, and then rank them from most appropriate to least appropriate.**

A. Fetch the patient's medication, before finding the nurse responsible for this, and ensuring that she apologises profusely to the patient.

B. Tell the patient that you don't have time to deal with ridiculous complaints.

C. Apologise to the patient, and fetch his medication. Following this, find the nurse responsible, and question her over her behaviour.

D. Apologise to the patient. Ask him to come with you to the senior manager's office, so that you can file an internal review against the nurse.

E. Fetch the patient's medication for him.

| 1 | 2 | 3 | 4 | 5 |
|---|---|---|---|---|
| C ✓ | E x A | A x E | D ✓ | B ✓ |

---

**Q16.** You have been working in your local hospital for a period of just over a year now. Over the past two days, a number of patients have come to you to discuss a sensitive issue. Amongst these patients, are Mr Wiggins, Mrs Flack and Mr Earnshaw:

**Mr Wiggins:** *'I don't mean to be rude, or cause a fuss…but I'm having a bit of a problem with Dr Pardew. I think that maybe he doesn't realise about the smell he gives off…or I don't know. I'm sorry, I know it sounds awful to say. Is there any chance I could see someone else instead?'*

**Mrs Flack:** *'I'm terribly sorry but I just really don't think I can deal with Dr Pardew anymore… it's the smell. I don't know whether he hasn't washed for a few days…I feel a bit rude just saying it to be honest, sorry.'*

**Mr Earnshaw:** *'Pardew smells. I want a new doctor.'*

Take a look at the responses below, and then rank them from **most appropriate** to **least appropriate**.

A. Pull Dr Pardew to one side, and inform him that Mr Wiggins, Mrs Flack and Mr Earnshaw are being reassigned to a new doctor. If he asks why, tell him that it's for scheduling reasons.

B. Pull Dr Pardew to one side, and demand that he takes a bath.

C. Pull Dr Pardew to one side, and quietly discuss the problem with him, in a sensitive manner.

D. Tell the patients that Dr Pardew's smell does not impact on his ability to treat them, and that they will just have to deal with it.

E. Ask one of your colleagues to have a quiet word with Dr Pardew.

| 1 | 2 | 3 | 4 | 5 |
|---|---|---|---|---|
| C ✓ | E ✓ | B ✓ | D ✓ | A ✓ |

**Q17.** Over the past week, it has become apparent that medical interns in your department are not getting the proper training. The head of radiology – Steve – has called you and several other staff members together, to decide what should be done about this.

**Steve:** *Okay guys. I want you to go away and brainstorm some ideas. We'll meet again tomorrow to discuss what you've come up with.*

**Take a look at the responses below, and then rank them from most appropriate to least appropriate.**

A. Tell Steve that the term 'brainstorm' is offensive. Refuse to take part in the exercise.

B. Meet up with your colleagues once you are free, so that you can all work together to come up with new ideas.

C. Go off and come up with your own ideas. Aim to bring them to Steve before anyone else has the chance. You snooze, you lose.

D. Ask Steve why he's delegating this task to you and your colleagues, when he should be doing it himself.

E. Spend some time researching ideas during the evening, which you can bring to the meeting the next day.

| 1 | 2 | 3 | 4 | 5 |
|---|---|---|---|---|
| D | B | E | C | A |

*(handwritten annotations: under 1: E ✗; under 2: ✓; under 3: ✗ C; under 4: ✗ D; under 5: ✓)*

**Q18.** You are on your lunchbreak at Ficshire Hospital, where you are a senior doctor. As you walk past the main entrance, you notice a junior doctor picking flowers from the hospital car park lawn. The man is clearly trying to be discreet. Next to him is a big sign which reads **DO NOT PICK THE FLOWERS.**

**Take a look at the responses below, and then rank them from most appropriate to least appropriate.**

A. Ignore the man. Picking flowers is not a big deal.

B. Draw the man's attention to the sign. Ask him to stop picking the flowers.

C. Call hospital security. This man is vandalising hospital property.

D. Tell the man to stop picking the flowers and get back to work. Warn him that you will call security if you ever see it happen again.

E. Take discreet photos of the man, and share them on the internet. That way, everyone will know what he's done.

*(handwritten answer: B, D, C, A, E — with ✗ ✗ ✓ ✓ ✓ and D B below)*

| 1 | 2 | 3 | 4 | 5 |
|---|---|---|---|---|
|   |   |   |   |   |

> **Q19.** One of your patients is shortly due to go in for an operation on his lungs. The patient in question is a heavy smoker. The patient's name is Paul. Paul's wife recently passed away from lung cancer, and he has been having grief counselling sessions at the hospital, in a bid to deal with this. He has made several attempts on his life in the past, and doctors are worried about the likelihood that he will try this again.
>
> Come operation time, there is no sign of Paul. He seems to have vanished. You find him outside the hospital doors, smoking a cigarette. The hospital has a strict no smoking rule anywhere on the premises.
>
> **Paul:** *'Alright doc, wanna fag?'*

**Take a look at the responses below, and then rank them from most appropriate to least appropriate.**

A. Inform Paul that the hospital has a no smoking on the premises policy.

B. Tell Paul that if he doesn't stop smoking, you will postpone his operation.

C. Thank Paul for his kind offer. Join him for a cigarette.

D. Tell Paul that if he does not stop smoking, you will ask security to escort him from the premises.

E. Go and ask another staff member what they think you should do.

| 1 | 2 | 3 | 4 | 5 |
|---|---|---|---|---|
| A ✓ | E  X B | B X  D X | D X  E | C ✓ |

> **Q20.** Today you are meeting with a woman named Pauline, to discuss her cancer treatment. Pauline's brain cancer is at an advanced stage. Pauline does not have any other family than her husband, who has come in with her.
>
> After discussing the details of chemotherapy, Pauline decides to decline treatment. Pauline's husband, Mike, is shocked by this:
>
> **Mike:** *'You can't decline treatment, I won't let you!'*
>
> **Pauline:** *'It's my choice, Mike.'*

**Take a look at the responses below, and then rank them from most appropriate to least appropriate.**

A. Inform Mike that the decision is down to Pauline.

B. Tell Pauline that as long as Mike refuses to accept her decision, she will be unable to decline treatment.

C. Ask Pauline to step outside of the room. Tell her that you and Mike will make a decision on what she will do.

D. Ask Pauline whether she has thought about her decision, and whether she needs some extra time to consider her options.

E. Tell Pauline that although the decision is hers to make, she should have a serious talk with Mike about whether this is the right thing to do.

| 1 | 2 | 3 | 4 | 5 |
|---|---|---|---|---|
| D | E | A | B | C |

E, D

Q21. The day is Tuesday. At approximately 2 o 'clock in the afternoon, a young man was admitted to the ECU. He had been in a devastating motorbike accident. The man's mother is at the scene. She informs you that he is a promising young footballer, with a future career in the professional game ahead of him.

Unfortunately, as a result of his injuries, the man's leg will need to be amputated. He will probably never be able to play football again. It is your job to break the news to his mother – as the man is unconscious and being prepped for surgery.

**Take a look at the responses below, and then rank them from most appropriate to least appropriate.**

A. Ask a junior doctor to break the news. You have more important things to be getting on with.

B. Take the man's mother into a private room, and gently explain that in order to save the life of her son, his leg will need to be amputated.

C. Quickly explain to the man's mother about what operation is going to be performed, then ask security to remove her. She'll only cause a scene.

D. Take the man's mother to one side, and quietly explain the seriousness of the situation. Try to lighten the mood by making a few jokes.

E. Wait until after the operation to give the mother the news.

| 1 | 2 | 3 | 4 | 5 |
|---|---|---|---|---|
| B | D | A | C | E |

A, E, D, C

**Q22.** It's the day after the operation. The man's leg has been amputated, and he remains unconscious. Although his mother was devastated by the news, she accepted it as the right thing to do. Unfortunately, the man's football agent – Paulo – has now arrived at the hospital. He is demanding a meeting with you, to discuss the consequences of the operation.

**Paulo:** *'Do you have any idea what you've done? You've cost me – sorry my client – so much money.'*

**You:** *'I appreciate your concern for your client's wellbeing, but the operation was necessary, in order to save the patient's life.'*

**Paulo:** *'He had an agreement with a top-flight team. I – sorry he – was going to be a millionaire. You've ruined everything. I'll have you for this…we'll see what the courts have to say.'*

Paulo starts to become aggressive. He stands up and knocks a lamp off your desk.

**Take a look at the responses below, and then rank them from most appropriate to least appropriate.**

A. Call hospital security and ask them to escort Paulo from the premises.

B. Inform Paulo that he is free to discuss any legal issues with the hospital's legal team. Ask him to leave your office.

C. Tell Paulo that he will need to pay for the lamp that he has broken. Ask him to leave.

D. Inform Paulo that it is the job of the hospital legal department to resolve such claims. Call security to escort him from the premises.

E. Tell Paulo that you've seen his client on TV, and he never would have made it at a top-flight club in the first place.

| 1 | 2 | 3 | 4 | 5 |
|---|---|---|---|---|
| B | D | A | C | E |

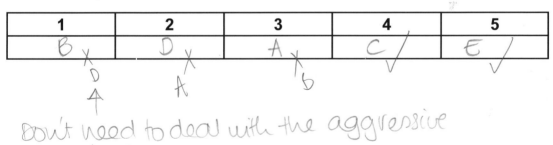

Don't need to deal with the aggressive behaviour

**Q23.** You've recently been treating a patient who was diagnosed with gonorrhea, after cheating on his girlfriend. Whilst you tried to establish what was wrong with the patient, he has been admitted to the GUM Clinic Ward. His girlfriend has come with him. Upon discovering that he is suffering from gonorrhea, the patient begs you not to inform his girlfriend. Both you and the junior doctor whom is shadowing you, agree not to inform her.

The next day, you walk into the hospital, to witness the following conversation:

**Junior doctor:** 'Your boyfriend has gonorrhea! Sorry!'

**Girlfriend:** 'What? How? How can you say this? I don't believe you.'

**Junior doctor:** 'It's true. He begged us not to tell you.'

**Girlfriend:** 'Oh my god...'

**Junior doctor:** 'Hey, it's okay. Listen, I know it's terrible, but I'm single...we can get through it together.'

**Take a look at the responses below, and then rank them from most appropriate to least appropriate.**

A. Take the junior doctor to one side, and inform him that he has broken the doctor patient confidentiality protocol. Ask him to go and consult the hospital legal team immediately, as there could be serious consequences.

B. Pretend that you never heard the conversation. It's the junior doctor's problem from now on – he can suffer the consequences.

C. Take the junior doctor to one side, and rebuke him for his behaviour. Inform him that there could be serious legal consequences for this.

D. Pull the junior doctor to one side, and congratulate him. Tell him that he has done the right thing, and that he can face his impending lawsuit with his head held high.

E. Ask to speak to the girlfriend in private, and apologise on behalf of the intern. Beg her not to take legal action.

| 1 | 2 | 3 | 4 | 5 |
|---|---|---|---|---|
| A | C | E | D | B |

**Q24.** You have been assigned to a male patient in the hospital. The man is named Kevin. Kevin is suffering from severe stomach pains. It is your job to find out what is wrong with him. Today you are meeting with Kevin for the first time:

**You:** 'Hi Kevin, my name is Doctor Freeman. I'll be taking care of you whilst you are here. How are you feeling?'

**Kevin:** 'I asked to be treated by a female doctor.'

**You:** 'Please be assured, I am fully trained and will provide you with an excellent level of care. Furthermore, there are always nurses on hand to assist you.'

**Kevin:** 'I don't care whether you are this or that…you aren't female. Male doctors, from my experience, are lazy and incapable. Women do a much better job.'

**Take a look at the responses below, and then rank them from most appropriate to least appropriate.**

A. Tell Kevin that his sexism is not appreciated, and that he will just have to accept that you are his doctor.

B. Tell Kevin that although you are more than capable of doing the job, if he is unwilling to be treated by you then you can try and make arrangements to find him another doctor.

C. Tell Kevin that he will not be treated until he changes his attitude towards hospital staff.

D. Tell Kevin that if he wants his stomach pain to go away, he'd better start being nicer to you.

E. Tell Kevin that although you can appreciate that he has had a negative experience with male doctors in the past, he can rest assured in the quality of your care and expertise.

| 1 | 2 | 3 | 4 | 5 |
|---|---|---|---|---|
| E | B | A | D | C |

**Q25.** You are working at the hospital's A&E walk in clinic. The session is closing up for the night, with only a few patients left to see. You are aware that two of your colleagues (who are also working the walk-in session) have finished, and so pop in for a quick chat with them before they go home. As you open the door, you notice that one of them has his head bent over the desk. He is snorting cocaine. Your other colleague is actively encouraging him, and has cocaine powder all over her fingers.

**Take a look at the responses below, and then rank them from most appropriate to least appropriate.**

A. Immediately rebuke your colleagues. Inform them that you have no choice but to take this to senior management.

B. Quietly close the door. You saw nothing.

C. Ask your colleagues what on earth they think they are doing. Tell them to dispose of the cocaine, before anyone sees it. ← Most inappropriate

D. Call the police.

E. Tell your colleagues that they are in violation of both the law and hospital guidelines. Tell them that they need to flush the cocaine down the toilet, and come with you to senior management.

| 1 | 2 | 3 | 4 | 5 |
|---|---|---|---|---|
| A ✓ | D ✓ | E ✓ | C ✗B | ✗ B C |

Q26. You have been working at your current hospital for a period of two years now. Over the past 2-3 months, the hospital has allowed a group of paid interns to come in and shadow the main staff. Whilst all of the interns started well, you have noticed that one of them – Brad – is now failing to pull his weight. He is frequently late for work, citing bus problems as a constant issue, and often seems disinterested in medical issues.

Today you have a progress meeting with Brad.

**Take a look at the responses below, and then rank them from most appropriate to least appropriate.**

A. Tell Brad that his performance is utterly unacceptable. Inform him that he is a sorry excuse for a doctor, and that you have no idea what he is even doing in an establishment such as this.

B. Tell Brad that his performance has dipped alarmingly, and that you are hugely concerned about whether he has what it takes to be a doctor.

C. Tell Brad that, despite his lateness, and his lack of interest in medicine, you are pretty pleased with his overall performance.

D. Tell Brad that his lateness, and lack of interest in medicine, are frankly embarrassing. Question him over whether this is the role he really wants to pursue.

E. Tell Brad that you are very disappointed by the way his performance has dipped over the last few months, and warn him that he needs to improve.

| 1 | 2 | 3 | 4 | 5 |
|---|---|---|---|---|
|   |   |   |   |   |

**Q27.** You are working as a surgical FY1. A patient has recently come into the hospital, with extreme pain in his arm. The patient is a diabetic smoker. His name is Martin.

**Martin:** *'Please, I'm really scared. I've heard stories of this kind of thing before. Do you think you'll have to amputate? I can't lose my arm, please.'*

**Take a look at the responses below, and then rank them from most appropriate to least appropriate.**

A. *'Please be assured, we will do our absolute best to ensure that things don't have to go that far. In any case, amputation is a last resort, so there's no need to start panicking about that right now. We'll need to arrange some tests, and once we get these back, one of our senior staff will consult with you. Trust me, you are in the safest hands possible.'*

B. *'There's a chance we'll have to amputate…but let's get the results back before we make any decisions.'*

C. *'I'll consult with our senior staff, and we'll run a few tests. Once we get the results back, I'll let you know the outcome.'*

D. *'Cheer up. Yes you'll lose your arm, but at least you're not dead.'*

E. *'Amputation is a last resort. It's very unlikely that this will happen. We'll run a few tests first, and then I'll ask one of our senior doctors to consult with you about the result. Don't panic, sir, you are in safe hands!'*

| 1 | 2 | 3 | 4 | 5 |
|---|---|---|---|---|
| A | C | B | E | D |

**Q28.** A patient – Miranda – is currently being treated for an infection of her right arm, which she picked up whilst on holiday in Brazil. Although the patient is making good progress, she is still scheduled to be in the hospital for a few more days, just as a precaution. As you walk into the patient's room, you see that she is getting ready to leave:

**Miranda:** *'I'm discharging myself. It's so boring here. To be honest, I feel like staying here is making me feel worse. I'd like to go home to my Mum – she can take care of me just fine.'*

**Take a look at the responses below, and then rank them from most appropriate to least appropriate.**

A. Tell Miranda that she cannot legally leave the hospital until she has been fully treated for the infection. Call hospital security to ensure that she stays.

B. Explain to Miranda about the risks of her leaving the hospital early, and what these risks are. Allow her to leave if she still persists, following this explanation.

C. Lie to Miranda, telling her that if she leaves hospital early, she is likely to die.

D. Tell Miranda that you would like to meet with her mother, to discuss the care that Miranda will need at home.

E. Tell Miranda that although she is taking a big risk, ultimately it's her choice.

| 1 | 2 | 3 | 4 | 5 |
|---|---|---|---|---|
|   |   |   |   |   |

**Q29.** You are working in the geriatric ward. One of your favourite patients is a woman named Mrs Connelly – who is being treated for lupus. Unfortunately, this afternoon, Mrs Connelly went into cardiac arrest – after taking a fall on her way to the bathroom. Although you did everything possible, Mrs Connelly died. The ward consultant has encouraged you to write down 'collapsed lung' as the cause of death. You disagree with this. Now that the ward consultant has gone home, you need to make a decision on how to proceed.

**Take a look at the responses below, and then rank them from most appropriate to least appropriate.**

A. Use your own judgement to decide which is the most appropriate cause of death.

B. Go and find the coroner. They are best placed to decide.

C. Agree with the consultant – they know better than you.

D. Leave the entry empty. It doesn't matter what the cause of death was.

E. Ask the victim's family what they believe the cause of death was.

| 1 | 2 | 3 | 4 | 5 |
|---|---|---|---|---|
|   |   |   |   |   |

**Q30.** You are working on the surgical ward round. Over the course of the round, you notice that the consultant in charge of the round is making some questionable decisions. Nobody else seems to have picked up on this.

**Take a look at the responses below, and then rank them from most appropriate to least appropriate.**

A. Stop the round, and ask the consultant in charge whether he has any idea what he is doing.

B. Encourage the other participants of the round to follow you instead, and start leading them on an alternative round.

C. Following the session, take the consultant to one side and question him over some of the decisions that he has made.

D. Say nothing. It's not your place to interfere.

E. From the point at which you notice something is wrong, ask the consultant to justify their decisions. Write this down as he does so.

| 1 | 2 | 3 | 4 | 5 |
|---|---|---|---|---|
|   |   |   |   |   |

**Q31.** You are working on the paediatric ward. One of your patients, a 14 year-old brain tumour patient by the name of Matthew, informs you that someone has stolen his bag from the side of his bed. The bag contained his laptop, some books and a wallet – containing £200.

By all accounts, Matthew is an extremely unpleasant young man. He spits and swears at staff, abuses the nurse call button, and throws a tantrum when he doesn't get his way.

**Take a look at the responses below, and then rank them from most appropriate to least appropriate.**

A. Tell Matthew that he needs to be more careful with his possessions in the future, and that this will teach him a valuable lesson.

B. Tell Matthew that this is karma for being such a spoilt little brat.

C. Tell Matthew that you'll get in touch with the nurses, to see if the bag has been picked up and put away for safekeeping.

D. Tell Matthew that you are happy to help him look through his belongings, to see if he has misplaced the bag.

E. Call the police.

| 1 | 2 | 3 | 4 | 5 |
|---|---|---|---|---|
|   |   |   |   |   |

**Q32.** You are working during a busy walk in clinic. As you pass by one of your colleague's doors, you overhear him on the phone. He is making fun of one of his previous patients:

**Patrick:** *'I know right…haha – these people come in here and think we can help them. Can't help you if you're fat, mate. I mean I feel bad for him, he said he's getting divorced from his wife…but who could blame her?'*

**Take a look at the responses below, and then rank them from most appropriate to least appropriate.**

A. Immediately go and find the clinic manager, to discuss what you have heard. This is utterly unacceptable.

B. Ignore it. It's not your place to comment on private conversations.

C. Knock on the door, interrupting the phone conversation, and then ask your colleague if you can have a quiet word about his behaviour.

D. Discuss with your other colleagues about what should be done.

E. Subtly open your colleague's door, so that everyone in the clinic can hear what he is saying.

| 1 | 2 | 3 | 4 | 5 |
|---|---|---|---|---|
|   |   |   |   |   |

---

**Q33.** You are working as a junior doctor in the gynaecology ward. One of your patients is suffering from pelvic inflammation, and you have prescribed them with a dose of antibiotics, in a bid to improve their condition. Before you leave work, you have the following conversation with one of the nurses:

**You:** *'I've prescribed Jane Edwards with a dosage of Maxipime. Please make sure she gets this tonight.'*

**Nurse:** *'Will do!'*

When you arrive in the morning, Jane has still not been given her antibiotics, and she is in significant pain from the inflammation.

**Take a look at the responses below, and then rank them from most appropriate to least appropriate.**

A. Angrily confront the staff at the desk as to why this medication wasn't given.

B. Apologise to Jane, notify the staff, and make sure you watch them administer the medication.

C. Go straight to the Director of Nursing, to tell her that her staff are incompetent.

D. Encourage Jane to pursue legal action against the hospital.

E. Calmly approach the nursing staff, to enquire as to why this wasn't administered.

| 1 | 2 | 3 | 4 | 5 |
|---|---|---|---|---|
|   |   |   |   |   |

---

**Q34.** You are working in the paediatric ward. A child comes in, complaining about a severe cough. Whilst examining her, you notice that she has a number of cuts and bruises on her arms, face and legs. Her mother claims that she picked up these injuries whilst playfighting with her sibling. The girl confirms her story. Apart from the cough, she appears to be perfectly happy.

**Take a look at the responses below, and then rank them from most appropriate to least appropriate.**

A. Call social services. It's obvious they are both lying.

B. Ask a few extra questions about the injuries, just to make sure their story makes sense.

C. Ask to speak to the mother in private. Accuse her of abusing her daughter.

D. Accept their story for now, but bring up your concerns with the head of department later in the day.

E. Take a look over the girl's medical history, to check for any previous signs of abuse.

| 1 | 2 | 3 | 4 | 5 |
|---|---|---|---|---|
|   |   |   |   |   |

**Q35.** Your work colleague, Nathan, is 36 years old today. Nathan is a surgeon at the hospital. You and some other colleagues have put together some money to purchase a fairly expensive bottle of wine for Nathan. You all get together at the end of the day, to present the gift to Nathan.

**You:** 'Happy birthday, Nathan! We've got together and bought you a small something...'

*Hands over the wine to Nathan*

**Nathan:** '...Is that it?'

**You:** 'Excuse me?'

**Nathan:** '36 years old, and all I get is a stinking bottle of wine. Wow. Nice to see I've got such good friends. Cheapskates.'

**You:** 'That's pretty ungrateful, Nathan. We all chipped in for that.'

In response, Nathan makes a racial slur towards another one of your colleagues.

**Take a look at the responses below, and then rank them from most appropriate to least appropriate.**

A. Tell Nathan that his behaviour is unacceptable. Ask him to give the wine back, so you can get a refund.

B. Offer to buy Nathan a better, more expensive gift.

C. Tell Nathan that his behaviour is completely unacceptable, and that you will be reporting him to senior management.

D. Take your colleague into a private room and attempt to comfort her over Nathan's language. Racism has no place in the workplace.

E. Tell Nathan that racism is unacceptable. Ask him to apologise to your colleague.

| 1 | 2 | 3 | 4 | 5 |
|---|---|---|---|---|
|   |   |   |   |   |

**Q36.** When you arrive at work on Tuesday, you are informed that one of your colleagues is sick, and therefore you will need to cover medical wards with another trainee – named Sarah. You and Sarah do not get along, and you know that it's going to be very difficult to work with her. In the past, Sarah has been extremely rude towards you, and even spread hurtful rumours about you in the hospital.

**Take a look at the responses below, and then rank them from most appropriate to least appropriate.**

A. Prior to your shift, ask Sarah to talk with you in private, in a bid to resolve your differences. This will make work much easier.

B. Tell the nurse in charge that you don't want to work with Sarah. Ask her to swap you with someone else.

C. Agree to work with Sarah, but resolve to make her look as bad as possible during the shift.

D. Agree to work with Sarah. Try to act as professionally as possible.

E. Tell the nurse in charge that you have some personal difficulties with Sarah. Ask her if it's possible for you to swap with someone else.

| 1 | 2 | 3 | 4 | 5 |
|---|---|---|---|---|
|   |   |   |   |   |

**Q37.** Mr Miggins has come in, complaining about frequent headaches, dizziness and even occasional blackouts. A brain scan shows that Mr Miggins has a tumour. Obviously, he is devastated by this diagnosis. Right after you've finished giving him the diagnosis, you receive a call from Mr Miggins's son. He wants to know if you've received the scan results, and what they are.

**Take a look at the responses below, and then rank them from most appropriate to least appropriate.**

A. Tell Mr Miggins's son that you have got the results back, but that he would be better off speaking to his father about the results directly.

B. Pass the phone straight to Mr Miggins.

C. Tell Mr Miggins's son that you have received the results, and unfortunately it's bad news.

D. Ask Mr Miggins whether he wants to tell his son the news directly, or whether it's okay for you to inform his son about it.

E. Announce loudly down the phone that Mr Miggins has a brain tumour, and that he doesn't have long to live.

| 1 | 2 | 3 | 4 | 5 |
|---|---|---|---|---|
|   |   |   |   |   |

---

**Q38.** This morning when you get into work, there is an email in your inbox from an intern named Morgan. Here is what it says:

*Hi Dr Pratchett,*

*I can't come in today, because I've got a splitting headache. I'm also feeling really sick, and was throwing up all night last night. I'll be in tomorrow though.*

*Cheers boss,*

*Morgan.*

This is not the first time that Morgan has been off for the exact same issues. You have at least three emails from the past 2 months, where Morgan has said more or less the same thing.

Later on during the day, you overhear two of the other junior doctors talking about how drunk Morgan was at the previous night's party, and that it's no wonder he's off today.

**Take a look at the responses below, and then rank them from most appropriate to least appropriate.**

A. Email Morgan back, informing him that as a result of his behaviour, you will be taking disciplinary action.

B. Email Morgan back, thanking him for letting you know about his absence, and tell him that you hope he gets better.

C. Thank Morgan for his hard work over the past year. Attach a P45 form to the email.

D. Email Morgan and tell him that you would like to have a meeting tomorrow, to discuss his absence.

E. Email Morgan and let him know in no uncertain terms that you are highly disappointed with him taking another absence.

| 1 | 2 | 3 | 4 | 5 |
|---|---|---|---|---|
|   |   |   |   |   |

**Q39.** You are the FY2 in the paediatric ward. In support of Movember, you have grown a full moustache, and have raised quite a bit of money for charity. As you get into work on the final day of the month, a woman comes up to you. She claims that you are scaring the children in the ward, and that you look unprofessional. The woman storms off before you can explain yourself.

Later, one of the nurses tells you that the woman has made an official complaint against you.

**Take a look at the responses below, and then rank them from most appropriate to least appropriate.**

A. See if you can arrange a meeting with the woman, to try and explain exactly why you have grown a moustache.

B. Meet with the head of the department, to address the complaint against you.

C. Ignore the complaint. Those in charge will see sense.

D. Shave your moustache immediately, find the woman and beg for forgiveness.

E. Resolve to keep your moustache beyond November. It's your choice.

| 1 | 2 | 3 | 4 | 5 |
|---|---|---|---|---|
|   |   |   |   |   |

**Q40.** You have been called into the paediatric ward, to see a 17 year-old boy. The boy was admitted to hospital after attempting to cut his wrists. Although his attempt failed, and he has been medically treated, the boy informs you that he wants to be discharged immediately. He tells you that once he leaves, he intends to kill himself.

**Take a look at the responses below, and then rank them from most appropriate to least appropriate.**

A. Allow the boy to leave. Ultimately, it's his choice.

B. Try and talk to the boy yourself, asking him to stay at the hospital and get the help that he needs.

C. Tell the boy that he will unfortunately need to be sectioned under the mental health act.

D. Arrange a phone call with the patient's relatives, to get their view on the situation.

E. Tell the boy that he has broken the law by attempting to commit suicide, and will now face criminal charges.

| 1 | 2 | 3 | 4 | 5 |
|---|---|---|---|---|
|   |   |   |   |   |

**Q41.** You are working with an elderly patient. Whilst treating the man for a standard infection, you notice that he is showing a number of signs of severe depression.

**Take a look at the responses below, and then rank them from most appropriate to least appropriate.**

A. You are treating the man for infection, not for depression. Ignore the issue.

B. Question the man further, querying his mood, his appetite and how he is feeling, to try and establish whether he is suicidal.

C. Take the issue directly to your senior GP.

D. Ask the patients in the waiting room what they think you should do.

E. Prescribe the man a course of anti-depressants.

| 1 | 2 | 3 | 4 | 5 |
|---|---|---|---|---|
|   |   |   |   |   |

**Q42.** You are working in the hospital surgical department. A patient has been admitted to the hospital, with appendicitis. However, once the patient arrives and is examined, the team finds no evidence of appendicitis whatsoever. One of your colleagues is pretty annoyed about this:

**Maria:** *'The admitting team at this hospital are absolute clowns. What the hell do they think they are playing at? I can assure you sir, you don't have appendicitis.'*

**Take a look at the responses below, and then rank them from most appropriate to least appropriate.**

A. *'You are so right. I can't believe how terrible they are. Only last week they admitted someone to the hospital with completely the wrong illness, and he died within 10 minutes of getting here…but don't worry I'm sure that won't happen to you sir.'*

B. *'There's only one clown in this hospital, and that's you, Maria. I can assure you sir, the admittance team are almost never wrong.'*

C. *'I'm sure they just made a mistake. They don't have access to the investigation results that we do. Not to worry though sir, we'll make sure we get this sorted for you and you'll be out of here in no time at all.'*

D. *'The admittance team don't have access to the same results that we do, therefore they can only make a preliminary diagnosis. In any case, we'll diagnosis you ourselves.'*

E. *'I'm sorry for my colleague's comments sir, she's having a bad day. We'll diagnose you ourselves, so don't worry.'*

| 1 | 2 | 3 | 4 | 5 |
|---|---|---|---|---|
|   |   |   |   |   |

**Q43.** Over the past few days, your team has been running investigations into the symptoms of Mr Naisbeck, a 40 year-old science teacher. Today, it has become apparent that he is likely to be suffering from bowel cancer. Whilst under the hospital's care, Mr Naisbeck is behaving in a very agitated and unhappy manner, and some of the nurses are very upset with this.

**Take a look at the responses below, and then rank them from most appropriate to least appropriate.**

A. Tell the patient that if his behaviour doesn't improve, you'll have him thrown out.

B. Sit down with the patient and talk to him about how he is feeling, and any concerns that he has.

C. Apologise to the nurses and tell them that you'll have a private word with Mr Naisbeck.

D. Tell Mr Naisbeck that although you understand he is feeling stressed and upset about being in hospital, he needs to try and be more polite to the staff.

E. Tell the nurses to stop overreacting.

| 1 | 2 | 3 | 4 | 5 |
|---|---|---|---|---|
|   |   |   |   |   |

**Q44.** You are working on medical wards with your colleague, named Stan. Stan is considered one of the top junior doctors at the hospital, and is a favourite amongst the nurses. Today you are dealing with an elderly patient – named Mr Bosworth. Mr Bosworth had a spinal tap procedure last week. You and Stan have the following conversation with Mr Bosworth:

**Stan:** *'Hello there Mr Bosworth, how are you doing today?'*

**Mr Bosworth:** *'A little better, thanks Stan.'*

**Stan:** *'How's your chest feeling?'*

**Mr Bosworth:** *'Mmmm...when I came in it was like a sharp pain right in my ribs, but now it's more like a dull ache.'*

*\*Stan checks Mr Bosworth over\**

**Stan:** *'Alright...I'm still a little concerned, so I'm going to prescribe you with some Dalteparin. How does that sound?'*

You are aware that Dalteparin could cause a bloodclot, if administered to patients who have just undergone a spinal tap.

**Take a look at the responses below, and then rank them from most appropriate to least appropriate.**

A. Agree with Stan. After all, he is one of the top junior doctors.

B. Tell Stan that Dalteparin is not the correct prescription, given that Mr Bosworth has just had a spinal tap.

C. Go behind Stan's back, and prescribe Mr Bosworth with different medication instead. That way, everybody wins.

D. Go straight to the head of medicine and tell them what Stan has just done. That will knock him off his perch.

E. Query Stan over why he has prescribed Dalteparin.

| 1 | 2 | 3 | 4 | 5 |
|---|---|---|---|---|
|   |   |   |   |   |

---

**Q45.** You walk into the hospital on Monday morning, to find a group of junior doctors standing around a patient, who they are prepping for surgery. Mrs Matthews has been diagnosed as clinically obese, and is going in for surgery later that morning. The doctors appear to be making fun of her. You hear one of them comment on how fat she is, and another one tells her that he doesn't know how they are going to cart her into the surgery room.

**Take a look at the responses below, and then rank them from most appropriate to least appropriate.**

A. Immediately walk up to Mrs Matthews and apologise profusely on behalf of the hospital. Ask them to finish prepping the patient, and then come with you to the Chief Physician's office.

B. Go over to Mrs Matthews and apologise on behalf of the junior doctors. Tell them to stop mucking around and finish off the preparation.

C. Ignore it and say nothing. They could turn on you too.

D. Consult with the nurses over what you have just heard.

E. Walk up to Mrs Matthews and apologise on behalf of the hospital. Inform her that the junior doctors will be punished severely for this unacceptable behaviour. Ask a nurse to finish prepping the patient instead.

| 1 | 2 | 3 | 4 | 5 |
|---|---|---|---|---|
|   |   |   |   |   |

**Q46.** Last week, a man named Charles Grayson was admitted to the hospital, after being in a severe motorcycle accident. Although you have had some verbal communication with the patient, who emphasised his desire to have his organs donated if he died, Charles's condition has been steadily declining for over a week now. When you come into the hospital for your evening shift, you are informed that Charles passed away two hours ago. Later that evening, his son James approaches you:

**James:** *'Thank you for looking after my father. I know you did everything you could to save him.'*

**You:** *'That's okay, I'm so sorry for your loss.'*

**James:** *'Listen, I know my dad is on the organ donor register, but we really don't want his organs donated. Is there anything you can do?'*

**Take a look at the responses below, and then rank them from most appropriate to least appropriate.**

A – Tell James that the decision is down to him and the rest of his family, and that the organs won't be donated without their permission.

B – Tell James that you will put him in touch with the hospital specialist, who deals with organ donation issues.

C – Tell James that although the organs won't be donated without his permission, he should think about the greater good.

D – Tell James that since his father was on the organ donor register, the decision on whether the organs will be donated is now out of the family's hands.

E – Tell James that you will donate his father's organs, whether he likes it or not.

| 1 | 2 | 3 | 4 | 5 |
|---|---|---|---|---|
|   |   |   |   |   |

**Q47.** You are working in the emergency care unit, when a 45 year old woman is rushed in. The woman fell off a ladder at work, and has suffered enormous blood loss. The medical team unanimously agrees that the patient needs a blood transfusion, or she'll die. However, the patient's husband disagrees:

**Husband:** *'You can't give her blood, it's against our religion!'*

**You:** *'Sir, if we don't perform a transfusion, then it's very likely that your wife will die.'*

**Husband:** *'Well then, at least she'll be with God.'*

**Take a look at the responses below, and then rank them from most appropriate to least appropriate.**

A – Perform the transfusion, regardless of the husband's wishes.

B – Ask the husband whether he wants to be held responsible for his wife's death.

C – Tell the husband that if he wants to prevent his wife from receiving blood, he needs to go and see the legal team.

D – Tell the husband that you are going to act in his wife's best interests, and perform the transfusion.

E – Ask the medical team to come up with some alternative solutions.

| 1 | 2 | 3 | 4 | 5 |
|---|---|---|---|---|
|   |   |   |   |   |

**Q48.** You have just started your shift, when a friend of yours walks into the hospital. He is going away on his honeymoon tomorrow, but his wife has a weak immune system, and is prone to infection. Your friend approaches you:

**Friend:** *'Alright Mick, can you do me a favour? We're going on our honeymoon tomorrow but Julie's got an infection…again. Can you prescribe me some antibiotics?'*

**Take a look at the responses below, and then rank them from most appropriate to least appropriate.**

A – Prescribe your friend the antibiotics. Wish him a good honeymoon.

B – Ask your friend to send Julie into the hospital, so that you can assess whether she needs the antibiotics.

C – Tell your friend that this is a request more suitable for his GP, and not something you can do.

D – Tell your friend to leave you alone, and stop pestering you at work.

E – Tell your friend that if he wants antibiotics, he should visit the hospital pharmacy.

| 1 | 2 | 3 | 4 | 5 |
|---|---|---|---|---|
|   |   |   |   |   |

**Q49.** You have been caring for a foreign-speaking patient for a few weeks now. Mrs Aillia is 49 years old, and does not speak a word of English. In order to communicate with her, staff have been using an extremely helpful translator, whom they hired from an external company.

Unfortunately, on the day when you need to gain consent from Mrs Aillia to perform a life-changing spinal operation, her translator is off sick. The company have sent over a replacement. When the replacement arrives, you realise that it's none other than your ex-wife's new husband. There is significant animosity between the pair of you, and you do not trust him to perform an accurate translation.

**Take a look at the responses below, and then rank them from most appropriate to least appropriate.**

A – Immediately call the translation service, and ask them to send over a different translator.

B – Take the man to one side and try to reach a reasonable agreement, for the best interests of the patient.

C – Ask the patient to sign the consent form, without the help of any translation service.

D – Proceed with the signing of the consent form as planned. Hopefully the translator doesn't have sinister intentions.

E – Fill in the consent form on behalf of the patient.

| 1 | 2 | 3 | 4 | 5 |
|---|---|---|---|---|
|   |   |   |   |   |

**Q50.** Unfortunately the translator from the previous question acted unprofessionally, and deliberately gave Mrs Aillia the wrong information! Mrs Aillia consented to the operation, without fully understanding the risks. Although the operation was a success, she is absolutely furious, and is threatening to sue the hospital. The translator in question has now been fired, but not before sending you a text that read: 'Lol!'

In light of the situation, your head of department has called you into his office, to explain the situation:

**Take a look at the responses below, and then rank them from most appropriate to least appropriate.**

A – Tell your head of department that although you understood there to be animosity between yourself and the translator, you trusted him to do his job to the best of his ability.

B – Tell your head of department that you are not responsible for the behaviour of the translator, and that it's the hospital's fault for hiring him.

C – Tell your head of department that although you can appreciate that you should have spoken to someone about the translator prior to gaining consent, they need to take issue with the translation company, and not with you – you were simply doing your job.

D – Tell your head of department that he better find himself a good lawyer, because Mrs Aillia is not happy.

E – Tell your head of department that you take full responsibility for the translator's actions, and that you are willing to take the legal consequences for the mistake.

| 1 | 2 | 3 | 4 | 5 |
|---|---|---|---|---|
|   |   |   |   |   |

**Q51.** You are working in the emergency care unit on a Saturday night. At around 7pm, a woman bursts into the ward. She is laughing and shouting, and starts kicking and punching hospital equipment. She climbs onto the bed of a sleeping patient, gets out her phone and starts playing loud music, singing at the top of her voice. It quickly becomes clear that the woman is extremely inebriated. One of the nurses informs you that she saw the woman in the A&E department earlier, being treated for alcohol intoxication.

**Take a look at the responses below, and then rank them from most appropriate to least appropriate.**

A – Call the security team to come and deal with the situation.

B – Try to move all of the other patients in the ward, out of the room, so that the woman can be dealt with.

C – Ask the nurses to fetch a sedation kit.

D – Try and restrain the patient yourself.

E – Call the A&E department to come and fetch their escaped patient.

| 1 | 2 | 3 | 4 | 5 |
|---|---|---|---|---|
|   |   |   |   |   |

**Q52.** You have been treating Mr Clement for the past few weeks now. Unfortunately Mr Clement is terminally ill, suffering from a brain tumour. On Saturday morning, you come into the hospital to find his son Paul, and his daughter Janice, gathered around his bedside:

**Mr Clement:** *'I'd really like to finish my last days in a hospice, Dr Mulgrew. I think I'd be much more comfortable there.'*

**Paul:** *'No, Dad! A hospice isn't the right place for you. Janice and I both agree, we want you to stay here.'*

**Mr Clement:** *'It's my decision, and that's final.'*

**Janice:** *'We'll see about that…'*

**Take a look at the responses below, and then rank them from most appropriate to least appropriate.**

A – Tell Janice and Paul that they have no say in what is done with their father.

B – Tell Mr Clement that because he is terminally ill, his children must decide what is done with him.

C – Tell Mr Clement that he is free to make his own decisions, but encourage him to involve his children in the decision-making process.

D – Encourage Mr Clement to accept his children's wishes.

E – Encourage Janice and Paul to accept their father's decision.

| 1 | 2 | 3 | 4 | 5 |
|---|---|---|---|---|
|   |   |   |   |   |

**Q53.** You are finishing your shift on Tuesday, when a patient calls you over to their bed. The patient in question is named Mrs Dalton. Although Mrs Dalton was given a low chance of survival when first admitted to the hospital, her condition has gradually improved, and she is now listed as stable.

**Mrs Dalton:** *'Dr McCarthy, I just wanted to say thank you so much for all your help over the last few weeks. You truly are a lifesaver!'*

**You:** *'That's no problem, Mrs Dalton. We are all just glad to see you doing better. I have my day off tomorrow, but I'll be back on Thursday, so we'll catch up then.'*

Unfortunately, when you arrive on Thursday morning, you are informed that Mrs Dalton died the previous evening. One of the nurses asks you to fill in Mrs Dalton's death certificate.

**Take a look at the responses below, and then rank them from most appropriate to least appropriate.**

A – Angrily blame the nurses for Mrs Dalton's death.

B – Ask the nurses to bring you a full set of notes on the events of yesterday, so that you can determine what went wrong.

C – Find out which members of staff were treating Mrs Dalton yesterday, to discuss the events with them.

D – Ask one of the nurses to fill in the death certificate instead.

E – Fill in the death certificate, based on Mrs Dalton's previous symptoms.

| 1 | 2 | 3 | 4 | 5 |
|---|---|---|---|---|
|   |   |   |   |   |

**Q54.** A patient has recently been admitted to your hospital with an infection, that they picked up whilst on holiday abroad. Your consultant has ordered a blood test. Unfortunately, when the results come back, they show that the patient is HIV positive. Your consultant has asked you to break the news sensitively to the patient, who has a fairly nervous disposition.

**Take a look at the responses below, and then rank them from most appropriate to least appropriate.**

A – Start by reminding the patient about why you took the blood test results in the first place, before gently breaking the unfortunate news.

B – Tell the patient that she is HIV positive, but the hospital can cure this for her.

C – Tell the patient that you have received the blood test results back, and unfortunately she is HIV positive. Follow this up by explaining the different treatment options available to her.

D – Ask the patient whether she had unprotected sex whilst abroad.

E – Break the news to the patient in a sensitive fashion. Pre-arrange for her friends and family to visit, so that they can support her at this difficult time.

| 1 | 2 | 3 | 4 | 5 |
|---|---|---|---|---|
|   |   |   |   |   |

**Q55.** Over the last few weeks, you have noticed that your FY2 colleague seems to be struggling. He's been late several times, and often seems downcast and disinterested. This morning, he walked out in the middle of his shift, with tears pouring down his face, after declaring that he was 'done with this place.'

**Take a look at the responses below, and then rank them from most appropriate to least appropriate.**

A – Follow after your colleague, demanding that he comes back into work.

B – Text your colleague to make sure he's feeling okay. Ask him to meet with you once you've finished your shift, so that you can discuss his behaviour.

C – Go and see your consultant to discuss your colleague's behaviour. Ask your consultant whether there is any support that can be offered to your colleague.

D – The next time you see your colleague, resolve to offer him your full support and confidence.

E – Contact your colleague's relatives, to see if they can provide any insight into his behaviour.

| 1 | 2 | 3 | 4 | 5 |
|---|---|---|---|---|
|   |   |   |   |   |

---

**Q56.** You are working in the emergency care unit. A 16-year-old girl has been admitted into your care, after attempting suicide. Upon stabilising the patient, and having a chat with her, it becomes apparent to you that the girl attempted suicide over her weight. She claims that she is being bullied at school. She has asked you whether she can have a liposuction procedure. Her parents also inform you that they'd like her to have liposuction.

Upon taking the girl's BMI, and weighing her, you notice that although she is slightly overweight, she is not considered obese or a significant health risk.

**Take a look at the responses below, and then rank them from most appropriate to least appropriate.**

A – Tell the girl that liposuction won't stop her being bullied.

B – Explain to the family that the girl is only slightly overweight, and that there are far less drastic measures of shedding pounds.

C – Run through the advantages and disadvantages of having liposuction. Encourage the family to consider other options.

D – Agree to the treatment. If that's what the family want, they can have it.

E – Arrange for the girl to undergo counselling at the hospital. Tell her parents that they need to be more supportive over their child's body image.

| 1 | 2 | 3 | 4 | 5 |
|---|---|---|---|---|
|   |   |   |   |   |

---

**Q57.** You are working the night shift, and have just finished visiting a patient. The patient in question is suffering from a minor infection, which they picked up whilst on holiday in the Caribbean. Although the infection is minor, it has the potential to become far more severe if it is not dealt with as a matter of urgency. Your team have agreed that the patient needs a course of antibiotics, but cannot agree on what antibiotics should be administered.

**Take a look at the responses below, and then rank them from most appropriate to least appropriate.**

A – Consult the hospital guidelines for a view on what antibiotics to prescribe.

B – Take a straw poll amongst your team, with the most popular antibiotic being the one that is prescribed.

C – Have a look on the internet to see what would be the best antibiotic.

D – Ask the patient what they think you should do.

E – Get in touch with your registrar, to see what they think.

| 1 | 2 | 3 | 4 | 5 |
|---|---|---|---|---|
|   |   |   |   |   |

**Q58.** You are working in the intensive care unit, when a patient whom you are familiar with is admitted, suffering from severe pneumonia. The patient is named Michelle, and she is your ex-husband's new wife. Although you do not get along with your ex-husband, you have an amicable relationship for the sake of your children. Your ex-husband is currently serving in the armed forces, so he cannot come and visit Michelle. However, the day after Michelle is admitted, you receive a phone call from Phil (your ex-husband):

**Phil:** *'Hi, Maggie. I'm sorry to bother you like this, but I just wondered if you can provide me with an update on how Michelle is getting along?'*

**You:** *'Have you contacted the hospital directly?'*

**Phil:** *'Yes, but they wouldn't give me any info.'*

**Take a look at the responses below, and then rank them from most appropriate to least appropriate.**

A – Tell Phil that unfortunately you can't give him any information over the phone, as this would be a breach of confidentiality.

B – Tell Phil that if he emails you written confirmation that you can request the info, then you'll do so on his behalf.

C – Tell Phil that his new wife is probably not going to make it.

D – Tell Phil that if he wants any information, he's going to have to visit the hospital in person.

E – Tell Phil that he should not contact you about such matters in the future.

| 1 | 2 | 3 | 4 | 5 |
|---|---|---|---|---|
|   |   |   |   |   |

**Q59.** You are working in the geriatric ward. It is Saturday morning. One of the patients in the ward is a woman named Mrs Entwhistle, who has recently been admitted. On Saturday morning, her son William comes in to visit her. He approaches you and says the following:

**William:** 'Hey, doc. Listen, I want you take special care of my mum. She's old and sick and I don't know how much longer she's got. Here's £100. Give her special treatment, please?'

**Take a look at the responses below, and then rank them from most appropriate to least appropriate.**

A – Thank William for the money, and assure him that his mother will be well looked after.

B – Tell William that he does not need to give you money, as his mother is already your favourite patient.

C – Hand back the money to William. Tell him that his mother will receive the same care as any other patient.

D – Thank William for his kind offer, but inform him that it won't be necessary, as the staff will take the best possible care of his mother, without any payments.

E – Inform William that it's against hospital policy to take gifts from patients.

| 1 | 2 | 3 | 4 | 5 |
|---|---|---|---|---|
|   |   |   |   |   |

**Q60.** Your hospital runs an extremely strict infection control policy. This policy states that all staff must not wear jewellery, watches or hand items (excluding medicinal gloves) below the elbow when working in clinical areas. However, wedding rings are allowed. Just as you walk into the surgical ward, you notice that your colleague has failed to remove the expensive-looking watch on his wrist. Although he hasn't touched anything, he has not made any attempt to take it off either.

**Take a look at the responses below, and then rank them from most appropriate to least appropriate.**

A – Politely draw your colleague's attention to his mistake. Tell him that because he has breached the infection control policy, you will have no choice but to report him to senior management.

B – Tell your colleague that as a result of his error, hundreds of people could die.

C – Push the hospital emergency alarm. This is a code-red situation, and your friend must be quarantined.

D – Take your friend to one side and tell him that if he doesn't take off his watch, you'll take it off for him…

E – Ask your friend to go back outside, take off his watch and clean his wrist thoroughly. Make sure he doesn't touch anything on the way out.

| 1 | 2 | 3 | 4 | 5 |
|---|---|---|---|---|
|   |   |   |   |   |

**Q61.** You are working in the geriatric ward, and have recently been treating a patient named Mrs Figgins. It's coming up to Christmas, and it's a particularly busy time at the hospital. Many of the nurses are complaining about a lack of beds for sick patients.

Mrs Figgins has recently been declared fit for discharge. However, before she about to leave, she approaches you and says the following:

**Mrs Figgins:** *'Hi, Doctor Osbourne. I don't mean to be a pain, but I really don't feel comfortable going home right now. I know my shoulder is better, but I live all by myself, and I don't know what will happen if something goes wrong.'*

**Take a look at the responses below, and then rank them from most appropriate to least appropriate.**

A – Inform Mrs Figgins that she can stay at the hospital, but she'll have to sleep on the floor.

B – Tell Mrs Figgins that the problems she has discussed can be resolved by an external social care team, and are nothing to do with the hospital.

C – Sit down with Mrs Figgins and ask her to elaborate on her concerns.

D – Arrange with the ward manager to delay Mrs Figgins's discharge, whilst these issues are dealt with.

E – Speak to the nursing team about how Mrs Figgins's problem can be resolved.

| 1 | 2 | 3 | 4 | 5 |
|---|---|---|---|---|
|   |   |   |   |   |

**Q62.** You are an FY2 working in the paediatric ward. As you get ready to finish your shift for the day, you notice a junior doctor named Ian opening up the controlled drugs cupboard, and putting several vials into his pocket. Upon noticing you, he tries to act nonchalant, as if nothing has happened:

**Ian:** *'Alright, mate? Just finishing your shift? It's been a long day!'*

**You:** *'What's that you put in your pocket?'*

**Ian:** *'It's nothing, don't worry about it.'*

**Take a look at the responses below, and then rank them from most appropriate to least appropriate.**

A – Ask Ian to empty his pockets, and accuse him of stealing from the hospital.

B – Allow Ian to leave, but then approach the head matron of the paediatric ward about what you have seen.

C – Loudly accuse Ian of being a drug addict.

D – Tell Ian that if he puts the drugs back, you won't tell anyone.

E – Tell Ian that he needs to put the drugs back immediately, and come with you to the Chief physician's office.

| 1 | 2 | 3 | 4 | 5 |
|---|---|---|---|---|
|   |   |   |   |   |

**Q63.** It is Christmas time, and the hospital is extremely busy. Just before a night shift is about to start, one of your colleagues calls in sick. This happens just as you are leaving. Later that night, you go out to a club, and spot her drinking and partying with her friends. She does not seem ill in the slightest. You will be working with the same staff member in two days' time, on the same shift.

**Take a look at the responses below, and then rank them from most appropriate to least appropriate.**

A – Wait until the next shift, when you are both working together, to confront your colleague about her behaviour. If she cannot provide a suitable explanation, then take this to a senior manager.

B – Leave the club, and call the hospital, to inform them about your colleague's behaviour. They need to be notified at once.

C – Ignore it. It's nothing to do with you.

D – Approach your colleague in the club, and tell her that if she doesn't want you to report her, she'll need to buy you a few drinks.

E – Wait until the next shift, to confront your colleague about her behaviour. Tell her that if she does it again, you'll report her.

| 1 | 2 | 3 | 4 | 5 |
|---|---|---|---|---|
|   |   |   |   |   |

**Q64.** You are working the night shift at a hospital. The patient you are most pre-occupied with, is a man named Mr Lewishham. Your team are a little bit stumped by Mr Lewishham's condition, and can't work out what to prescribe him. Eventually, one of your team suggests that they go and see the registrar, to get his opinion on the case. Everyone agrees that this is a good idea. Later, the member of your team returns. She seems very upset. Taking you to one side, she informs you that she caught the registrar watching pornography in his office, using the hospital internet.

**Take a look at the responses below, and then rank them from most appropriate to least appropriate.**

A – Reassure your colleague that this is something which will be taken very seriously. Immediately go to find the senior site practitioner.

B – Reassure your colleague that it's not her fault, and she shouldn't be embarrassed, but that the registrar can use his free time however he wishes.

C – Immediately go to registrar's office and confront him about his behaviour.

D – Ask Mr Lewishham what he thinks about the registrar watching pornography.

E – Ask your colleague if she would be happy to submit a written report on what she saw. Following this, go with her to the head of medicine's office to discuss the incident.

| 1 | 2 | 3 | 4 | 5 |
|---|---|---|---|---|
|   |   |   |   |   |

**Q65.** For the past few months, you have been treating a patient named Chad. Chad is a frequent visitor to the hospital, owing to his participation in physical sports at college. In the past 2 months alone, Chad has been in the hospital 5 times for injuries ranging from sports related head wounds, to a dislocated shoulder. Chad is exceedingly arrogant, and takes great pleasure in informing the male staff about the many women whom he has 'on the go'. On many occasions, Chad has actually come into the hospital with one girl, and left with another.

Today, Chad is due to be discharged from the hospital again. Just before he leaves, he has the following conversation with you:

**Chad:** 'And tonight, I'm going on a date with Melanie. Tomorrow, it's Jane. Have you got anyone to come home to, doctor?'

**You:** 'I don't think that's any of your business, Chad.'

**Chad:** 'Haha, of course you haven't, you loser! Meanwhile, I'm just irresistible.'

**Take a look at the responses below, and then rank them from most appropriate to least appropriate.**

A – Tell Chad that next time he comes back to the hospital, you won't be treating him.

B – Tell Chad that next time he comes back to the hospital, you won't be treating him.

C – Tell Chad that he should start treating women with more respect, if he ever wishes to be happy.

D – Tell Chad that you hope his sporting career is a failure.

E – Tell Chad that you don't need to put up with abuse from patients. Discharge him.

| 1 | 2 | 3 | 4 | 5 |
|---|---|---|---|---|
|   |   |   |   |   |

---

**Q66.** You are working as a surgical FY2. Whilst participating in rounds, you arrive at the bed of a 15-year-old male patient. As per usual, a series of discussions takes place about the condition of the patient and what the best solution would be. However, at the end of the discussion, the patient themselves speaks up. He points directly to your colleague, who has an extremely nervous disposition, and says the following:

**Patient:** *'You better get this operation right, because if my surgery goes wrong, I'll sue YOU!'*

Your colleague seems extremely distressed by this, and you are worried about her ability to participate in the surgery later.

**Take a look at the responses below, and then rank them from most appropriate to least appropriate.**

A – Ignore your concerns. Your colleague is a grown woman, she can handle it.

B – Speak to the head of the surgical team for that operation, and voice your concerns over your colleague's mindset.

C – Sit down with your colleague in private, and discuss how the patient's comments made her feel. Reassure her that you have the utmost confidence in her ability to take part in the operation.

D – Ask the head of the surgical team to consider removing your colleague from the operation.

E – Approach the patient and demand that he apologises.

| 1 | 2 | 3 | 4 | 5 |
|---|---|---|---|---|
|   |   |   |   |   |

**Q67.** For the past few weeks, you have been treating an entertainment performer for spinal and neck injuries. The entertainer is an amateur professional wrestler Unfortunately, scan results came back today that reveal the entertainer will not be able to perform in the ring again – with any significant bumps or drops presenting a genuine risk to her life. You will need to break the news to her.

**Take a look at the responses below, and then rank them from most appropriate to least appropriate.**

A – Sit down with the patient, and inform her that the scan results give her very little hope of wrestling again in the future.

B – Sit down with the patient, in a quiet and sensitive manner, to discuss her options moving forward. Ask her whether she has any friends/relatives whom she wants to discuss things with.

C – Inform the patient that while the scan results are extremely negative, you have hope that she'll be able to wrestle again in the future.

D – Ask a junior doctor to break the news. You have better things to do.

E – Tell the patient, in a quiet and sensitive manner, that the scan results show she won't be able to wrestle again. Book her an appointment with the counselling team.

| 1 | 2 | 3 | 4 | 5 |
|---|---|---|---|---|
|   |   |   |   |   |

**Q68.** You are an FY1 working in the paediatric ward. Two of your colleagues recently started dating, but have an extremely difficult relationship, and are prone to breaking up. This occurred last week, and has made the atmosphere within the ward extremely uncomfortable. Your colleagues have also commented on how uncomfortable things are, but are unwilling to speak to the pair, as they don't want to interfere in the relationship. Recently, the pair were assigned to work together on a particular case, but their discussions on the patient quickly turned into an angry shouting match – right in front of the child.

**Take a look at the responses below, and then rank them from most appropriate to least appropriate.**

A – Take both of your colleagues to one side, and inform them that their relationship is having a disruptive influence on the treatment of patients within the ward.

B – Gather a few of your other colleagues together, and sit down with the pair as a group, to discuss how things can be improved moving forward.

C – Go to the head of medicine, and ask for the pair to be placed in different sectors moving forward.

D – Try to take advantage of their recent breakup, by dating your male colleague yourself.

That way, there will be no more arguments.

E – Ignore it and say nothing.

| 1 | 2 | 3 | 4 | 5 |
|---|---|---|---|---|
|   |   |   |   |   |

> **Q69.** Two of your colleagues recently broke up, and there has been significant friction between the pair ever since. Despite working on the same ward, the pair barely speak to each other, and the atmosphere is extremely frosty. You are good friends with one party in the relationship, and belong to an online group chat with him and some colleagues. Recently, after a huge argument, your colleague resorted to sharing round explicit pictures of his ex. Many people in the workplace have seen these, and your colleague is continuing to show others in the workplace too. He has also published them on his social media page.
>
> His ex-partner doesn't seem to be aware of this.

**Take a look at the responses below, and then rank them from most appropriate to least appropriate.**

A – Immediately confront your colleague and tell him that he needs to stop sharing the images around.

B – Go to his ex-partner and explain to her what your colleague has done.

C – Go to a senior doctor and ask them what they believe the best course of action would be.

D – Tell your colleague that he has broken the law by sharing these images, and that he needs to hand himself in to the police.

E – Tell your colleague that as a result of his behaviour, you will have no choice but to report him to the police.

| 1 | 2 | 3 | 4 | 5 |
|---|---|---|---|---|
|   |   |   |   |   |

**Q70.** A very distressed women has come into A&E, with her 19-year-old son. Her son has taken an overdose of paracetamol tablets. The woman is begging you to treat him, as she believes he will die. Although the boy is not showing any signs of illness yet, you have the following conversation with him:

**You:** 'When did you take the tablets, and how many did you take?'

**Boy:** 'I'm not telling you anything. It's my choice to die.'

**Mum:** 'Please Johnny, please tell the doctor!'

Despite further encouragement, the boy refuses to give you any more information.

**Take a look at the responses below, and then rank them from most appropriate to least appropriate.**

A – Treat Johnny under the mental health act.

B – Tell Johnny that if he won't cooperate, you will need to enforce cannulation.

C – Discharge Johnny. There's nothing you can do if he won't cooperate.

D – Ask the nurses whether they think it's worth treating Johnny under the mental capacity act.

E – Inform Johnny's mother that if her son doesn't cooperate, there could be criminal charges levelled against her.

| 1 | 2 | 3 | 4 | 5 |
|---|---|---|---|---|
|   |   |   |   |   |

**Q71.** You are working as a junior doctor in the paediatric ward. You have only recently started working within this section, but already you feel very uncomfortable. The entire team is made up of senior staff, and they are making it very evident that you aren't welcome. Many of their comments are patronising, and it feels like you are being victimised because of your junior status within the ward. As a result of their behaviour, since you started working in the ward, it does not feel as if you have learned very much.

**Take a look at the responses below, and then rank them from most appropriate to least appropriate.**

A – Try and organise a sit-down meeting with your senior colleagues. Accuse them of bullying and harassment, and inform them that they are a disgrace to the profession.

B – Next time someone makes a patronising comment, call them out in front of the patients.

C – Ask your colleagues from other departments in the hospital for advice on what to do.

D – Approach a senior member of staff from outside of the ward for guidance on how you should deal with this. Ideally, this should be your educational supervisor.

E – Ignore it, and resolve to prove to the senior doctors in the ward that you have what it takes to survive.

| 1 | 2 | 3 | 4 | 5 |
|---|---|---|---|---|
|   |   |   |   |   |

**Q72.** A patient who was recently discharged from the hospital has made a formal complaint about her treatment. She claims that the medical team who were responsible for her, which was your team, were clumsy, disorganised and unwelcoming. You are aware that one of your colleagues in particular, named Chris, did not perform to his best on this patient. This was largely owing to personal difficulties at home.

Today, a senior doctor has called you into his office to discuss the situation. He is demanding to know who is to blame.

**Take a look at the responses below, and then rank them from most appropriate to least appropriate.**

A – Inform the senior doctor that it's all Chris's fault, and that he was to blame for all of the mistakes that occurred when dealing with this patient.

B – Tell the senior doctor that no one person is to blame for the entire problem, and that all members of the team must share the responsibility equally.

C – Tell the senior doctor that although you did your very best with this patient, other members of the team let you down.

D – Tell the senior doctor that every person in the team must share the blame equally for what occurred, but certain members were in the midst of personal issues while dealing with the patient.

E – Tell the senior doctor that certain members of your team did not perform to their best, but for this the entire team must share the responsibility.

| 1 | 2 | 3 | 4 | 5 |
|---|---|---|---|---|
|   |   |   |   |   |

**Q73.** Over the past few days, you have been treating a man named Gregg for an infection. Unfortunately, when his blood test results came back, it was revealed that Gregg is HIV positive. Gregg has revealed to you that he isn't intending on telling his new partner about this diagnosis, because he's scared that she will leave him. The two have not yet had sexual intercourse, but for religious reasons don't believe in using sexual protection.

**Take a look at the responses below, and then rank them from most appropriate to least appropriate.**

A – Inform Gregg that if he does not notify his partner, as a doctor you have a legal responsibility to notify her yourself.

B – Tell Gregg that he won't need to inform his partner, just as long as he starts using sexual protection.

C – Tell Gregg that he has a moral responsibility to notify his partner, but not a legal responsibility.

D – Tell Gregg that even though he has HIV, there's a good chance he can be cured.

E – Tell Gregg that he could be subject to criminal prosecution if he fails to notify his partner about his condition, in advance of having intercourse with her.

| 1 | 2 | 3 | 4 | 5 |
|---|---|---|---|---|
|   |   |   |   |   |

---

**Q74.** You are working as an FY2 in the Gynaecology ward. As you pass one of the beds, you hear a conversation between one of the nurses – Pauline, and a male member of staff – Graham.

**Graham:** *'Don't ever interrupt me like that again, Pauline.'*

**Pauline:** *'I didn't interrupt you, I was really polite. I thought you ought to know that Mrs Flaherty was showing negative symptoms.'*

**Graham:** *'Look, lady. I'm a senior doctor here. You're just a nurse. You're a nobody. I've worked my way up, you work on the desk. I don't need your input.'*

Later on, you see Pauline standing by the desk looking extremely upset. She confesses to you that Graham is frequently rude and demeaning towards her and the other nurses.

**Take a look at the responses below, and then rank them from most appropriate to least appropriate.**

A – Encourage Pauline to speak to some of the other nurses, and then take the issue to senior management.

B – Tell Pauline that she shouldn't have interrupted Graham.

C – Find a member of senior management, with whom you can discuss the issue.

D – Confront Graham about his behaviour. Accuse him of being disrespectful towards the nurses.

E – Speak to the other nurses about how they feel on the issue.

| 1 | 2 | 3 | 4 | 5 |
|---|---|---|---|---|
|   |   |   |   |   |

**Q75.** You are an FY2 at your local hospital. Unfortunately you have been suffering from severe insomnia lately. The last time you attempted to work without sleep, you performed extremely poorly, and made a number of bad mistakes.

Last night, you barely got any sleep. You know you cannot work without sleep, and you don't want to harm the patients. However, you know that if you call in sick, you will be risking your job.

**Take a look at the responses below, and then rank them from most appropriate to least appropriate.**

A – Call the consultant to explain the situation, and tell him that you feel you would only be harming the patients by coming into work in this state.

B – Try and wake yourself up with a coffee, and go into work.

C – Call your friend working at the hospital, and ask her to try to cover your shift, whilst you take a quick nap.

D – Call the consultant to explain the situation, and offer to work extra time over the next few days to make up for it.

E – Call the consultant, but lie telling him that you are stuck in traffic. Take a quick nap for a few hours.

| 1 | 2 | 3 | 4 | 5 |
|---|---|---|---|---|
|   |   |   |   |   |

**Q76.** It's Wednesday and you have just started your shift, when you start to feel extremely ill. After an hour or so of trying to shake off the feeling, you head to the hospital toilet and vomit violently. Unfortunately things have got really busy, so it's a very bad time to leave.

**Take a look at the responses below, and then rank them from most appropriate to least appropriate.**

A – Pack your things and leave without telling anyone. They'll manage without you just fine.

B – Speak to your consultant and explain to her what has just happened. Ask her for permission to go home.

C – Take a paracetamol from the medicinal cupboard and continue with your shift.

D – Continue working for an hour, to see if the sickness wears off. If not, ask for permission to go home.

E – Speak to one of the nurses and ask them whether it's okay for you to leave.

| 1 | 2 | 3 | 4 | 5 |
|---|---|---|---|---|
|   |   |   |   |   |

**Q77.** You are sitting down to lunch with a colleague of yours – Miranda, who is also a close friend. Your friend seems extremely downcast today, and isn't responding much to conversation. Suddenly, in the middle of lunch, she bursts into tears:

**Miranda:** *'I can't stand it anymore, I just can't do it! My consultant is an absolute nightmare. It's like he expects me to know everything about everything. Do I look like an encyclopaedia of medical knowledge? I only just started here and I can't cope anymore. Honestly, the next time he asks me something I'm going to punch him, I swear it.'*

**Take a look at the responses below, and then rank them from most appropriate to least appropriate.**

A – Tell Miranda that she needs to get a grip of herself if she wants to succeed in medicine.

B – Tell Miranda that she needs to have a talk with her consultant about how she feels. Offer to go with her for support, if she would prefer.

C – Sympathise with Miranda and implore her to go into more detail about how she is feeling.

D – Speak to a senior doctor about Miranda's troubles.

E – Go and speak to Miranda's consultant by yourself.

| 1 | 2 | 3 | 4 | 5 |
|---|---|---|---|---|
|   |   |   |   |   |

**Q78.** You are working on the paediatric ward during the evening shift, when there is an enormous commotion behind you. A young male, who is 14 years old and suffers from schizophrenia, has become extremely agitated. A nurse tries to calm him down, but he punches her in the face, and then attempts to leave through the exit door. You do not believe that he is of sound mental state to leave the ward.

**Take a look at the responses below, and then rank them from most appropriate to least appropriate.**

A – Immediately call security. They are the best placed people to deal with this, and restrain the patient, if necessary.

B – Run to the nurse's aid, to check whether she is okay after being punched.

C – Shout and yell at the patient to get back in his bed.

D – Take a calm and persuasive approach, to try and get the patient to return to his bed.

E – Try to tackle the patient, physically, yourself.

| 1 | 2 | 3 | 4 | 5 |
|---|---|---|---|---|
|   |   |   |   |   |

---

**Q79.** You are working in the A&E department, when a foreign man comes in experiencing stomach pains. He speaks extremely poor English. After some minor questioning, it is established that the man is suffering from constipation. After providing the man with the necessary medication, the man confides in you that he is on the run from the police. He begs you not to tell anyone.

**Take a look at the responses below, and then rank them from most appropriate to least appropriate.**

A – Tell the man that unfortunately you have no choice but to call the police.

B – Call up the department who are in charge of international patient issues, and ask them to send a representative down to discuss the issue.

C – Tell the man that he needs to leave the hospital within the next 10 minutes, or you'll call the police.

D – Go to the front desk and ask the nurse in charge what should be done.

E – Pass the patient over to another colleague.

| 1 | 2 | 3 | 4 | 5 |
|---|---|---|---|---|
|   |   |   |   |   |

---

**Q80.** You are an FY2, working on the surgical team. You are due to take part in an operation in 15 minutes time. Unfortunately, nobody seems to be able to locate your colleague Maureen – who will also be taking part in the operation. The head of the surgical team has asked you to go and find her. After a quick search, you find her in the breakroom, fast asleep.

Upon waking Maureen up, she confesses to you that she feels extremely tired, and just had a quick nap to try and combat this, although it doesn't seem to have worked.

**Take a look at the responses below, and then rank them from most appropriate to least appropriate.**

A – Ask Maureen whether she feels capable of performing the operation.

B – Tell Maureen that she needs to speak to the head of the surgical team, and tell him that she's too tired to participate in the operation.

C – Tell Maureen that the operation is taking place in 10 minutes, so she'd better wake herself up before then.

D – Tell Maureen that she can go back to sleep. You'll find a suitable replacement for her.

E – Ask Maureen to come with you to the head of the surgical team, so that you can explain why she won't be participating.

| 1 | 2 | 3 | 4 | 5 |
|---|---|---|---|---|
|   |   |   |   |   |

**Q81.** You have been working in your current hospital for two years now. Recently a junior doctor joined the staff. Her name is Rebecca. Rebecca has only been at the hospital for three weeks, but you have noticed that she is avoiding dealing directly with patients, and seems to be all too happy to pass them off onto other doctors or staff. When confronted about this, Rebecca claims that she really dislikes working directly with people, and is quite scared of talking to patients.

**Take a look at the responses below, and then rank them from most appropriate to least appropriate.**

A – Tell Rebecca that if she dislikes working with people, she's probably in the wrong career.

B – Tell Rebecca that this is a serious problem, and she needs to speak to her clinical supervisor in order to try and resolve it.

C – Tell Rebecca that she needs to try and overcome her fear of people if she is to succeed as a doctor.

D – Sympathise with Rebecca, and encourage her to try and be brave with patients in future. Offer to help her out with her next patient.

E – Tell Rebecca that if she doesn't improve her patient skills, she is liable to be fired from the hospital.

| 1 | 2 | 3 | 4 | 5 |
|---|---|---|---|---|
|   |   |   |   |   |

**Q82.** For the past few days, you have been treating a young man who was involved in a severe car accident. The man's brother, Aaron, has been at the hospital every single day since the accident, waiting for his sibling to wake up. Unfortunately the prognosis is not good. On Friday evening, the patient starts crashing, and the team is forced to begin resuscitation attempts. The man's brother becomes extremely distressed:

**Aaron:** *'What the hell is happening? Do something, please!'*

**Nurse:** *'Please sir, I'm going to have to ask you to leave the room.'*

**Aaron:** *'No! No way, I'm staying right here.'*

**Nurse:** *'Sir, please. I assure you we will do everything that we possibly can to help your brother but we need you to leave the room immediately.'*

**Aaron:** *'No!'*

**Take a look at the responses below, and then rank them from most appropriate to least appropriate.**

A – Tell Aaron that he needs to leave the room immediately, or you will call security to escort him out.

B – Correct the nurse. Tell her that Aaron is allowed to stay, but he must remain at the back of the room and not behave disruptively.

C – Tell Aaron that he is allowed to stay, but he must be prepared for the worst.

D – Tell Aaron that he can stay in the room. Ask a member of the ward staff to stand next to him and explain what is happening.

E – Tell the nurse that she is wrong to try and make Aaron leave. He can stay, but he must remain completely silent during the process.

| 1 | 2 | 3 | 4 | 5 |
|---|---|---|---|---|
|   |   |   |   |   |

**Q83.** You are working as an FY1 in the Emergency Care Unit. You've been working in this unit for several weeks now, but you are growing concerned with the level of work that's being given to you. So far, you've only been assigned minor admin-based tasks, and have had very little practice or opportunity to enhance your clinical skills. Today, one of the senior doctors asked you to fetch him a cup of tea, whilst he worked on a patient.

**Take a look at the responses below, and then rank them from most appropriate to least appropriate.**

A – Approach the doctor who asked you to make him a tea, and question him over whether he thinks you are fit to work here.

B – Speak to your supervising consultant about the issue. They are well placed to give you advice.

C – Accept that there is a bedding in period for junior doctors in hospitals, and that it will take time before the doctors in the unit can trust you.

D – Try and make an appointment with the Chief Physician, to see what can be done to resolve this.

E – Try and make yourself available for as many jobs as possible in future. If you can prove to the doctors what you are capable of, then this could be resolved.

| 1 | 2 | 3 | 4 | 5 |
|---|---|---|---|---|
|   |   |   |   |   |

**Q84.** You have recently been placed on rotation with a highly respected consultant, and you are desperate to go out of your way to create a good impression. On Tuesday, the consultant approaches you and says the following:

**Consultant:** *'Hi, Linda, I'd like you to complete a research project for me. This needs to be done by Friday. Thanks!'*

Unfortunately, you already have three other projects on the go right now, and all of them are due for Friday! You know that it's pretty much impossible for you to complete all 4 of these assignments for the due date.

**Take a look at the responses below, and then rank them from most appropriate to least appropriate.**

A – Ignore the other projects, in order to make sure this one is finished. You could really advance your career if this goes well.

B – Get in touch with all of the other project supervisors, explaining to them that you need to give this new project priority, as it will impress the consultant.

C – Speak to the consultant and inform her that unfortunately you have three other projects on the go at the moment. However, if she would be willing to extend the deadline, then you could get it completed for next week.

D – Tell the consultant that you won't be able to take part in the project, as you have other projects to complete.

E – Ask the consultant whether you should give her task priority over the other three projects.

| 1 | 2 | 3 | 4 | 5 |
|---|---|---|---|---|
|   |   |   |   |   |

**Q85.** You are working in the emergency care unit on a busy Friday night. An FY1 approaches you, and informs you that although his shift was meant to finish at 5pm, the time is now 9pm. He still has a number of tasks to complete, and needs to be home for a dinner date with his partner at 10pm. Over the past few months, his relationship has started to suffer, as he is coming home later and later from work, and is frequently exhausted.

You need to give him some advice on what to do.

**Take a look at the responses below, and then rank them from most appropriate to least appropriate.**

A – Tell him that he needs to go and see his supervising consultant, to discuss the impact that his exhaustion could have on patient wellbeing.

B – Tell him that he needs to go and see his supervising consultant, to discuss the fact that he is working past his expected timeframe, on some occasions.

C – Tell him that he should avoid going to see his supervising consultant, because his inability to manage the workload could reflect poorly on his performance.

D – Tell him that he needs to go and see his supervising consultant, to discuss the impact that his workload is having on his personal life.

E – Tell him that he needs to go and see his supervising consultant, to discuss working different shift patterns.

| 1 | 2 | 3 | 4 | 5 |
|---|---|---|---|---|
|   |   |   |   |   |

**Q86.** You are working within one of the most respected and well-renowned hospitals in the country. You have been assigned to the gynaecology ward, and are treating a patient named Abigail, for a suspected STI. Following your meeting with her, she says the following:

**Abigail:** *'Look, doctor, this is really embarrassing. I've got a girlfriend, and if she finds out that I've been cheating on her then it will all be over. I know this hospital has a really great reputation, but I don't want my case to be published in any research papers or anything like that.'*

**Take a look at the responses below, and then rank them from most appropriate to least appropriate.**

A – Inform Abigail that she has no choice in whether her case is published in a research paper.

B – Inform Abigail that the hospital would never publish information such as this without gaining her full consent beforehand.

C – Tell Abigail that although her case won't be published, she should do the right thing and inform her girlfriend.

D – Encourage Abigail to speak to the hospital legal department, who can give better advice on the publication of such material.

E – Ask Abigail whether she would pursue legal action, if the hospital published her case without her permission.

| 1 | 2 | 3 | 4 | 5 |
|---|---|---|---|---|
|   |   |   |   |   |

**Q87.** The time is 4pm, and you have just finished your shift. You've worked for 2 hours extra than the allocated shift end time, and can't wait to get home. Throughout the day, you've been dealing with a patient named Mrs Harley, who is suffering from a blood infection. As you pack up your things, you are approached by Michelle, an FY2, who is just starting her shift. She will be dealing with Mrs Harley for the evening. After you attempt to give her a quick update on Mrs Harley's situation, and what needs to be done, Michelle informs you that she won't be able to help Mrs Harley tonight, as she has too many other patients to see. She tells you that you need to stick around to treat Mrs Harley.

**Take a look at the responses below, and then rank them from most appropriate to least appropriate.**

A – Tell Michelle that you will try to find another doctor to treat Mrs Harley, before you leave.

B – Agree with Michelle. Stay at the hospital so that you can treat Mrs Harley.

C – Tell Michelle that Mrs Harley is her patient, and that she will need to take responsibility for treating her.

D – Tell Michelle that she needs to speak to the Chief Physician, if she doesn't want to treat Mrs Harley.

E – Leave a note on Mrs Harley's bed, then go home. Hopefully another doctor will see it and take action.

| 1 | 2 | 3 | 4 | 5 |
|---|---|---|---|---|
|   |   |   |   |   |

**Q88.** You are working the evening shift at your local hospital. Halfway through your shift, you receive a text from your FY2 – Dr Blake, informing you that she is running over an hour late due to her child being sick. She does not mention any of her patients. Half an hour later, one of her patients, named Martin, approaches you.

**Martin:** *'Hi Doctor Bradley, can I talk to you about something?'*

**You:** *'Sure, Martin. What can I help you with?'*

**Martin:** *'I've got a dinner date with my wife in an hour's time. Dr Blake said that she would discharge me once she got into work, but now I can't find her anywhere.'*

**Take a look at the responses below, and then rank them from most appropriate to least appropriate.**

A – Discharge Martin, so that he can have the dinner date with his wife.

B – Go and find a senior colleague, who can review Martin's condition before he is discharged.

C – Explain to Martin that you don't have the power to discharge patients, so he will just have to wait until Dr Blake arrives at the hospital.

D – Call Dr Blake and ask her whether she agreed to discharge Martin.

E – Allow Martin to leave without signing a discharge form.

| 1 | 2 | 3 | 4 | 5 |
|---|---|---|---|---|
|   |   |   |   |   |

**Q89.** You are working with your consultant – Dr Chaudry, in the paediatric ward. The two of you are assessing a young girl, who has come in complaining about significant pain in her lower back. Halfway through the assessment, a nurse approaches you:

**Nurse:** *'Hi, I'm really sorry to interrupt, but there's a bit of a developing situation upstairs. Mr Fletcher is in a bad way...I think we need your advice, Dr Chaudry.'*

**Dr Chaudry:** *'I'm really busy at the moment, can it wait?'*

**Nurse:** *'No, not really. We need you right away.'*

**Dr Chaudry:** *'For goodness sake, fine. Sorry Miranda, you'll need to finish this up.'*

**You:** *'Me? What do I need to do?'*

In response, Dr Chaudry asks you to perform a procedure on the young girl that you have never done before.

**Take a look at the responses below, and then rank them from most appropriate to least appropriate.**

A – Agree to perform the procedure, while Dr Chaudry deals with the patient upstairs.

B – Inform the patient that although you've never done this procedure before, you'll give it your best shot.

C – Take Dr Chaudry to one side and ask him for advice on the best way to perform the procedure.

D – Ask another colleague to perform the procedure instead of you.

E – Tell Dr Chaudry that you have never done this procedure before, so it would be too risky for you to do so now.

| 1 | 2 | 3 | 4 | 5 |
|---|---|---|---|---|
|   |   |   |   |   |

**Q90.** You are working in the paediatric ward, as an FY2. A 5-year-old girl was recently admitted to the ward, suffering from severe abdominal pain. Preliminary assessments have not yielded any results, and therefore the team have requested that the patient has an X-ray on her chest. Unfortunately, when the results come back it, it appears that the scan was done incorrectly and will need to be re-performed. When you tell the family about this, they are livid, and react extremely badly. They want to make a formal complaint.

**Take a look at the responses below, and then rank them from most appropriate to least appropriate.**

A – Apologise to the family, and assure them that you will personally ensure that the scan is done properly this time.

B – Tell the family that mistakes happen, and they will just have to accept that you need another scan.

C – Tell the family that this is the fault of the relevant department, and not anything to do with you.

D – Apologise to the family, and carefully lay out the procedure for making a formal complaint.

E – Apologise to the family, and offer to do the next scan yourself.

| 1 | 2 | 3 | 4 | 5 |
|---|---|---|---|---|
|   |   |   |   |   |

---

**Q91.** You are taking part in medical ward rounds, when it is pointed out that one of your colleagues, Craig, is missing. The consultant in charge of the rounds requests that you go and find him. He tells you that if you can't find Craig within 5 minutes, then you should return immediately. Upon locating Craig, you find him in the staff room, playing games on his mobile phone.

**You:** 'Craig, you are supposed to be joining us for rounds!'

**Craig:** 'That's pretty boring, I'll stay here thanks.'

---

**Take a look at the responses below, and then rank them from most appropriate to least appropriate.**

A – Leave Craig to his own devices. Return to the consultant and tell him about what happened.

B – Try and convince Craig to join you on rounds. Tell him that you will need to report this behaviour if not.

C – Go back to the consultant, and tell him that you couldn't find Craig.

D – Sit down with Craig and question him over his lack of interest in medical rounds.

E – Ask Craig about what his top score on the game is. Challenge him to a match.

| 1 | 2 | 3 | 4 | 5 |
|---|---|---|---|---|
|   |   |   |   |   |

---

**Q92.** You are taking part in medical ward rounds. Following assessment of an elderly patient, the consultant in charge of the rounds – Dr Smith – decides that the patient will need an MRI scan. Although nobody in the group says anything, you are aware of a ripple of discontent. Later on, you hear the following conversation between your colleagues who took part in the session:

**Melanie:** 'That Dr Smith doesn't have a clue what he's doing, I'll tell you.'

**John:** 'I know right. Why the hell did he order an MRI scan? What a waste of time!'

**Steve:** 'I know...he's clueless. I'm already a better doctor than him. I didn't want to say anything though, because it's bad to contradict the consultant, you know?'

**Melanie:** 'Yeah, I know what you mean. I don't think we should argue with him. If he gets it wrong then that's his fault.'

---

**Take a look at the responses below, and then rank them from most appropriate to least appropriate.**

A – Say nothing. This issue has nothing to do with you.

B – Approach your colleagues and encourage them to speak to the consultant if they disagree with his decision making.

C – Approach your colleagues and inform them that you will have no choice but to report this conversation to the consultant.

D – Approach the consultant and tell him that a few of your colleagues are unsure about his decision-making.

E – Ask your colleagues what could be done to make them feel more confident about raising their opinion during rounds.

| 1 | 2 | 3 | 4 | 5 |
|---|---|---|---|---|
|   |   |   |   |   |

---

**Q93.** There is a new senior doctor operating in the emergency care unit. His name is Dr Barnes. The two of you are assessing a patient named Mr Hibbs, who is recovering from a lung condition. You have working in the unit for a while, and with Mr Hibbs for a significant period of time – much longer than the new doctor has. In the past, Mr Hibbs has suffered allergic reactions to certain types of drugs, and some of these incidents were nearly fatal. As a result, it was decided by the staff that he would no longer be given these drugs or similar types. Unfortunately the new doctor has asked you to prescribe the same type of drug to the patient on this occasion. When you question him, he becomes irate:

**Dr Barnes:** *'Are you questioning my expertise? How dare you! You think because you've been here a while you're now Mr Big Shot? Don't forget that you are just a junior doctor, kid.'*

**Take a look at the responses below, and then rank them from most appropriate to least appropriate.**

A – Immediately apologise and agree with Dr Barnes. You spoke out of turn here.

B – Ask Dr Barnes to take a look at the patient history, to show him why he's wrong.

C – Tell Dr Barnes that he needs to treat you with more respect. Inform him that Mr Hibbs could die if he is prescribed with this type of drug.

D – Ask one of the other doctors to explain to Dr Barnes why he is wrong.

E – Inform Dr Barnes that you are indeed, a big shot. Tell him that if he prescribes Mr Hibbs with the drugs, he will be risking his career.

| 1 | 2 | 3 | 4 | 5 |
|---|---|---|---|---|
|   |   |   |   |   |

**Q94.** You have been treating a patient named Earl for a number of weeks now. Earl is a professional sportsman, who is currently in the emergency care unit for a severe leg injury. Earl needs to go in for surgery. The surgery in question is extremely risky. If it doesn't go right, then Earl's career could be over.

Earl is due to have his operation in less than 24 hours. However, upon speaking to him, it becomes clear to you that is not fully aware of what the risks involved in the surgery are, or even what is being operated on. Despite this, Earl has already given his consent to the surgical team. You are part of the clinical medicine team.

**Take a look at the responses below, and then rank them from most appropriate to least appropriate.**

A – Consult with the surgical team. Ask them to send round a representative, who can ensure that Earl understands everything about the operation, before he goes into theatre.

B – Try and explain the risks involved in the surgery to Earl yourself.

C – Ignore the situation. Earl has signed a consent form, so it doesn't matter.

D – Tell Earl that it would be a good idea for him to speak to a specialist within the next 24 hours.

E – Ask Earl why he signed the consent form without proper understanding of the situation.

| 1 | 2 | 3 | 4 | 5 |
|---|---|---|---|---|
|   |   |   |   |   |

**Q95.** You are working in the geriatric ward. Unfortunately, one of your patients has been diagnosed with terminal lung cancer. He has elected to stay at the hospital, rather than go to a hospice, but his family have requested that he is given a private room at the hospital, so that he can spend his final moments in peace and privacy. You have agreed to fulfil this request. However, when you come in the next day, you find that one of the nurses has reversed the request. Upon confronting her, she informs you that there was only one private room left, and that this has been taken up by another patient – Mrs Fleming. You are aware of Mrs Fleming's condition. She is not seriously ill, and is due to be discharged within the next two days.

**Take a look at the responses below, and then rank them from most appropriate to least appropriate.**

A – Inform the nurse that your patient has a greater need for the room than Mrs Fleming.

B – Enquire with the nurse about why Mrs Fleming needs a private room.

C – Return to your patient and inform him that unfortunately there are no private rooms available.

D – Speak to the nurse about your patient's request. If she does not agree with you, take the issue to someone more senior.

E – Confront Mrs Fleming, asking her to leave the private room immediately.

| 1 | 2 | 3 | 4 | 5 |
|---|---|---|---|---|
|   |   |   |   |   |

**Q96.** You are working on a patient named Nathaniel. Nathaniel is 14 years old, and requires an MRI scan. You have booked him in for a test tomorrow, but recently received a response from the radiology department, informing you that they have rejected your request. There are no specified reasons for this.

The response comes from a member of the department named Chris, who you do not get on with. You suspect that Chris has rejected your request simply because he doesn't like you. Nathaniel's family are very anxious about his condition.

**Take a look at the responses below, and then rank them from most appropriate to least appropriate.**

A – Send a response back, accusing Chris of letting his personal feelings get in the way of good practice.

B – Give Chris the benefit of the doubt. Send a polite response back, asking the department why your request has been rejected, and what you can improve to ensure it gets accepted.

C – Go down to the radiology department and angrily confront Chris. If he won't listen to reason, it's time to get physical.

D – Speak to your clinical consultant about why the department rejected your request.

E – Go down to the radiology department and ask them about the case. Try and speak to another staff member than Chris, if possible.

| 1 | 2 | 3 | 4 | 5 |
|---|---|---|---|---|
|   |   |   |   |   |

**Q97.** You are working with an elderly patient, named Mr Barkley. Yesterday, Mr Barkley was diagnosed with terminal cancer, and he does not have long to live. Since Mr Barkley was admitted to hospital, his family have been there every single day to visit him. Mr Barkley has confessed to you that he doesn't want to tell his family about the terminal diagnosis, because he doesn't want to upset them. He has lied to his family, telling him that his condition is improving and he'll be out of hospital soon.

**Take a look at the responses below, and then rank them from most appropriate to least appropriate.**

A – Tell Mr Barkley that he is acting against the law, by failing to inform his family of the circumstances surrounding his illness.

B – Encourage Mr Barkley to participate in counselling sessions, so that he can come to terms with his illness, and be honest with his family.

C – Encourage Mr Barkley to be open and honest with his family about the circumstances surrounding his illness.

D – Ask Mr Barkley whether he wants you to inform his family, to make it easier for him.

E – Inform Mr Barkley that he cannot stay at the hospital unless he is honest with his family.

| 1 | 2 | 3 | 4 | 5 |
|---|---|---|---|---|
|   |   |   |   |   |

**Q98.** You are working with another FY1, named Cassie. The two of you have working together for a few weeks now. Although things started well, it has become apparent to you that Cassie is doing less and less work on the ward, and seems to be spending enormous amounts of time completing projects for various consultants. When you question her about this, she brushes it off as a minor issue. She does not seem prepared to change the way she's doing things.

**Take a look at the responses below, and then rank them from most appropriate to least appropriate.**

A – Ask Cassie if she would be happy to meet with you and your educational supervisor, to discuss the recent issues.

B – Tell Cassie that she is being highly unprofessional, and should consider resigning from the hospital.

C – Offer to help Cassie with the extra research projects that she is taking on.

D – Speak to the relevant ward consultant about the issue.

E – Ask your other colleagues whether they have had any issues with Cassie and her workload.

| 1 | 2 | 3 | 4 | 5 |
|---|---|---|---|---|
|   |   |   |   |   |

**Q99.** You have been working with a patient names Mrs Andrews for a few days now. Mrs Andrews is the mother of your close friend, Sue. The team have been running tests for a few days now, and unfortunately today the result has come back – Mrs Andrews has bowel cancer. After informing Mrs Andrews about the result, she tells you that she'd like to speak to Sue about it directly, and asks you not to tell her.

Later that day, Sue arrives at the hospital. She immediately approaches you and asks for news about her mother.

**Take a look at the responses below, and then rank them from most appropriate to least appropriate.**

A – Tell Sue that her mother has been diagnosed with bowel cancer.

B – Tell Sue that you will take her to see her mother, right away.

C – Tell Sue that she will need to book an appointment to see her mother.

D – Sit Sue down in a quiet room, and inform her that her mother has been diagnosed with a serious illness.

E – Ask another member of the team to escort Sue to her mother.

| 1 | 2 | 3 | 4 | 5 |
|---|---|---|---|---|
|   |   |   |   |   |

**Q100.** You are walking past the nurse's staff room, when you hear one of the nurses having a conversation with her colleague:

**Mandy:** *'Look, I've been working here for ten years now. All I'm saying is that nobody ever checks whether you are wearing gloves or whether you put disinfectant on your hands. Nobody checks, and nobody cares. Yesterday I walked around the ward picking my nose and nobody said a thing. You can get away with anything here.'*

**Sarah:** *'Mandy, that's awful!'*

**Mandy:** *'Yesterday I walked around the ward without washing my hands and nobody said a thing.'*

**Take a look at the responses below, and then rank them from most appropriate to least appropriate.**

A – Speak to Sarah once she leaves the staff room, to clarify what you have just heard. Ask her to come with you to see a senior member of the nursing staff.

B – Walk into the staffroom and berate Mandy for her comments. Call her unprofessional and disgusting.

C – Confront Mandy about her comments. Tell her that she is behaving unacceptably.

D – Resolve not to wash your hands next time you walk into the Emergency Care Unit.

E – Poke your head round the door and remind Mandy of why disinfectant, and wearing gloves, is important.

| 1 | 2 | 3 | 4 | 5 |
|---|---|---|---|---|
|   |   |   |   |   |

---

**Q101.** You are treating a professional footballer, who has been in a serious car accident. The patient is in stable condition, and has been recovering well over the past two weeks. Although he is not ready for discharge, the team are confident that he will be able to leave the hospital within two weeks.

Today, the footballer's manager has visited the hospital. He approaches you and says the following:

**Manager:** 'Listen, I want you to discharge Matthew. He's walking, talking…he's ready to get out of the hospital now.'

**You:** 'Matthew won't be ready for discharge for at least a week, and even then he won't be available to play football for a month or two. He needs time to recover.'

**Manager:** 'What? No way! Listen, here's £500. I need this guy out of hospital as soon as possible, or we'll get relegated. Please.'

**Take a look at the responses below, and then rank them from most appropriate to least appropriate.**

A – Tell the manager that if he wants you to discharge his player, it will take a lot more than £500.

B – Tell the manager that Matthew won't be discharged for at least a week, and that you won't accept his money.

C – Ask the manager to have a quiet chat with you, so that you can discuss the seriousness of his player's situation.

D – Tell the manager that you are willing to discharge Matthew, but only on the condition that he doesn't play football for a month.

E – Inform the manager that you support a rival team, so there's no chance of you discharging Matthew.

| 1 | 2 | 3 | 4 | 5 |
|---|---|---|---|---|
|   |   |   |   |   |

**Q102.** You are a junior doctor, working in the emergency care unit. At the end of his shift, the specialist consultant approaches you, and together you proceed to make an assessment of an elderly patient. At the end of your discussion, the consultant prescribes the patient with a course of antibiotics. He then goes home. 10 minutes later, you realise that the antibiotics prescribed are in contradiction to the other medicine being given to the patient.

**Take a look at the responses below, and then rank them from most appropriate to least appropriate.**

A – Find a senior colleague and bring the error to their attention. Ask them whether a different drug would be more suitable.

B – Visit your consultant at his home to discuss the issue.

C – Text your consultant, to enquire about the mistake.

D – Do nothing. The consultant must have prescribed this for a reason.

E – Tell the patient that there's been a mix up, and ask for him to be patient whilst you resolve the medication issue.

| 1 | 2 | 3 | 4 | 5 |
|---|---|---|---|---|
|   |   |   |   |   |

**Q103.** You are working in the A&E department for the evening. There is a man sitting in the waiting room, who is clearly extremely drunk. The man is being extremely rude to other patients, and seems to be upsetting some of them. At one point he gets up, stands in front of the desk, and demands to be seen right at that moment. The nurse tells him to wait his turn.

Although the man has not turned violent yet, your colleague confides in you that she is worried he will start acting aggressively.

**Take a look at the responses below, and then rank them from most appropriate to least appropriate.**

A – Call security to escort the man from the premises.

B – Ask the other patients in the waiting room whether the man's behaviour is upsetting them.

C – Ask the man to go outside, and come back when he has calmed down.

D – Take the man to one side and inform him that if he does not calm down, you will have to ask him to leave.

E – Try to treat the man as quickly as possible, so that he can leave.

| 1 | 2 | 3 | 4 | 5 |
|---|---|---|---|---|
|   |   |   |   |   |

**Q104.** You have made a mistake when treating an elderly patient. Although the mistake is not a major issue, and can be corrected, it has had a detrimental impact on her care and she has spent the past few days vomiting. As of yet, nobody seems to know that you did it.

**Take a look at the responses below, and then rank them from most appropriate to least appropriate.**

A – Approach the patient and admit that her bout of sickness was down to your error. Apologise profusely, and tell her that it won't happen again.

B – Go to your educational supervisor and admit that you made a mistake. Ask her what your next step should be.

C – Say nothing. Hopefully nobody will ever find out.

D – Resign. Hopefully this way you can avoid a potential lawsuit.

E – Consult with the legal team about what your next steps should be.

| 1 | 2 | 3 | 4 | 5 |
|---|---|---|---|---|
|   |   |   |   |   |

**Q105.** You have been working on the paediatric ward for number of weeks now. Although you feel like you are making great progress, you have run into problems with a senior doctor working on the ward. The doctor in question seems to be making frequent attempts to undermine you. On many occasions, he has approached you in front of patients, and openly questioned your diagnosis. Nobody else whom you have spoken to seems to have had any problems with this doctor.

When you confront the man about this issue, he informs you that he doesn't believe in your ability as a doctor, and that he is hoping you'll be let go from the hospital.

**Take a look at the responses below, and then rank them from most appropriate to least appropriate.**

A – Inform the doctor that his behaviour is extremely unprofessional, and that he's the one who should be let go.

B – Ask the doctor what you can do to convince him that you are capable and competent.

C – Ask the doctor to clarify the reasons why he feels you are a poor doctor.

D – Agree with the doctor. Resign immediately.

E – Inform the doctor that if he doesn't stop with this behaviour, you will report him to senior management.

| 1 | 2 | 3 | 4 | 5 |
|---|---|---|---|---|
|   |   |   |   |   |

**Q106.** You are just about to finish your shift. As you finalise things for the evening, preparing to hand over your notes to another FY2, you notice that one of your younger patients is about to consume his medication. The medication in question was prescribed by your consultant yesterday, and is to be taken twice daily. Your patient has four pills in his hand, and is clearly ready to consume them all. When you confront him about this, and take the pills away, the patient says the following:

**Patient:** *'My dad said that I have to take all four pills if I want to make the pain go away!'*

The patient's father has gone home for the evening, and won't be in till tomorrow.

**Take a look at the responses below, and then rank them from most appropriate to least appropriate.**

A – Tell the patient that he is to take two pills, and two pills only. Then go home.

B – Give the patient two pills, and leave the rest of the medication with the nursing team.

C – Once you leave work, call the patient's father and demand that he explain himself.

D – Give the patient two pills. Wait until the next day, to have a serious talk with the patient's father. Make the nursing team aware of what has just occurred.

E – Call the police, to report the patient's father.

| 1 | 2 | 3 | 4 | 5 |
|---|---|---|---|---|
|   |   |   |   |   |

**Q107.** You are working as an FY1 in the paediatric ward. One of your patients, a 5-year-old girl, is causing major problems for the staff. She continually pushes the nurse call button, without good reason. Today alone she has pushed the button on 4 separate occasions. Once to inform the nurses that her toe was a bit sore, once to announce to the nurses that it was raining outside, once to tell the nurses that there was a bird on the windowsill, and once to tell everyone the nurses that she'd run out of chocolate milk. The nurses on the ward are exasperated with her, and don't know what to do. The patient's parents won't be back at the hospital for another 2 days.

**Take a look at the responses below, and then rank them from most appropriate to least appropriate.**

A – March up to the girl and call her a spoilt little brat. Tell her that the next time she pushes the button without reason, there will be serious consequences.

B – Have a quiet chat with the girl, to try and explain why the nurse call button is so important, and must only be used on the most special of occasions.

C – Tell the nurses that the next time the button is pushed without good reason, they have permission to remove it altogether.

D – Call the patient's parents, and ask them if they can come in to have a quick word about her behaviour.

E – Tell the nurses that they need to be more sympathetic towards the child's behaviour.

| 1 | 2 | 3 | 4 | 5 |
|---|---|---|---|---|
|   |   |   |   |   |

**Q108.** You have just started your evening shift. Tonight you are due to meet a new patient, named Sophie. Sophie is a 30-year-old woman, who is also a famous pianist. She has just had elbow surgery. When you take a look at the notes for Sophie, you can see that she is recovering well and making good progress.

Unfortunately, when you approach her bed, Sophie's girlfriend approaches you. She seems extremely angry, and claims that Sophie is still suffering from pain in her elbow following the surgery.

You can see from the patient notes, that mild discomfort is a normal symptom given the operation that Sophie has just had.

**Take a look at the responses below, and then rank them from most appropriate to least appropriate.**

A – Assure the woman that you will take the utmost care of Sophie, and will now take steps to examine her elbow.

B – Ask the woman to calm down. Inform her that mild discomfort is a normal symptom following such an operation, but promise to examine Sophie's elbow anyway.

C – Tell the woman that since Sophie is still experiencing elbow pain, she'll probably need to go back in for repeat surgery.

D – Call security and ask them to escort Sophie's girlfriend out of the hospital.

E – Tell Sophie's girlfriend that you will have a discussion with the surgical team, and get back to her.

| 1 | 2 | 3 | 4 | 5 |
|---|---|---|---|---|
|   |   |   |   |   |

**Q109.** Today you are working in the Emergency Care Unit, as an FY2. A new junior doctor has recently joined the hospital. Her name is Melissa. Throughout the day, you notice that Melissa is extremely timid, and seems very reluctant to get hands on with paperwork based tasks – although she is happy to speak to patients directly and has a good bedside manner. At the end of the day, a colleague approaches you. She seems extremely nervous, and tells you that she suffers from severe dyslexia, so she is scared to fill in any prescription forms or drug charts.

**Take a look at the responses below, and then rank them from most appropriate to least appropriate.**

A – Sympathise with Melissa, but reinforce that this is a serious issue which she will need to deal with.

B – Tell Melissa that she has your full support in this issue, but that this could cause safety issues for patients.

C – Tell Melissa that this is something she should discuss with her educational supervisor, but that she has your full support.

D – Tell Melissa that unfortunately her dyslexia will likely mean that she has to resign.

E – Tell Melissa that you will raise her concerns with a senior member of staff.

| 1 | 2 | 3 | 4 | 5 |
|---|---|---|---|---|
|   |   |   |   |   |

**Q110.** Recently you have become aware that one of your FY2 colleagues is not putting in his share of work at the hospital. He is frequently late, disorganised and takes mid-work breaks to play on his phone. When you have questioned him about various medical matters, he seems vacant and can't give a good response. Unfortunately, nobody else seems to have noticed this. The individual in question is extremely popular. All of the senior staff get on with him very well, and all of your other colleagues love having him around. It seems like you are the only person who has spotted his behaviour. Upon questioning your colleagues about his poor behaviour, they all seem shocked and appalled at you raising the subject. Even your senior colleagues have refused to listen.

**Take a look at the responses below, and then rank them from most appropriate to least appropriate.**

A – Quietly start gathering video evidence of your colleague's ineptitude. Plan to show the video on the projector screen at the next big meeting.

B – Pass off your concerns as nothing. If nobody else can see it, then maybe it's just you.

C – Do your best to help out your colleague. Maybe he's just going through a temporary struggle.

D – See if you can arrange a meeting with a senior consultant to discuss the issue.

E – Take your colleague aside for a one-to-one chat, and inform him that you have noticed him struggling, even if nobody else has. Encourage him to go and see a senior manager about the situation.

| 1 | 2 | 3 | 4 | 5 |
|---|---|---|---|---|
|   |   |   |   |   |

**Q111.** You are working within the A&E department on a busy Friday night. Midway through your shift, you receive a phone call, informing you that your brother has been involved in a serious road accident and has been hospitalised. Naturally, your first inclination is to leave the hospital immediately to go and be with your family. However, when you explain the situation to your colleague, she says the following:

*'You can't leave, sorry. We're massively understaffed right now.'*

**Take a look at the responses below, and then rank them from most appropriate to least appropriate.**

A – Agree with your colleague and stay at the hospital. The wellbeing of patients must come first.

B – Seek out a senior member of staff, explain the situation, and ask for permission to leave.

C – Tell your colleague that she is wrong. Leave immediately.

D – Tell your colleague that you need to leave, but first try to find someone who can cover your shift.

E – Explain to your colleague that she is being quite insensitive, and that you need to leave immediately.

| 1 | 2 | 3 | 4 | 5 |
|---|---|---|---|---|
|   |   |   |   |   |

**Q112.** In the past few weeks, you have noticed that one of your colleagues, Henry, is spreading rumours about another colleague, Melvin. You know for a fact that these rumours are untrue, and that they could be harmful for the overall group dynamic between FY1s in the hospital. Upon confronting Henry about the rumours, and asking him to stop spreading them, Henry simply laughed in your face – and even threatened to start spreading rumours about you too!

Melvin does not seem to be aware of the rumours being spread.

**Take a look at the responses below, and then rank them from most appropriate to least appropriate.**

A – Approach Melvin and inform him about Henry's behaviour. He has a right to know about the rumours going around.

B – Ignore the situation. You have better things to do than deal with childish gossip.

C – Go to a senior manager and report the situation.

D – Ask your other colleagues to stop engaging with Henry in malicious behaviour. If everyone else stops, then he will have to as well.

E – Spread rumours yourself, to try and stop Henry.

| 1 | 2 | 3 | 4 | 5 |
|---|---|---|---|---|
|   |   |   |   |   |

**Q113.** You are just starting your shift in the geriatric ward. As you walk past the beds, one of the patients calls you over. She is in great pain, and seems very unhappy. She begs you to prescribe her with a laxative, and complains that she has not been to the toilet for over 48 hours. Upon further questioning, you discover that the doctor from the previous shift refused to prescribe her with a laxative, although you do not know why. Looking at the patient notes, it does not seem as if this would be a problem.

**Take a look at the responses below, and then rank them from most appropriate to least appropriate.**

A – Tell the patient that, because of her previous doctor's refusal to do so, you will also be unable to prescribe her with a laxative.

B – Tell the patient that she'll need to hold her bowels for at least another 24 hours if she wants a laxative.

C – See if you can get in touch with the doctor from the previous shift, to establish his reasons for refusing to prescribe a laxative.

D – Do a full assessment of the patient yourself, and if you deem it appropriate, prescribe a laxative.

E – Ask the nurses whether there was a specific reason why the patient couldn't be given a laxative.

| 1 | 2 | 3 | 4 | 5 |
|---|---|---|---|---|
|   |   |   |   |   |

**Q114.** You have just started your shift at the hospital, when a patient's husband – Michael – comes up to you. He is extremely angry, and begins yelling in your face:

**Michael:** *'Doctor, I'm really angry. I was informed by one of the junior staff two days ago that Sally would be discharged today. We had plans to celebrate her getting out, we had booked dinner and a romantic boat ride…and yet nobody has told us anything today! Where's the discharge form? She wants to leave, NOW!'*

You quickly realise that the junior doctor has made a mistake. Sally is not due to be discharged for another 4 days.

**Take a look at the responses below, and then rank them from most appropriate to least appropriate.**

A – Inform Michael that there has been a mistake with the discharge dates, and that Sally won't be released until 4 days from now.

B – Find the junior doctor responsible for the error, and get him to explain himself to Michael.

C – Ask Michael to please try and calm down. Inform him that you are extremely sorry on behalf of the hospital, but that there appears to have been a mix-up with the discharge dates.

D – Tell Michael that he needs to try and calm down. Ask him to come back once he has stopped yelling, so that you can discuss the discharge dates.

E – Tell Michael that if he does not stop shouting at you, you'll be forced to get physical.

| 1 | 2 | 3 | 4 | 5 |
|---|---|---|---|---|
|   |   |   |   |   |

**Q115.** A patient who was under your care has recently passed away, after a long battle with cancer. In the time that the patient spent at the hospital, you have grown quite close to their family. Although you do not agree with him, your consultant – who has been closely observing the case – does not believe that your patient died as a result of the cancer. He thinks that there was an underlying genetic condition which may have caused the patient's death. In order to test for this, he wants to arrange a post-mortem, and bypasses you to try and convince the family to allow this. The family consent. Prior to the post-mortem, the patient's son, Neil, approaches you:

**Neil:** 'Hi Doctor Bishop. Can I talk to you about something?'

**You:** 'Sure, Neil, what's up?'

**Neil:** 'We've all been talking…me and Mum and Grandma that is, and we just don't feel comfortable with this post-mortem. It feels a lot like we were forced into doing it…we didn't want to say no because the hospital has been so good to us and you've all been so helpful, but we aren't comfortable with this being done.'

**Take a look at the responses below, and then rank them from most appropriate to least appropriate.**

A – Tell Neil that since the family have already consented, there's nothing you can do to stop the post-mortem from going ahead.

B – Tell Neil that you will have a word with the consultant, and the post-mortem will be cancelled for the time being.

C – Confront the consultant and accuse him of acting unprofessionally in these circumstances.

D – Sit down with Neil to explore the reasons why the family don't feel comfortable with having a post-mortem.

E – Ask the consultant to speak with the family again, but emphasise to him that he needs to avoid putting pressure on them.

| 1 | 2 | 3 | 4 | 5 |
|---|---|---|---|---|
|   |   |   |   |   |

**Q116.** You are participating in medical ward rounds, with a group of other FY1 colleagues. One of your colleagues is named Osman. Osman has been fasting for the month of Ramadan, and therefore has completed 6 hours of work without having anything to eat or drink. He began fasting earlier this week.

As rounds draw to a close, you notice that Osman is looking quite pale. When the consultant asks him a question, he doesn't seem to be aware of what was said, and he is shivering. The consultant doesn't really notice the issue, and continues on with what he was doing. Osman appears a little unsteady on his feet as you move to the next patient.

**Take a look at the responses below, and then rank them from most appropriate to least appropriate.**

A – Immediately draw the consultant's attention to Osman's condition. Ask someone to fetch Osman a glass of water.

B – Politely excuse yourself, take Osman to one side, and demand he has something to eat.

C – Quietly ask Osman whether he is feeling okay.

D – Take the consultant to one side and explain to him your concerns about Osman's condition.

E – Loudly declare that Osman is putting patients at risk by refusing to have a drink.

| 1 | 2 | 3 | 4 | 5 |
|---|---|---|---|---|
|   |   |   |   |   |

**Q117.** You and your consultant are having a discussion about a patient named Remy. Remy is a 12-year-old boy, who is prone to tears and tantrums. He often claims that he is being picked on by the staff, who are then forced to jump through hoops to make him feel better. Generally, he is not particularly liked by the doctors and nurses. Your consultant says the following:

**Consultant:** *'Remy has a slight allergy to doxycycline, so we can't give him that. It wouldn't kill him, but he'd have a bit of swelling around his face. What do you suggest as an alternative?'*

In response to your consultant, Remy starts accusing the pair of you of picking on him. Later that day, you notice that the nurses are about to administer Remy with 2 doxycycline capsules.

**Take a look at the responses below, and then rank them from most appropriate to least appropriate.**

A – Let Remy take the medicine. It will serve him right for being a whiney little brat.

B – Immediately approach the nurses and tell them that Remy has an allergy to doxycycline.

C – Question the nurses over why they are prescribing Remy with doxycycline.

D – Allow the nurses to administer the medicine, but question the consultant over it next time you see him.

E – Take the doxycycline from the nurses, and inform them Remy is allergic to both this, and penicillin.

| 1 | 2 | 3 | 4 | 5 |
|---|---|---|---|---|
|   |   |   |   |   |

---

**Q118.** You are sitting in the staff room, on your break. You have just started eating a delicious cheese sandwich that your girlfriend made for you, when an FY1 colleague approaches you. Her name is Bethany. She sits down at your table and says the following:

**Bethany:** *'Hi, I have something really serious that I want to discuss with you.'*

**You:** *'Go ahead, I'm listening.'*

**Bethany:** *'Well, my Mum is really into private healthcare, and she doesn't really like the NHS. The other day she went to see a private doctor, for some help with her back.'*

**You:** *'Alright…'*

**Bethany:** *'Anyway, you'll never guess who the doctor was? It was Bradley, from this hospital! She couldn't believe it, because she'd seen him on my social media wall before.'*

**You:** *'That's breaking the rules, you aren't allowed to work private if you're an FY1. The hospital forbids it.'*

**Bethany:** *'I know! What shall we do?'*

---

**Take a look at the responses below, and then rank them from most appropriate to least appropriate.**

A – Try and arrange a meeting with Bradley, so that you can discuss the issue. Question him on whether he's aware that his behaviour is contradictory to hospital rules.

B – Go straight to senior management. This is completely unacceptable behaviour.

C – Arrange a meeting with Bradley. Suggest to him that there are better ways to make money, that don't involve circumventing the hospital's rules.

D – Meet with Bradley, to discuss joining him in this profitable venture.

E – Ask your educational consultant on whether you should report this issue.

| 1 | 2 | 3 | 4 | 5 |
|---|---|---|---|---|
|   |   |   |   |   |

---

**Q119.** You have been working with a colleague named Gus for several weeks now. Gus is a great doctor, very popular amongst the other members of staff, and generally seems to have a bright future ahead of him. You are pleased to have met such a good friend. On Tuesday, you and Gus are sitting in the break room eating sandwiches. Gus informs you that he is feeling slightly dizzy, and then all of a sudden he faints. He regains consciousness within 5 minutes, and declares that it's time to get back to work.

---

**Take a look at the responses below, and then rank them from most appropriate to least appropriate.**

A – Ask Gus whether he is sure that this is the right thing to do.

B – Allow Gus to go back to work, but inform all of his patients that he has just passed out.

C – Tell Gus that he can't go back to work straight after passing out. Ask a nurse to escort him to one of the hospital beds.

D – Inform a senior doctor on the ward about what has just occurred.

E – Tell Gus he needs to rest for a period of at least five minutes, before he returns to work.

| 1 | 2 | 3 | 4 | 5 |
|---|---|---|---|---|
|   |   |   |   |   |

**Q120.** You have been assigned a group project, along with some other FY2s. The project is research-based, and requires the group to investigate the relationship between the dietary and lifestyle habits of expectant mothers, and the health of their offspring. The consultant who ordered the research project has specifically requested that the material presented is original.

One of the members of the group is called Kevin. Two days before the assignment is due, Kevin announces that he has made a major breakthrough, and then proceeds to show the rest of the group some rather impressive looking graphs, facts and figures. Nobody questions him on this. Come deadline day, the consultant who ordered the research project is highly impressed with Kevin. He asks Kevin to attend a research seminar with him in a month's time, so that he can present his findings.

Later that day, as you browse the internet, you discover that Kevin has taken all of his information from an external website.

**Take a look at the responses below, and then rank them from most appropriate to least appropriate.**

A – Go straight to the consultant and inform him that Kevin cheated on this task.

B – Find Kevin and confront him about what you have found. Ask him if he understood the concept of 'original content'.

C – Gather the other members of the group project together, excluding Kevin, and submit a formal complaint to the head of medicine.

D – Do nothing. Kevin simply outsmarted you all.

E – Find the consultant and inform him that Kevin doesn't deserve to take part in the research seminar.

| 1 | 2 | 3 | 4 | 5 |
|---|---|---|---|---|
|   |   |   |   |   |

**Q121.** You have just got home from the hospital, after finishing your evening shift. For much of the shift, you were dealing with a patient named Mr Fernandez, who speaks very poor English. Mr Fernandez has recently had a blood test. Tonight you received the blood test results back, but forgot to hand the paperwork over to the doctor replacing you on the shift. The paperwork is still in your pocket, which you only realise when you start to change clothes.

**Take a look at the responses below, and then rank them from most appropriate to least appropriate.**

A – Wait until tomorrow, to provide Mr Fernandez with the results.

B – Drive back to the hospital to provide the staff with the necessary paperwork. Apologise for the error.

C – Call the hospital, and ask them to get the new doctor to look up the results, using the hospital system. Apologise for the error.

D – Text your friend, who works in the hospital canteen, asking him to provide Mr Fernandez with the test results.

E – See if you can get in touch with the replacement doctor directly, to explain the situation.

| 1 | 2 | 3 | 4 | 5 |
|---|---|---|---|---|
|   |   |   |   |   |

**Q122.** You are working in the emergency care unit. One of your colleagues, named Jade, is still finding her feet in the hospital. Although she continuously struggles, she is doing her best, and the doctors have noticed a marked improvement in her performance. Your hospital has a strict policy on paperwork mistakes. If a doctor makes two mistakes within a 2-week period, when filling in patient paperwork, then they will be required to attend extra hours training. If a doctor makes three or more mistakes within a 2-week period, they will need to see a senior member of staff to evaluate their job position – and could be released from their employment.

In the past 2 weeks, Jade has made two mistakes already. She is due to attend training tomorrow. Unfortunately, today, you have realised that Jade has made another error with her paperwork.

**Take a look at the responses below, and then rank them from most appropriate to least appropriate.**

A – Approach Jade and gently inform her that unfortunately she's made another mistake with her paperwork. Tell her that she will need to speak with a senior manager about this.

B – Speak to a senior doctor and inform them that Jade has made another error. Encourage them to sack her.

C – Approach Jade and inform her that as a result of her error, she will need to see a senior manager.

D – Correct the error and don't say anything. Jade is improving, you can cut her some slack.

E – Inform Jade that the hospital operates on a '3 strikes and you're out' policy. Tell her that she needs to leave immediately.

| 1 | 2 | 3 | 4 | 5 |
|---|---|---|---|---|
|   |   |   |   |   |

**Q123.** You have just got home after a long day at work. As is customary at this time, you log in to your social media page to see what all of your friends have been getting up to. One of your colleagues from the hospital has made a long post, which says the following:

*'Oh my god what a day! So sick of patients and doctors moaning at me. Do this do that waaa waaa waaa…grow a pair you crybabies! First there was Mr Parsley, who has a bladder infection. Oh my pillow isn't comfy enough, my feet hurt, my back hurts. Mate, your head's gonna hurt if you don't stop moaning, because I'll knock you out! Then there was Belinda, some snotty little kid, who has appendicitis. Man up. Your appendix doesn't even do anything!*

*Tomorrow I have the day off, and I'm going to have NOTHING TO DO with patients!'*

**Take a look at the responses below, and then rank them from most appropriate to least appropriate.**

A – Contact your colleague, and tell him that he really needs to remove the social media post.

B – Speak to a consultant about the post, and what should be done.

C – Reply to the post, stating that you found it amusing.

D – Contact your colleague, informing him that you will be reporting the post to a senior manager.

E – Message your colleague, informing him that appendicitis is actually really painful.

| 1 | 2 | 3 | 4 | 5 |
|---|---|---|---|---|
|   |   |   |   |   |

**Q124.** You have just started your shift, when an angry patient approaches you. She informs you that her surgery has been delayed by 2 extra days, and that this is unacceptable. She demands to know what you are going to do about it. The woman is not your patient, and this is the first time that you have met her.

**Take a look at the responses below, and then rank them from most appropriate to least appropriate.**

A – Inform the woman that she is not your patient, and therefore she needs to find someone else to deal with the problem.

B – Consult the patient notes, to discover who is treating the woman. Promise to raise the issue with her current doctor and then get back to her.

C – Ask the woman what surgery she needs.

D – Take the woman down to the legal department, so that she can pursue a formal complaint.

E – Tell the woman that you will speak to the surgical team and see what they can do.

| 1 | 2 | 3 | 4 | 5 |
|---|---|---|---|---|
|   |   |   |   |   |

**Q125.** You have been treating a patient named Miles. Miles suffers from severe spinal issues, and therefore has been at the hospital for over 2 months now. In a week's time, he is due to be released, and he is throwing a huge party to celebrate. Miles is very excited to be released. Today, when you are treating him, he says the following:

**Miles:** *'Listen doctor, you've been so good to me. Honestly, I couldn't have asked for a better carer.'*

**You:** *'That's okay, Miles, I'm just doing my job. We are all glad to see you getting better.'*

**Miles:** *'When I get out of here, I'm throwing a massive party. It's going to be huge, hundreds of people, balloons and everything. I want you to attend, and I won't take no for an answer!'*

Your hospital has a very strict policy, which forbids doctors from interacting with patients on a social basis, outside of the hospital.

**Take a look at the responses below, and then rank them from most appropriate to least appropriate.**

A – Inform Miles that there's nothing you would rather do less, than attend his party.

B – Berate Miles for asking you to risk your job in such a manner.

C – Tell Miles that the hospital rules forbid you from attending.

D – Thank Miles for his invite, but tell him that you don't want to attend.

E – Thank Miles for the invite, but inform him that you will be busy working that day.

| 1 | 2 | 3 | 4 | 5 |
|---|---|---|---|---|
|   |   |   |   |   |

**Q126.** You are working in the surgical team. This morning you are participating in an operation. The surgery is taking place in just fifteen minutes. While everyone else has prepped and is ready, unfortunately one of your colleagues – Brian – has failed to show up. 10 minutes before the operation is about to take place, you receive a phonecall:

**Brian:** *'Hi mate. I'm really sorry I'm not there, I'm in a bit of a trouble.'*

**You:** *'Trouble? What trouble? We are doing the operation in 10 minutes Brian, where are you?'*

**Brian:** *'Mate I've been nabbed by the police. I was late, so I was speeding, and I've knocked someone down. They aren't seriously hurt but the police are telling me that they have to take me back to the station.'*

**You:** *'That's a really serious situation, Brian.'*

**Brian:** *'I know. Listen, I've got the police officer here…I can get out of this and get to the surgery but I need you to corroborate my version of events. Can you just tell him over the phone who I am and that I am actually needed at the hospital?'*

**Take a look at the responses below, and then rank them from most appropriate to least appropriate.**

A – Inform Brian that you will speak to the head surgeon and ask him to delay the operation, whilst Brian deals with the police.

B – Tell Brian that you will arrange for someone to replace him during the operation. Encourage him to cooperate with the police.

C – Agree to talk with the police officer, and try to persuade him about why Brian is needed at the surgery.

D – Tell Brian that he needs to face the consequences of his actions, and that you will tell the head surgeon about what has happened.

E – Pass the phone over to the lead surgeon to deal with this issue.

| 1 | 2 | 3 | 4 | 5 |
|---|---|---|---|---|
|   |   |   |   |   |

**Q127.** One of your colleagues approaches you and informs you that he feels extremely disappointed in the level of teaching at this hospital. He claims that his education consultant doesn't seem to be at the level your colleague expected. Your colleague says that he is thinking about transferring to another hospital, where the standards are higher.

You have not experienced the issues that your colleague has mentioned, and feel that the hospital operates to an extremely high standard.

**Take a look at the responses below, and then rank them from most appropriate to least appropriate.**

A – Inform your colleague that in your opinion, the hospital has very high standards, and great teaching.

B – Encourage your colleague to sit down with his education consultant and discuss these issues in depth.

C – Tell your colleague that he is being ungrateful, and needs to change his attitude.

D – Ask your colleague whether he would consider himself an arrogant person.

E – Ask your colleague why he thinks another hospital would provide a better standard of teaching than this one.

| 1 | 2 | 3 | 4 | 5 |
|---|---|---|---|---|
|   |   |   |   |   |

**Q128.** You are an FY2 working in the emergency care unit. As you finish up your shift, an FY1 approaches you. Her name is Kayla. Kayla says the following:

**Kayla:** 'Hi, Dr Parson. I'm having a bit of trouble with filling in patient records. Could help me?'

**You:** 'Sure, Kayla, what's the problem?'

**Kayla:** 'Well, I just don't understand why it's so important for us to fill in the time and date on the records when we create them. I mean what does it matter? The records are the records, they just show details of the patient's symptoms and behaviour. Why do we need to time them?'

**Take a look at the responses below, and then rank them from most appropriate to least appropriate.**

A – Ask Kayla how she even gained employment at the hospital, if she has to ask such a question.

B – Tell Kayla not to ask you stupid questions.

C – Inform Kayla that the primary reason for putting the time and date on records is for hospital protection against potential lawsuits.

D – Inform Kayla that the reason for putting the time and date on records is so that every single doctor for a patient can see how the patient has been treated, whilst at the hospital.

E – Inform Kayla that the reason for putting the time and date on records is so that if a doctor makes a mistake, the hospital can point out when and by whom the mistake was made, thus ensuring the right person is fired.

| 1 | 2 | 3 | 4 | 5 |
|---|---|---|---|---|
|   |   |   |   |   |

**Q129.** You are an FY2 working in the paediatric ward. In the past few months, you have developed a good working relationship with an FY1, named Kelsie. Kelsie frequently comes to you for advice over her patients. Unfortunately, in the last two weeks, you have found Kelsie to be increasingly overbearing. Although you have informed Kelsie that you are happy to help, you find that she is coming to you more and more for help with patients, and it's started to impact on your work. Kelsie does not seem to have any idea that she's doing anything wrong.

**Take a look at the responses below, and then rank them from most appropriate to least appropriate.**

A – Pull Kelsie to one side and inform her that, as from this moment, you will be unable to assist her with any medical matters.

B – Carry on as you are. It's great to help out your colleagues.

C – Tell Kelsie that although you are always happy to help her, this behaviour cannot continue if she wishes to be a successful doctor.

D – Tell Kelsie that she needs to try and take some more responsibility for her own patients.

E – Tell Kelsie that although you are always happy to offer guidance, she needs to speak to her education consultant if she wants extra help.

| 1 | 2 | 3 | 4 | 5 |
|---|---|---|---|---|
|   |   |   |   |   |

**Q130.** You are working with a doctor named Ruben, in the emergency ward. Two patients come in. One of them is morbidly obese. Upon seeing the patients, Ruben informs you that he 'does not want to deal with the fat one.' Before you have time to speak to him about the remark, he has welcomed the other patient in, and begins treating them in a separate room. Meanwhile, you deal with the obese patient. Whilst treating this patient, it becomes clear that Ruben has left his door open. You hear him talking with his patient:

**Ruben:** 'Mate, I'm glad I've got you. Did you see the size of that guy? My word.'

**Patient:** 'Well...'

**Ruben:** 'He was huge! I don't even know if he'd have fit in this room to be honest.'

Your patient does not show any response to this, but you can tell that he is quite upset.

**Take a look at the responses below, and then rank them from most appropriate to least**

**appropriate.**

A – Go and shut Ruben's door, so that nobody else can hear his inappropriate remarks.

B – Apologise sincerely to the patient, and assure him that Ruben is just having a bad day.

C – Go and speak to Ruben. Inform him that his comments are totally unacceptable.

D – Once you have finished with your patient, go and tell a senior doctor about what has just happened.

E – Once you have finished with your patient, inform Ruben that there could be serious consequences for his behaviour.

| 1 | 2 | 3 | 4 | 5 |
|---|---|---|---|---|
|   |   |   |   |   |

---

**Q131.** You are dealing with a patient named Joel. By all accounts, Joel is an extremely pleasant young man. He is polite, well-mannered and always positive. Joel's condition is steadily improving, and you are hoping that he will be ready for release within the next 2 weeks. On Sunday night, you are scheduled to work the night shift. At 11pm you walk through the ward. Joel is still awake, which concerns you. He has large bags under his eyes and looks very tired. Upon questioning him, he informs you that 'he just can't sleep'. The next time you walk through the ward, two hours later, Joel is still awake. You then notice that his bed is positioned close to the nurse station, and one of the nurses is chatting on the phone very loudly.

**Take a look at the responses below, and then rank them from most appropriate to least appropriate.**

A – Ask Joel whether the noise from the nurse station is bothering him.

B – Approach the nurse in question and ask her to try and keep the noise down.

C – Wait until the next day, and then go and see the ward manager to enquire about whether Joel can move to a new location on the ward.

D – Do nothing. It's bad luck that Joel's bed is next to the nurse station, but that's life.

E – Wait until the nurse has finished talking on the phone, and then unplug it when nobody is looking. That will stop the noise.

| 1 | 2 | 3 | 4 | 5 |
|---|---|---|---|---|
|   |   |   |   |   |

**Q132.** You have just walked into the hospital to begin your shift, when a patient approaches you. Her name is Lauren. Lauren is quite upset. She informs you that she would like to discharge herself from the hospital, because she feels that the ward she is on is too noisy. She claims that she is suffering from headaches as a result, isn't getting enough sleep, and doesn't feel that staying at the hospital is benefitting her.

When you look at Lauren's paperwork, you realise that she is not due to be discharged for another three days. However, the previous doctor to have seen Lauren has noted down that she is almost ready to leave, and could be considered for early discharge if possible.

**Take a look at the responses below, and then rank them from most appropriate to least appropriate.**

A – Apologise sincerely to Lauren for the problems that she has been having. Inform her that if she is willing to wait for a few minutes, you will go and find out whether it's possible to move her to another ward.

B – Tell Lauren that you are happy to discharge her, but will need to conduct a short medical assessment first.

C – Tell Lauren that she is not due for discharge for another three days. Inform her that she'll have to stay put.

D – Tell Lauren that it would be a good idea for her to purchase some noise-cancelling headphones.

E – Tell Lauren that you'll have her moved to another ward immediately.

| 1 | 2 | 3 | 4 | 5 |
|---|---|---|---|---|
|   |   |   |   |   |

**Q133.** It is Monday evening, and you are just about to finish your shift. Just as you are leaving, one of the senior consultants for the ward you are working on, calls you into her office. Her name is Barbara.

**Barbara:** *'Sit down, Michael. I'm afraid I've got some bad news. Over the last few days, we've had a number of complaints about you from some patients. I'll list a few of them:*

*-Firstly, Mr Wiggins claims that your bedside manner was quite abrupt and cold.*

*-Secondly, Pam Earnshaw from the nursing team said that she saw you being rude to a patient.*

*-Thirdly, Mrs Oliver said that last night, you failed to bring her dinner, so she went hungry for two hours.*

*What do you have to say for yourself?'*

You were not aware of any of the above incidents, or that you had done anything wrong.

**Take a look at the responses below, and then rank them from most appropriate to least appropriate.**

A – Tell Barbara that you are very confused by the comments about your behaviour. Ask her if there has been a case of mistaken identity.

B – Tell Barbara that you are shocked and appalled by these comments about your behaviour, especially coming from someone as incompetent as her.

C – Tell Barbara that you weren't aware of any wrongdoing, but that you are happy to apologise to the patients in person.

D – Tell Barbara that you weren't aware of any wrongdoing, but will do your utmost to improve your patient handling skills.

E – Ask Barbara for tips on how to avoid being spotted, the next time you do something wrong.

| 1 | 2 | 3 | 4 | 5 |
|---|---|---|---|---|
|   |   |   |   |   |

**Q134.** You are an FY1 in your local hospital. During medical ward rounds, the consultant in charge of the rounds asks you to administer an IV to a patient. You have no idea of how to do this, and informed the consultant of this. After giving you a demonstration, the consultant in question said the following:

*'In two days' time, we'll be doing another session. By then, I want you to be able to perform this procedure.'*

Two days later, the consultant asks you to administer an IV to another patient. You still don't have any clue of how to do it.

**Take a look at the responses below, and then rank them from most appropriate to least appropriate.**

A – Be honest with the consultant and inform him that you still don't feel comfortable performing this procedure.

B – Try and perform the procedure to the best of your ability.

C – Tell the consultant that you don't feel comfortable performing this. Ask him to give you another demonstration.

D – Ask someone else in the group to do it, whilst you watch.

E – Start crying. Hopefully the consultant will feel sorry for you.

| 1 | 2 | 3 | 4 | 5 |
|---|---|---|---|---|
|   |   |   |   |   |

**Q135.** You are an FY1, who has recently started work at a new hospital, and have been assigned to the paediatric ward. Since you are a new doctor, the hospital have provided you with one of their top supervisors – a woman named Amanda. Amanda will be providing both your clinical and educational supervision. A few weeks ago, you had your first meeting with Amanda, in her office. It did not go well. Amanda was very standoffish with you, and ended the meeting early.

Since that meeting, you have had absolutely no contact with Amanda. She has not responded to any of your emails, or any phone messages. She also never appears to be in her office when you go to visit.

**Take a look at the responses below, and then rank them from most appropriate to least appropriate.**

A – Wait for Amanda to contact you. She's clearly very busy.

B – Leave an angry note on Amanda's door, stating that you believe she is unprofessional and rude.

C – Try and get in touch with the Foundation Programme Director, to inform them about the lack of communication from Amanda.

D – Send Amanda an email titled URGENT REQUEST PLEASE RESPOND IMMEDIATELY. She will surely at least open this.

E – Speak to one of the senior doctors on the ward, about arranging an appointment with Amanda.

| 1 | 2 | 3 | 4 | 5 |
|---|---|---|---|---|
|   |   |   |   |   |

**Q136.** You are discussing with a consultant about an elderly patient on the ward. Whilst the two of you discuss things, you notice that the consultant smells very strongly of alcohol. However, he is not slurring his words, and there is nothing in his behaviour to suggest that he is under the influence.

**Take a look at the responses below, and then rank them from most appropriate to least appropriate.**

A – Take the consultant to one side and question him about the smell.

B – Wait until the consultation is finished, and then question your colleagues about whether they have noticed the smell.

C – Ask the consultant, in front of the patient, why he smells of alcohol.

D – Do nothing. It's not your place to question a senior member of staff.

E – Take the consultant to one side and inform him that he stinks of alcohol.

| 1 | 2 | 3 | 4 | 5 |
|---|---|---|---|---|
|   |   |   |   |   |

**Q137.** You are participating in medical ward rounds with the lead consultant, Dr Green. Dr Green seems to be in a rush today. As you move from your first patient to your second, one of your colleagues speaks up:

**Emma:** *'Dr Green, I hope you don't mind me saying, but you haven't washed your hands. Doesn't this need to be done before you can examine the next patient?'*

**Dr Green:** *'I don't have time to listen to trainee nonsense. Shut up and do your job, or I'll have you thrown out of this hospital.'*

Dr Green proceeds to move onto the next patient, without washing his hands.

**Take a look at the responses below, and then rank them from most appropriate to least appropriate.**

A – Concur with Dr Green. Inform Emma that she is rude and disrespectful.

B – Stand up for your colleague. Inform Dr Green that he is in breach of hospital guidelines.

C – Tell Emma that if she ever wants to get promoted, she needs to treat Dr Green with more respect.

D – Refuse to take part in the rest of the round, until Dr Green washes his hands and apologises to Emma.

E – Tell Dr Green that his behaviour is out of line, and that he should apologise to Emma.

| 1 | 2 | 3 | 4 | 5 |
|---|---|---|---|---|
|   |   |   |   |   |

**Q138.** You are dealing with a patient, who has fallen sick whilst on holiday in the UK. The patient's name is Eileen. Eileen's condition has worsened significantly over the past week. Although she is not considered to be at risk of death, she will almost certainly need to remain at the hospital for a few more weeks.

Today, Eileen's daughter has come to visit her at the hospital. She has brought Eileen's dog along. Your hospital has a strict policy of not allowing dogs anywhere other than the reception area. A petting area is in the process of being constructed, it is not yet ready for use. Due to Eileen's condition, she is unable to come down to the reception area.

When Eileen's daughter is informed that she cannot bring the dog into the main hospital, she becomes irate.

**Take a look at the responses below, and then rank them from most appropriate to least**

**appropriate.**

A – Apologise for the inconvenience caused, but make it clear that dogs are not allowed in the main hospital building.

B – Tell Eileen's daughter that she can bring the dog upstairs, but it must be kept on a leash.

C – Call the police and have Eileen's daughter arrested.

D – Enquire with a senior doctor as to whether the dog can enter the main hospital building.

E – Tell Eileen's daughter that she will need to come back without the dog, if she wishes to see her mother.

| 1 | 2 | 3 | 4 | 5 |
|---|---|---|---|---|
|   |   |   |   |   |

**Q139.** One of your patients is ready to return home, after a lengthy stay at the hospital. His name is Mr Ingram. He is an elderly man, and has no friends or family. He seems quite reluctant to leave. When the time comes for him to leave the hospital, Mr Ingram informs you that it's not convenient for him to be discharged at this time, as his carer won't be available now until the morning. The nurses inform you that since he was ready for discharge, Mr Ingram's bed has already been given to someone else.

**Take a look at the responses below, and then rank them from most appropriate to least appropriate.**

A – Tell Mr Ingram that his personal problems are no concern of the hospital. Ask him to leave.

B – Tell Mr Ingram that if he doesn't want to leave by himself, you can ask security to escort him out.

C – Ask Mr Ingram if an alternative carer can be arranged.

D – Tell Mr Ingram that you will speak to the relevant person, and try to find him a new bed for the night.

E – Ask the nurses to find out if there are any available beds in which Mr Ingram can stay.

| 1 | 2 | 3 | 4 | 5 |
|---|---|---|---|---|
|   |   |   |   |   |

**Q140.** You have recently started working at a new hospital. Although things started out very stressful, you have found your feet and are now very confident in your new surroundings. The reports that you are receiving from senior doctors and your supervisor are extremely good. Your supervisor is named Eileen.

On Thursday morning, you log in to your emails, to discover a lengthy email from a colleague named Rhotunda. The email goes into great length about Eileen, declaring her as incompetent, useless and unhelpful. Rhotunda claims that Eileen should be sacked and is incapable of doing her job. She has copied in 20 other FY1 doctors to the email, and the head physician of the hospital, along with Eileen herself, and declared that every single member of the FY1 group is in total agreement with her.

You have not been informed in advance of this email, and you have not given your consent or signature to this. You strongly disagree with Rhotunda's comments.

Take a look at the responses below, and then rank them from most appropriate to least appropriate.

A – Immediately seek out Eileen, and assure her that you did not give any consent for Rhotunda to sign your name on this email. Tell her that she has your full support.

B – Contact Rhotunda and inform her that you strongly disagree with her opinion.

C – Do nothing. If that's how the rest of the FY1s feel, then who are you to argue?

D – See if you can arrange a meeting with the head physician to discuss Rhotunda's comments.

E – Seek legal advice. Your name has been used without permission.

| 1 | 2 | 3 | 4 | 5 |
|---|---|---|---|---|
|   |   |   |   |   |

**Q141.** You are working in the paediatric ward, assisting a 10-year-old patient. The patient is named Benjamin, and he is very excited as this is his first time in a hospital. Whilst you consult with him and his parents, he takes out his mobile phone and begins to film you. You haven't authorised him to do this.

Take a look at the responses below, and then rank them from most appropriate to least appropriate.

A – Tell Benjamin that you do not consent to being filmed, and therefore legally he must delete the footage.

B – Politely ask Benjamin's parents if he could stop filming. Explain that you aren't very comfortable appearing on film.

C – Take Benjamin's mobile phone from him and delete the footage yourself.

D – Tell Benjamin that you would appreciate it if he didn't film during your consultation.

E – Ignore it. He's just a child.

| 1 | 2 | 3 | 4 | 5 |
|---|---|---|---|---|
|   |   |   |   |   |

**Q142.** The next day, you walk into the ward to see a junior doctor talking with Benjamin and his family. Although things seem to be going well, they quickly take a turn for the worse, when Benjamin whips off his phone and starts filming the junior doctor, who takes offence to this. After demanding that Benjamin turns the camera off, the junior doctor takes out his own phone and starts filming Benjamin back. He proceeds to yell at Benjamin: 'LET'S SEE HOW YOU LIKE IT!'

Benjamin's parents are horrified by this, and ask the junior doctor to delete the footage.

**Take a look at the responses below, and then rank them from most appropriate to least appropriate.**

A – Walk over and inform the junior doctor that he will need to delete the footage immediately.

B – Ask a senior doctor for advice on what to do.

C – Ask the junior doctor to step outside and calm down, whilst you apologise to the family for his behaviour.

D – Tell the junior doctor that he has no legal requirement to delete the footage, as he was being filmed first.

E – Ask Benjamin's family whether they are happy for the footage to appear on the internet.

| 1 | 2 | 3 | 4 | 5 |
|---|---|---|---|---|
|   |   |   |   |   |

**Q143.** One of your patients has recently died. Although the patient in question has been in hospital for many months, his death was still very unexpected, and both you and the consultant agree that a post-mortem would be the best course of action. The man's family are members of a religion that believes in immediate burial of loved ones following death. They have informed you that if their relative is to pass on to the afterlife, he must be buried within a 48-hour period following death. They do not want a post-mortem, as this will delay the burial.

**Take a look at the responses below, and then rank them from most appropriate to least appropriate.**

A – Agree to the family's wishes. A post-mortem cannot take place if consent from the patient's relatives is withheld.

B – Ignore the family's request. In this instance, a post-mortem would be extremely beneficial, and could help save the lives of future patients.

C – Tell your consultant that although the family haven't consented to the post-mortem, you think it would be a good idea to go through with it anyway.

D – Sit down with the family and explain that their religious views are a load of nonsense. Urge them to consider the post-mortem.

E – Ask the family whether they would consent to a post-mortem, if it could be conducted within the 48-hour period.

| 1 | 2 | 3 | 4 | 5 |
|---|---|---|---|---|
|   |   |   |   |   |

**Q144.** You are an FY1, working in the A&E department on a busy Saturday night. A man comes in with a large splinter in his hand, which he claims he got from chopping wood. After treating the man, he suddenly gets extremely angry. He declares that you are a racist, and that he wishes to speak to a senior doctor about your behaviour. The man is becoming increasingly irate.

You have not behaved in any way that you could see would offend him, and have clearly kept to the guidelines laid out by the GMC.

**Take a look at the responses below, and then rank them from most appropriate to least appropriate.**

A – Ask the man what exactly you have said that has offended him so badly.

B – Agree to fetch a senior doctor. Resolve to argue your case after the man has spoken to them.

C – Inform the man that you are confused and upset by his comments. Assure him that you have not meant to cause any offence.

D – Tell the man that he cannot see a senior doctor. Ask him to leave.

E – Tell the man that he could ruin your career with such accusations.

| 1 | 2 | 3 | 4 | 5 |
|---|---|---|---|---|
|   |   |   |   |   |

**Q145.** You are an FY1, and are treating a patient named Desmond. Desmond has come into the hospital complaining about severe chest pain. As a new doctor, you do not have much experience in this field, and feel as if you are not the best person to deal with it. You have spoken to one of your colleagues, who agrees that the best course of action would be to pass Desmond over to the ward specialist for these issues. Unfortunately, you can't seem to find her anywhere.

**Take a look at the responses below, and then rank them from most appropriate to least appropriate.**

A – Deal with the patient as best as you can. Keep him overnight in the hospital, so that the specialist can deal with him when she's available.

B – Find a senior doctor and ask them to assist you with the patient. Explain to the patient that you would like your colleague's advice on this issue.

C – Tell the patient that you aren't confident enough to deal with him, and that you'll be right back when you find someone else who can.

D – Ask the nurses whether they can find a doctor who is more suitable to treating this type of patient.

E – Find a senior doctor, and ask them if they would be able to deal with this patient instead of you.

| 1 | 2 | 3 | 4 | 5 |
|---|---|---|---|---|
|   |   |   |   |   |

**Q146.** One of your colleagues is frequently turning up late to work. She has informed you that she is losing interest in medicine, and is considering giving up because she doesn't feel that she is good enough.

**Take a look at the responses below, and then rank them from most appropriate to least appropriate.**

A – Tell your colleague that if she is losing interest in medicine, the best thing would be to resign immediately.

B – Ask your colleague to speak to her educational supervisor about how she feels. Encourage her to do what makes her happy.

C – Tell your colleague that she is selfish for losing interest in medicine, and clearly doesn't care about saving lives.

D – Ask your colleague to speak to the ward consultant about this issue.

E – Tell your colleague that she has your full support, and that you are always available if she needs someone to talk to.

| 1 | 2 | 3 | 4 | 5 |
|---|---|---|---|---|
|   |   |   |   |   |

**Q147.** One of your patients has been diagnosed with terminal cancer. Obviously, she is very upset by the news. When she informs her son, Tim, he immediately becomes very upset:

**Tim:** *'This hospital…it's your fault! You could have saved her, but all of the doctors here didn't even bother. Now my mum is dying and it's your fault. I can't believe this.'*

Tim starts to become very emotional and angry. He punches the wall in frustration.

**Take a look at the responses below, and then rank them from most appropriate to least appropriate.**

A – Ask Tim to come and sit down with you in a quiet room, so that you can discuss the situation and his options moving forward.

B – Tell Tim that if he does not calm down then you will be forced to call security, who will escort him from the building.

C – Tell Tim that you will give him and his mother some privacy.

D – Offer to bring Tim a hot beverage, in the hopes that it will comfort him.

E – Assure Tim that the doctors at the hospital have done their very best to save his mother.

| 1 | 2 | 3 | 4 | 5 |
|---|---|---|---|---|
|   |   |   |   |   |

**Q148.** One of the patients in the paediatric ward is refusing to eat. He claims that hospital food is all poisoned and will kill him. The patient hasn't eaten for two days. The nurses have informed you that you need to speak to the patient's parents the next time they visit, or they may have to force-feed him.

**Take a look at the responses below, and then rank them from most appropriate to least appropriate.**

A – Tell the patient's parents that they will need to ask their son to eat, or else…

B – Inform the patient's parents that their son isn't eating hospital food. Tell them that this is a serious problem which could significantly hinder his recovery.

C – Ask the patient's parents to have a serious chat with their son about his behaviour.

D – Ask the patient's parents whether they could bring in a burger from the local fast food restaurant for their son.

E – Sit down with the patient and try to talk to him about why he won't eat the hospital food.

| 1 | 2 | 3 | 4 | 5 |
|---|---|---|---|---|
|   |   |   |   |   |

**Q149.** You are just about to start your shift for the day. As usual, you approach the doctor whose shift you are taking over. Today, his name is Darren. Darren informs you that he has had no patients today, and promptly strolls off out the exit doors. Through the window, you witness him taking off his lanyard and throwing it into a nearby bush.

You do not believe that Darren didn't have any patients.

**Take a look at the responses below, and then rank them from most appropriate to least appropriate.**

A – Go to the nurse desk and ask them if they can provide you with a full report on Darren's activity for the day.

B – Go and see your educational supervisor and ask them what you should do.

C – Hang around with your colleagues for the rest of your shift, helping them out with their patients.

D – Chase after Darren and ask him whether he has resigned.

E – Speak to the consultant on the ward, and explain to him what has just happened.

| 1 | 2 | 3 | 4 | 5 |
|---|---|---|---|---|
|   |   |   |   |   |

**Q150.** Over the last few weeks, a number of your colleagues have come to you to complain about the behaviour of another junior doctor, named Mark. Your colleagues claim that Mark is making jokes about them losing their jobs, and that they find these jokes offensive and hurtful. On Tuesday, you walk into the hospital, to witness the following conversation:

**Amanda:** *'Oh god, I've forgotten to pass over the blood test results for Mrs McKenzie.'*

**Mark:** *'You're fired. LOL.'*

**Take a look at the responses below, and then rank them from most appropriate to least appropriate.**

A – Take Amanda to one side and ask her whether she feels hurt by Mark's comment.

B – Approach Mark and inform him that his jokes are not very funny.

C – Ask Mark for a quiet chat. Tell him that he needs to be more considerate towards the feelings of his colleagues.

D – Go and see the Chief Physician about Mark's behaviour.

E – Tell Mark that the hospital is no place for humour.

| 1 | 2 | 3 | 4 | 5 |
|---|---|---|---|---|
|   |   |   |   |   |

You have now finished the first section of practice questions. Check your answers before moving on to the next set of practice questions.

# ANSWERS TO PRACTICE QUESTIONS SECTION 1

**Q1.**

1 – D. Explain to the patient that although you can appreciate his concerns, he is not the only person on the ward. Assure him that he now has your attention.

**Explanation:** This is the best response to the situation. The patient is behaving unreasonably. If his behaviour still persists following your explanation, then you can move onto option A – but the best immediate course of action is to try and reassure the patient yourself.

2 – A. Apologise to the patient, and go fetch a senior doctor to deal with the situation.

**Explanation:** This is the second best response to the situation. You should try to take responsibility first, before calling a senior doctor, but at least here you are apologising and providing a solution to the issue.

3 – E. Go fetch a senior doctor.

**Explanation:** This is the third best option, although it's not a great response. You aren't apologising to the patient, or attempting to deal with the situation yourself.

4 – C. Leave the patient and go find a senior nurse. She will be able to offer you advice.

**Explanation:** This is the fourth best option, but it's not a good response. You cannot just leave the patient on his own while you go to consult a nurse, without apologising or attempting to explain what is going on.

5 – B. Wheel the patient to the exit doors, and wish him good luck. Rudeness will result in immediate discharge.

**Explanation:** This is, by some distance, the worst option. This is not how you would deal with a sick patient.

**Q2.**

1 – B. Ask the mother to leave the room, so that you can conduct a full physical examination of the boy, checking for signs of abuse.

**Explanation:** In this case, this is the best response listed to the situation. Normally under circumstances like this you would need to document the boy's claims and then conduct further questioning. The next thing would be to conduct a physical examination, to further establish his claims.

2 – D. Ask the boy to leave the room with a nurse, so that you can further question the mother.

**Explanation:** This is the second best response listed. Although it does not constitute a great response, you would need to consult with the boy's mother before any further action could be taken, or before the situation could be escalated, so therefore of all the options listed this is ranked at number two. That being said, based on her behaviour, the mother does not appear to be a trustworthy source.

3 – C. Call social services. The mother has essentially admitted to her guilt.

**Explanation:** This is not a good response, as there are protocols in place which need to be met before escalating the situation to this level. However, it's the third best option on the list, as you are at least taking action.

4 – E. Prescribe the boy some painkillers for his back pain, and then discharge him. There is no substantial evidence for abuse here.

**Explanation:** This is a really bad response, as you are ignoring the evidence presented to you – which points to abuse. Therefore, you are failing to do your job properly, and placing the child at risk.

5. A – Tell the boy to stop lying.

**Explanation:** This is the worst response. You are belittling the child's claim, and ignoring the evidence presented to you.


**Q3.**

1 – E. Apologise to the doctor. Tie your hair back, but query him about the earrings.

**Explanation:** This is the best response to the situation. Although you should always follow instructions from one of your senior doctors, you have a right to query him if you believe there has been a mistake.

2 – A. Tell the doctor that although you are happy to tie your hair back, you won't be taking out your earrings.

**Explanation:** This is the second best response. Although you are being extremely to the point and blunt about doing so, at least you are standing your ground on what you believe to be a mistake.

3 – D. Apologise to the doctor. Tie your hair back, and take out your earrings.

**Explanation:** This is the third best response. Although you are being polite and showing respect to a senior member of staff, you should not take out your earrings if you think there's been a mistake.

4 – C. Explain to the doctor that there is nothing in the rules about wearing earrings. Refuse to tie your hair back, as a result of his mistake.

**Explanation:** This is a bad response, as you are acting very irrationally, and disrespectfully.

5 – B. File an junior doctoral complaint against the doctor. Sexism in the workplace is not acceptable.

**Explanation:** This is a terrible response, and a complete overreaction. Clearly the doctor is not being sexist here, and this does not warrant an junior doctoral complaint.


**Q4.**

1 – B. Smile and nod. Tell the woman that hopefully her boyfriend will be patched up soon.

**Explanation:** Although E might seem like the best option here, it is better for you not to get involved in the situation at all. You should treat the patient to the best of your ability, and then leave him to get on with his life. His personal situation is nothing to do with you.

2 – E. When the patient wakes up, inform him that although you are bound by confidentiality, he should consider telling his girlfriend the truth.

**Explanation:** Although this isn't the best option, it's not the worst either. You are at least acting in a morally passable manner, and giving the patient some good advice.

3 – C. Ask the woman not to discuss personal matters with you.

**Explanation:** This is not an ideal response, as you are being rude and insensitive, but you would at least be releasing yourself from the pressure of the situation – which is better than breaking the doctor-patient confidentiality rules.

4 – D.  Wake the man up and announce that he has something to tell his girlfriend.

**Explanation:** This is a bad response, as you are putting the man in a very difficult situation. Although he could simply lie his way out of this, you would be acting irresponsibly here.

5 – A. Immediately tell the man's girlfriend that he is cheating on her. You have a moral responsibility.

**Explanation:** This is the worst response. You would breaking the code of conduct, and involving yourself in a situation which has nothing to do with you.


**Q5.**

1 – E. Ask your colleague for guidance on what you've done wrong, but make it clear that this is not an appropriate way for him to address you in future.

**Explanation:** This is a good, rational response. You are clearly asking for advice on how to improve, whilst standing your ground and ensuring that your colleague is in no doubt that his behaviour is unacceptable.

2 – D. Calmly but firmly tell your colleague that you do not need to put up with such abuse, and that he can come and speak to you when he has calmed down.

**Explanation:** This is another good response. The reason that we have put this as second on the list is because it would be better to get feedback on what mistakes your colleague believes you've made. However, this could easily be interchanged with option E.

3 – A. Ask your colleague what exactly you have done wrong. Tell him that you are really surprised by the criticism.

**Explanation:** This is a good and rational response. However, you need to show your colleague in no uncertain terms that his behaviour is unacceptable.

4 – B. Tell your colleague that he needs to calm down and treat you with more respect, if he wants you to take him seriously.

**Explanation:** This is a reasonable response, but at the same time you still want to behave in an acceptable manner yourself. Yes your colleague does need to treat you with more respect, but this isn't the way to tell him that.

5 – C. Break down and cry. Hopefully he'll feel sorry for you.

**Explanation:** This is the worst response on the list. You should stand up for yourself in this situation, and tell your colleague that he is being very rude.

## Q6.

1 – B. Go straight to the lead surgeon for the operation, and inform him about your friend's condition.

**Explanation:** This is a sensible response to the situation. Yes, you could follow after your friend and try to persuade him, or even threaten to tell the surgeon in charge, but the best course of action would really be just to go to the surgeon yourself. If your friend has been drinking, you cannot rely on him to make sensible decisions, and therefore he cannot be allowed to proceed with surgery. Likewise, you may need to spend some time convincing your inebriated friend that this is the right course of action – which will lead to a delay with the surgery. It's better to just go and inform the lead surgeon yourself.

2 – E. Tell your friend that if he isn't honest with the lead surgeon about the fact he's been drinking, you will tell the surgeon yourself.

**Explanation:** This is a good response, although you shouldn't leave things in the hope that your friend will tell the surgeon. You need to make absolutely sure that your friend doesn't participate in the surgery, and for that reason the best course of action is just to go straight to the surgeon yourself, saving time in the process.

3 – D. Follow after your friend and try to persuade him to pull out of the operation.

**Explanation:** This is an adequate response, but it's still not a good one. Simply trying to persuade your friend isn't enough, you need to make sure that he does pull out of the operation.

4 – A. Go straight to the head of surgery's office, and inform him about your friend. Hopefully he'll be fired – you never liked him much anyway.

**Explanation:** This is a bad response. The best response in this scenario is to go and see the surgeon participating in the operation, not the head of surgery. If the surgeon in charge decides to raise the issue with the head of surgery then that's his prerogative.

5 – C. Trust in your friend's ability. A little bit of alcohol never hurt anyone.

**Explanation:** 'A bit of alcohol' could have disastrous consequences in this case. Your friend is clearly not in a fit state to perform surgery, making this by far the worst option.

## Q7.

1 – B. Thank the patient for their gift, but politely decline. Explain to them that you were just

doing your job.

**Explanation:** This is a great response. You are being polite and grateful, whilst ensuring that you keep to the hospital's rules and regulations.

2 – D. Ask one of the senior doctors about whether you can keep the chocolates.

**Explanation:** This isn't a good response, but is still the next best option on the list. It's not a good response, because you know the rules and regulations surrounding gifts from patients.

3 – A. Accept the chocolates. Nobody is going to know.

**Explanation:** This is a very bad response, as you would be breaking the hospital rules by accepting the gift.

4 – E. Tell the patient that for your hard work, you expected a better gift.

**Explanation:** This is a very bad response. Not only are you being extremely rude, but you are also implying that it's okay for the patient to buy you gifts.

5 – C. Ask the patient to share the chocolates with you over a dinner date.

**Explanation:** This is the worst response, as it is completely inappropriate.

**Q8.**

1 – A. Go straight to senior management and file a complaint. They are the best placed people to deal with this.

**Explanation:** This is the best possible response in this situation. Your colleague's behaviour is unacceptable, and needs to be dealt with by senior management.

2 – E. Tell your colleague that if he doesn't stop then you are going to report him to senior management.

**Explanation:** This is the second best option. Although it's still not great, because you have already asked your colleague to stop, at least you are taking sustained action to prevent him from continuing.

3 – B. Confide in another doctor, and ask them what you should do.

**Explanation:** This is an acceptable solution, although it would be better to take the issue to senior management.

4 – D. Quit. There are plenty of other jobs, in other hospitals. You don't need to put up with this.

**Explanation:** This is a very bad response. You shouldn't allow someone else to bully you out of a job. Senior management can deal with this issue.

5 – C. Take physical retaliation against your colleague. If he won't listen to verbal warnings, then there's only one solution.

**Explanation:** This is the worst response. Violence is never the answer, and this will likely lead to you losing your job, and you could face criminal charges.

**Q9.**

1 – E. 'Okay, thank you for bringing this to my attention. My advice is to list all of these issues down, and then we can bring it to the attention of a senior member of staff.'

**Explanation:** This is the best response to the situation. You are assuring the junior doctors that this will be dealt with by a senior member of staff, whilst at the same time making sure that when they do approach the senior member of staff – they have a comprehensive list of things that need to be discussed.

2 – B. 'Thank you for letting me know your concerns. If you would like, I can accompany you to a senior doctor's office, so that we can discuss this further.'

**Explanation:** This is the second best option. You are taking very firm and immediate action to deal with the situation. The reason this is the second best option is that you cannot simply march up a senior doctor's office with a list of complaints – this needs to be done in an organised fashion. Therefore, it would be better to make an appointment, and get all of the complaints down in a neat list, before the meeting.

3 – D. 'That's terrible to hear. I will bring these issues to the concern of a senior member of staff immediately. Please be assured that we will deal with this as a matter of priority.'

**Explanation:** This is an acceptable solution, although it's still not ideal. The reason for this is that you haven't taken the time to note down all of their concerns, nor are you involving the junior doctors in the process of dealing with the complaint.

4 – A. 'If you don't like it, there's the door. I'm sure there's plenty of hospitals who would love to take on a bunch of ungrateful trainees…'

**Explanation:** This is a very bad response. You are completely dismissing their complaints, many of which are serious in nature. This will only harm the hospital.

5 – C. 'I'm sorry to hear that you are unhappy. If it helps, I am happy to offer one-to-one tuition, to get you all get up to speed with things…I charge £30 per hour.'

**Explanation:** This is the worst response. Although you are offering tuition, you are charging them for the time – thereby profiting from the hospital's ineptitude.

**Q10.**

1 – E. Go straight to the head of the course, and report Melanie for her behaviour.

**Explanation:** This is the best response to the situation. Melanie is a cheater, therefore you should take direct action and report her.

2 – B. Tell Melanie that cheating is unethical, and that you'll play no part in this.

**Explanation:** This is a good response. You don't need to get involved in this, although you should still report Melanie.

3 – C. Tell Melanie that there's no guarantee those are the actual answers, and therefore she could be wasting her time.

**Explanation:** This is an okay response, but it's not great. Although you are encouraging Melanie not to cheat, you are only doing this on the basis that they might not be the right answers – and not because cheating itself is wrong.

4 – D. Announce loudly to everyone in the library that Melanie is cheating.

**Explanation:** This is not a particularly helpful response. It's nothing to do with the other people in the library, and should be dealt with by someone senior.

5 – A. Take a pen and quickly jot down the answers. This will save you a whole lot of time revising.

**Explanation:** This is the worst response. You are only cheating yourself.


**Q11.**

1. C – Tell Karen that she should be more respectful towards Marvin, but query the dosage yourself.

**Explanation:** This is the best response. Karen is being quite rude, which should be addressed, but at the same time the dosage does need to be queried.

2 – A. Speak up. Tell Marvin that Karen is actually correct, and query the dosage yourself.

**Explanation:** This is a good response. You have noticed a mistake, so you should bring this up. However, you should also point out to Karen that she is being rude towards a senior member of staff.

3 – D. Change the dosage yourself, without telling Marvin.

**Explanation:** This is a bad response. Although you are taking action to amend the mistake, you are going behind a senior member of staff's back to do so.

4 – E. Wait until rounds have finished, and then approach Marvin in private, to query the dosage.

**Explanation:** This is a very bad response. As Karen has pointed out, the dosage prescribed could kill the patient, so it needs to be addressed as soon as possible. You shouldn't wait until after rounds have finished.

5 – B. Say nothing. This is not your argument to get involved in.

**Explanation:** This is the worst response. You need to speak up if you've spotted a mistake, especially one as serious as this.

## Q12.

1 – A. Inform Joel that he is incorrect. Tell the girl that you are happy to prescribe her with contraceptive pills, but that first you need to ask her a few routine questions about her relationship.

**Explanation:** This is the best response to the situation. The General Medical Council guidelines make it clear that underage people should still be given contraception, as it is in their best interests. That being said, you should still ask some questions, to ensure that the sex is consensual and the patient is not being abused.

2 – C. Prescribe her the pills.

**Explanation:** This is the second-best response. You are giving the patient what she needs, but you should still follow up with welfare check-up questions, to ensure the relationship is consensual.

3 – E. Prescribe the girl with the pills, and give her your work/office contact number, so that she has someone to talk to about future sexual health issues.

**Explanation:** This is the third best response, but it's very problematic. You don't need to give the patient your work contact number. You could give her the number of a specialist to contact for these issues, but giving her your number could cause lots of problems.

4 – D. Go and find a senior manager, to see what they think you should do.

**Explanation:** This is not a very good response. You should be aware of the guidelines surrounding underage sex and contraception, and respond accordingly.

5 – B. Perform a citizen's arrest. The girl has broken the law by having underage sex – she must be detained.

**Explanation:** This is definitely the worst response. You are massively overreacting, and causing significant distress to the patient.

## Q13.

1 – C. Sympathise with the woman, and tell her that you will do your very best to bring her the results as soon as possible.

**Explanation:** This is the best response to the situation. You are reassuring the woman that the staff at the hospital are doing their best for her son, which will hopefully calm her down a little.

2 – A. Inform the woman that there is nothing you can do to speed up the results, but that you will bring them to the family as soon as you hear anything.

**Explanation:** This is the second best response to the situation. You are being very honest with the woman, whilst still reassuring her that she'll receive the results as soon as possible. It would be better to be a little more tactful here. Telling the woman that there is nothing you can do, is not going to reassure her.

3 – D. Ask the woman to take a seat, and try to calm down. Once she's calmed down, explain to her that rudeness won't make the scan go any faster.

**Explanation:** This is not a great response. Whilst it's true that you shouldn't accept rudeness from patients/their relatives, this woman is clearly distressed and upset about her son. As a member of staff, it is your job to try and reassure her, and calm her down.

4 – E. Inform the woman that as a result of her rudeness, it will now be even longer before she receives the scan results.

**Explanation:** This is a poor response. The woman is distressed about her son's condition. Spitefully holding onto the results until she is more polite will only make things worse.

5 – B. Call security, and ask them to throw the woman and her son out of the hospital.

**Explanation:** This is a complete overreaction, and will make things much worse.


## Q14.

1 – E. Tell David that you cannot do this for him. Try to encourage him towards fighting the illness.

**Explanation:** This is the best response to the situation. You are trying to reinforce positive emotions within the patient, and encouraging him. If this doesn't work, then you can establish what the next best course of action should be

2 – B. Ask David to try and explain to you why he feels this way.

**Explanation:** This is the second best response to the situation. You are dealing with the patient in a sensitive and sympathetic manner, which will allow you to establish what the next course of action should be.

3 – C. Book David an appointment with the palliative care team, for the next morning.

**Explanation:** This is the third best response. Although it would be better to try and talk him through the issues first, as he is your patient, it is also acceptable to put him in the care of the palliative team – who are well placed to deal with issues such as these.

4 – D. Tell David that you cannot help him to die, but that you'll try and find a doctor who might be more willing to do so.

**Explanation:** Euthanasia is illegal in the United Kingdom. You should not be showing the patient that there are doctors working in the hospital who are willing to break the law. Not only is this false (hopefully!) but you should be encouraging the patient to fight through his illness.

5 – A. Agree to help David die. Triple the dosage.

**Explanation:** As mentioned, Euthanasia is against the law. This is by far the worst response.

## Q15.

1 – C. Apologise to the patient, and fetch his medication. Following this, find the nurse responsible, and question her over her behaviour.

**Explanation:** This is the best response to the situation. You are apologising immediately to the patient, as a representative of the hospital, and also finding the nurse to ensure that she amends her mistake for the future.

2 – A. Fetch the patient's medication, before finding the nurse responsible for this, and ensuring that she apologises profusely to the patient.

**Explanation:** This is the next best response to the situation. The patient is receiving an apology from the member of staff who has acted wrongly, but at the same time it would better for you to apologise on the nurse's behalf – as a representative of the hospital, before quietly discussing the situation with the nurse. Dragging her over to apologise to the patient could be quite embarrassing.

3 – E. Fetch the patient's medication.

**Explanation:** This is an okay response, but it's still very flawed. You need to offer the patient a sincere apology, as well as correcting the nurse's behaviour.

4 – D. Apologise to the patient. Ask him to come with you to the senior manager's office, so that you can file an junior doctoral review against the nurse.

**Explanation:** This is not a great solution. Your aim should be to resolve this situation without having to involve senior management, apologising to the patient and correcting the nurse's behaviour. The patient certainly shouldn't have to come with you all the way to the senior manager's office, as he is unwell.

5 – B. Tell the patient that you don't have time to deal with ridiculous complaints.

**Explanation:** You are completely belittling the patient's, very serious, concerns. This is not acceptable.

## Q16.

1 – C. Pull Dr Pardew to one side, and quietly discuss the problem with him, in a sensitive manner.

**Explanation:** This is the best response to the situation. You are being reasonable, polite and considerate, towards the feelings of both Dr Pardew and the patients.

2 – E. Ask one of your colleagues to have a quiet word with Dr Pardew.

**Explanation:** This is the second best response. Although you should deal with the issue yourself, at least something is being done to resolve it.

3 – B. Pull Dr Pardew to one side, and demand that he takes a bath.

**Explanation:** This is a pretty rude and abrupt response, but it's still the third best option on the list. There are far more tactful ways to deal with the problem, but at least you are doing something about it.

4 – D. Tell the patients that Dr Pardew's smell does not impact on his ability to treat them, and that they will just have to deal with it.

**Explanation:** This is a bad response. Dr Pardew's smell does impact on his ability to treat patients, as it is making them feel uncomfortable. They shouldn't 'just have to deal with it'.

5 – A. Pull Dr Pardew to one side, and inform him that Mr Wiggins, Mrs Flack and Mr Earnshaw are being reassigned to a new doctor. If he asks why, tell him that it's for scheduling reasons.

**Explanation:** This is the worst response. You are lying to Dr Pardew, and therefore causing more problems. The issue won't be resolved, and this could lead more patients to complain/ having to deal with it.

**Q17.**

1 – E. Spend some time researching ideas during the evening, which you can bring to the meeting the next day.

**Explanation:** This is the best response. You are doing exactly what has been asked of you, so that you can be productive and helpful in the meeting.

2 – B. Meet up with your colleagues once you are free, so that you can all work together to come up with new ideas.

**Explanation:** This is an okay response. You are being productive and a great team player, but at the same time you don't know other people's schedules – and you are all going to be discussing the ideas tomorrow anyway. It would be better to just go away and write down your own ideas, with the aim of reporting back and mixing them together at the meeting.

3 – C. Go off and come up with your own ideas. Aim to bring them to Steve before anyone else has the chance. You snooze, you lose.

**Explanation:** This is a bad response. You are not being a team player, and Steve has asked you to give your ideas at the meeting tomorrow. That being said, at least you are coming up with ideas.

4 – D. Ask Steve why he's delegating this task to you and your colleagues, when he should be doing it himself.

**Explanation:** This is really rude and unhelpful. You are part of the department team, and therefore you should be helping Steve to improve the standards of work within the hospital.

5 – A. Tell Steve that the term 'brainstorm' is offensive. Refuse to take part in the exercise.

**Explanation:** Refusing to take part in the exercise altogether will not help anyone, and will come across extremely badly.

## Q18.

1 – D. Tell the man to stop picking the flowers and get back to work. Warn him that you will call security if you ever see it happen again.

**Explanation:** This is the most reasonable explanation. You are being firm but fair, and showing the man that his behaviour is against hospital rules.

2 – B. Draw the man's attention to the sign. Ask him to stop picking the flowers.

**Explanation:** This is an okay response, but you need to be a little firmer. The question says that the man is trying to be discreet – which means that he has probably seen the sign and knows he is breaking the rules.

3 – C. Call hospital security. This man is vandalising hospital property.

**Explanation:** This is an acceptable response, although it could be seen as a slight overreaction. The man is breaking the rules, so you are well within your rights to call hospital security to deal with the issue, but it would probably better just to deal with it yourself.

4 – A. Ignore the man. Picking flowers is not a big deal.

**Explanation:** Hospital rules are there for a reason. Although it doesn't warrant a massive reaction, like calling security, it's still important to make sure that the rules are being followed. Therefore, you shouldn't ignore the man, because it is a big deal.

5 – E. Take discreet photos of the man, and share them on the junior doctoret. That way, everyone will know what he's done.

**Explanation:** This is very immature, and could get you into trouble for taking unauthorised photos of another member of staff.

## Q19.

1 – A. Inform Paul that the hospital has a no smoking on the premises policy.

**Explanation:** This is the best response to the scenario. You are clearly showing Paul that his behaviour is incorrect.

2 – B. Tell Paul that if he doesn't stop smoking, you will postpone his operation.

**Explanation:** This is an okay response, as you are giving Paul a firm but fair warning. He is clearly in breach of pre-operational protocol.

3 – D. Tell Paul that if he does not stop smoking, you will ask security to escort him from the premises.

**Explanation:** This is not a very good response, and constitutes a big overreaction. Yes, you should ask Paul to stop smoking, but threatening him with removal from the hospital is quite over the top.

4 – E. Go and ask another staff member what they think you should do.

**Explanation:** This is a bad response. You should take responsibility for the problem.

5 – C. Thank Paul for his kind offer. Join him for a cigarette.

**Explanation:** This is a very bad response. You shouldn't be encouraging Paul to smoke, nor should you participate in breaking hospital rules yourself.


## Q20.

1 – E. Tell Pauline that although the decision is hers to make, she should have a serious talk with Mike about whether this is the right thing to do.

**Explanation:** This is the best response to the situation. You are clearly emphasising that the decision is down to the patient, whilst also encouraging her to discuss it with her husband, which reduces the chances of conflict later down the line. In situations such as these it is very important to consider the wishes of the patient's family, whilst still respecting that the decision is down to the patient themselves.

2 – D. Ask Pauline whether she has thought about her decision, and whether she needs some extra time to consider her options.

**Explanation:** This is a good response because you are encouraging the patient to think carefully about her options and whether this is the right thing to do, but you should also encourage her to consult with her husband and take his feelings into account.

3 – A. Inform Mike that the decision is down to Pauline.

**Explanation:** This is not a great response. Although it's true that the decision does ultimately rest with Pauline, it is extremely important that her relative's feelings are taken into account and that they are included in the decision-making process.

4 – B. Tell Pauline that as long as Mike refuses to accept her decision, she will be unable to decline treatment.

**Explanation:** This is untrue, and insensitive.

5 – C. Ask Pauline to step outside of the room. Tell her that you and Mike will make a decision on what she will do.

**Explanation:** This is the worst option. You are treating the patient in a very insensitive and rude manner.


## Q21.

1 – B. Take the man's mother into a private room, and gently explain that in order to save the life of her son, his leg will need to be amputated.

**Explanation:** This is a good response, to a highly sensitive situation. The man's mother will be devastated, naturally, so you need to ensure that you are extremely sympathetic to her feelings.

2 – A. Ask a junior doctor to break the news. You have more important things to be getting on with.

**Explanation:** This is a pretty bad response. You shouldn't put this responsibility on a junior doctor, it would be better coming from you.

3 – E. Wait until after the operation give the mother the news.

**Explanation:** Again this is not a good response, but it is still the third best option available. In any case, this would simply be a case of easing the mother's mind – there is nothing that she can do for her son until the operation is over. That being said, you should still be sensitive to how she is feeling, and therefore it would be much better to keep her informed.

4 – D. Take the man's mother to one side, and quietly explain the seriousness of the situation. Try to lighten the mood by making a few jokes.

**Explanation:** This is a terrible response. It is completely inappropriate to make jokes in this instance, which will upset the man's mother even further.

5 – C. Quickly explain to the man's mother about what operation is going to be performed, then ask security to remove her. She'll only cause a scene.

**Explanation:** This is the worst response. You are being completely unreasonable and insensitive towards the mother's feelings, as well as assuming that she'll 'cause a scene'.


**Q22.**

1 – D. Inform Paulo that it is the job of the hospital legal department to resolve such claims. Call security to escort him from the premises.

**Explanation:** This is the most reasonable response to the situation. You do not have to deal with such aggressive behaviour from Paulo, and you are directing him to the proper place.

2 – A. Call hospital security and ask them to escort Paulo from the premises.

**Explanation:** This is the second best response. You don't need to put up with such rude behaviour from Paulo, and are perfectly justified in calling security here.

3 – B. Inform Paulo that he is free to discuss any legal issues with the hospital's legal team. Ask him to leave your office.

**Explanation:** This is the third best response. However, you are being very lenient here. Calling security would be a better option. Paulo is very angry and could cause problems for the rest of the staff in the hospital if you simply ask him to leave your office.

4 – C. Tell Paulo that he will need to pay for the lamp that he has broken. Ask him to leave.

**Explanation:** This is a reasonable response, but not one that really deals with the issues at hand.

5 – E. Tell Paulo that you've seen his client on TV, and he never would have made it at a top-flight club in the first place.

**Explanation:** This is highly inflammatory, and will only serve to make the situation worse.

## Q23.

1 – A. Take the junior doctor to one side, and inform him that he has broken the doctor patient confidentiality protocol. Ask him to go and consult the hospital legal team immediately, as there could be serious consequences.

**Explanation:** This is the best response to the situation. The junior doctor has behaved in a completely unacceptable manner, and this needs to be dealt with by the legal team as a matter of urgency.

2 – C. Take the junior doctor to one side, and rebuke him for his behaviour. Inform him that there could be serious legal consequences for this.

**Explanation:** This is the next best response to the situation. You are treating the situation with the utmost seriousness. That being said, it would be better to just send the junior doctor straight to the legal team.

3 – E. Ask to speak to the girlfriend in private, and apologise on behalf of the junior doctor. Beg her not to take legal action.

**Explanation:** This is the third best response, although it's not great. You are offering an apology on behalf of the junior doctor, but begging her not to take legal action could cause more problems, and in any case you are not in a position to talk about legal matters.

4 – B. Pretend that you never heard the conversation. It's the junior doctor's problem from now on – he can suffer the consequences.

**Explanation:** This is a bad response. The junior doctor has committed a serious mistake, that could have extremely severe consequences. Therefore, ignoring the conversation altogether is not an option.

5 – D. Pull the junior doctor to one side, and congratulate him. Tell him that he has done the right thing, and that he can face his impending lawsuit with his head held high.

**Explanation:** This is a terrible response. You are not helping at all here. The junior doctor is in big trouble, and you are making light of the situation.

## Q24.

1 – E. Tell Kevin that although you can appreciate that he has had a negative experience with male doctors in the past, he can rest assured in the quality of your care and expertise.

**Explanation:** This is the most reasonable response to the situation. You are being polite and considerate in the face of the patient's rudeness, and making a real effort to show him that you are the right doctor to treat him.

2 – B. Tell Kevin that although you are more than capable of doing the job, if he is unwilling to be treated by you then you can try and make arrangements to find him another doctor.

**Explanation:** This is the second best response to the situation. If the patient is refusing to work with you then it would be better to try and find another doctor.

3 – A. Tell Kevin that his sexism is not appreciated, and that he will just have to accept that you are his doctor.

**Explanation:** This is the third best response to the situation. You are being very firm with the patient, and making it clear that his behaviour is unacceptable. However, you should try and reassure him that you are more than capable of treating him.

4 – D. Tell Kevin that if he wants his stomach pain to go away, he'd better start being nicer to you.

**Explanation:** This is a bad response. You will only make the patient feel worse, and if anything this will strengthen his belief that you are unprofessional.

5 – C. Tell Kevin that he will not be treated until he changes his attitude towards hospital staff.

**Explanation:** This is the worst response. You have no grounds to tell Kevin this. It is up to you to try and correct his behaviour. Threatening him is the wrong way to go about this.

## Q25.

1 – A. Immediately rebuke your colleagues. Inform them that you have no choice but to take this to senior management.

**Explanation:** This is the best response to the situation. You are dealing with things in a responsible manner. Your colleagues need to be reported to senior management immediately.

2 – D. Call the police.

**Explanation:** This is the next best response. Although this is very severe, and taking the matter to senior management is the best option, your colleagues are breaking the law and therefore this is a police issue.

3 – E. Tell your colleagues that they are in violation of both the law and hospital guidelines. Tell them that they need to flush the cocaine down the toilet, and come with you to senior management.

**Explanation:** This is not a good response. Although it's good that you are taking the matter to senior management, you are helping your colleagues to dispose of the evidence!

4 – B. Quietly close the door. You saw nothing.

**Explanation:** This is a very bad response. You cannot simply ignore this issue.

5 – C. Ask your colleagues what on earth they think they are doing. Tell them to dispose of the cocaine, before anyone sees it.

**Explanation:** This is the worst response. You are actively helping your colleagues to dispose of the evidence, becoming complicit in a major breach of hospital rules, and the law.

## Q26.

1 – E. Tell Brad that you are very disappointed by the way his performance has dipped over the last few months, and warn him that he needs to improve.

**Explanation:** This is the best response to the scenario. You need to show Brad that his performance is unacceptable, but it would be unprofessional to a) question his career prospects, or b) berate him. Ideally, you need to establish what can be done to help him improve.

2 – B. Tell Brad that his performance has dipped alarmingly, and that you are hugely concerned about whether he has what it takes to be a doctor.

**Explanation:** This is the second best response to the scenario, although it's not ideal. While you do need to tell Brad that his performance has been poor, it's a little unprofessional to question his career aspirations.

3 – D. Tell Brad that his lateness, and lack of interest in medicine, are frankly embarrassing. Question him over whether this is the role he really wants to pursue.

**Explanation:** This is similar to option B, but in this option you are essentially just berating Brad in a fashion that will be hugely humiliating for him. This is unprofessional, and you should be trying to find a constructive solution.

4 – A. Tell Brad that his performance is utterly unacceptable. Inform him that he is a sorry excuse for a doctor, and that you have no idea what he is even doing in an establishment such as this.

**Explanation:** This is really unprofessional, and humiliating for Brad. It's even worse than option D, because you are just yelling at him.

5 – C. Tell Brad that, despite his lateness, and his lack of interest in medicine, you are pretty pleased with his overall performance.

**Explanation:** This is the worst option, as you are not fixing the problem.

## Q27.

1 – A. 'Please be assured, we will do our absolute best to ensure that things don't have to go that far. In any case, amputation is a last resort, so there's no need to start panicking about that right now. We'll need to arrange some tests, and once we get these back, one of our senior staff will consult with you. Trust me, you are in the safest hands possible.'

**Explanation:** This is the best and most professional response possible. You are making sure that the patient isn't panicking about the results, and reassuring him that amputation is highly unlikely.

2 – E. 'Amputation is a last resort. It's very unlikely that this will happen. We'll run a few tests first, and then I'll ask one of our senior doctors to consult with you about the result. Don't panic, sir, you are in safe hands!'

**Explanation:** This is the second best response. Again, you are being very professional here, albeit it would be good to reassure the patient that you are doing everything you can for him.

3 – C. 'I'll consult with our senior staff, and we'll run a few tests. Once we get the results back, I'll let you know the outcome.'

**Explanation:** This is the third best response. It's not a great response, because you aren't being very reassuring – but at least you are being professional.

4 – B. 'There's a chance we'll have to amputate…but let's get the results back before we make any decisions.'

**Explanation:** This is a bad response. You are being very unprofessional, and will make the patient feel even more stressed.

5 – D. 'Cheer up. Yes, you'll lose your arm, but at least you're not dead.'

**Explanation:** This is a terrible response. The patient is very distressed, so making jokes is incredibly unprofessional.

## Q28.

1 – B. Explain to Miranda about the risks of her leaving the hospital early, and what these risks are. Allow her to leave if she still persists, following this explanation.

**Explanation:** This is the best response to the situation. There is no legal requirement to keep Miranda at the hospital, provided that you have clearly informed her about all of the risks of leaving, and are assured that she understands these.

2 – D. Tell Miranda that you would like to meet with her mother, to discuss the care that Miranda will need at home.

**Explanation:** This is a good and reasonable response to the situation, as you are ensuring that the patient gets the proper care.

3 – E. Tell Miranda that although she is taking a big risk, ultimately it's her choice.

**Explanation:** This is not a great response, as you should be informing Miranda of what the risks are, rather than simply allowing her to leave without any advice or precautionary measures in place.

4 – C. Lie to Miranda, telling her that if she leaves hospital early, she is likely to die.

**Explanation:** This is obviously not a good response. You are flat out lying to the patient.

5 – A. Tell Miranda that she cannot legally leave the hospital until she has been fully treated for the infection. Call hospital security to ensure that she stays.

**Explanation:** This is the worst response. There is no legal basis to keep Miranda at the hospital. You can't keep her there against her will.

## Q29.

1 – A. Use your own judgement to decide which is the most appropriate cause of death.

**Explanation:** This is the best response to the scenario. You should follow your gut instinct, and put down the cause of death that you believe is the most accurate. You should not simply write down 'collapsed lung' just because the ward consultant told you to, the decision is yours to make. If you believe there was a different cause of death, then write this down.

2 – B. Go and find the coroner. They are best placed to decide.

**Explanation:** In this case, it would be fair to describe the patient's death as 'unexpected'. Her death is (most likely) the result of the fall, and not from lupus. Therefore, if you cannot reach a suitable conclusion by yourself, and you don't agree with the consultant, then the coroner would be the best placed person to deal with this.

3 – C. Agree with the consultant – they know better than you.

**Explanation:** Your ward consultant likely has medical training and expertise that exceeds your own. Therefore, you shouldn't just dismiss what they have said. If their explanation makes sense then it would be wise to consider it.

4 – D. Leave the entry empty. It doesn't matter what the cause of death was.

**Explanation:** You can't simply ignore the cause of death, this is key medical protocol and someone needs to make a decision on what caused this to happen.

5 – E. Ask the victim's family what they believe the cause of death was.

**Explanation:** This is really insensitive. The family will trust in the expertise in the hospital to come to a decision, they are not medical professionals and asking them what they believe was the cause of death is likely to lead to more problems.

## Q30.

1 – E. From the point at which you notice something is wrong, ask the consultant to justify their decisions. Write this down as he does so.

**Explanation:** This is the best response. It might be the case that the consultant has some extra information that you are not aware of. Therefore, it's a good idea to ask them to justify their decisions, whilst ensuring that any extra information is noted down.

2 – A. Stop the round, and ask the consultant in charge whether he has any idea what he is doing.

**Explanation:** This is the next best response. Yes, you are being very rude and unprofessional, but if you feel like the consultant is making poor decisions then you should stand up and say something right then and there.

3 – C. Following the session, take the consultant to one side and question him over some of the decisions that he has made.

**Explanation:** This is the next best response. You aren't being rude about questioning his decisions. However, you should take immediate action if you feel like bad decisions are being made, so waiting till afterwards isn't helpful.

4 – D. Say nothing. It's not your place to interfere.

**Explanation:** This is a bad response. You should say something if you believe that mistakes are being made.

5 – B. Encourage the other participants of the round to follow you instead, and start leading them on an alternative round.

**Explanation:** This is the worst response. You are being extremely unprofessional and completely unhelpful.


## Q31.

1 – C. Tell Matthew that you'll get in touch with the nurses, to see if the bag has been picked up and put away for safekeeping.

**Explanation:** This is the best response to the scenario. It's entirely possible that one of the staff has placed the bag somewhere, so this should be your first port of call.

2 – D. Tell Matthew that you are happy to help him look through his belongings, to see if he has misplaced the bag.

**Explanation:** This is the next best response. You are helping the patient to conduct a thorough search, before escalating the issue.

3 – E. Call the police.

**Explanation:** Calling the police should only be done as a last resort. However, if after a thorough search the bag cannot be found, then it might be the case that the police will need to be involved.

4 – A. Tell Matthew that he needs to be more careful with his possessions in the future, and that this will teach him a valuable lesson.

**Explanation:** This is not helpful at all. The patient is distressed because he has lost his possessions, and you are only making the situation worse.

5 – B. Tell Matthew that this is karma for being such a spoilt little brat.

**Explanation:** This is extremely unprofessional and will make the situation much worse.

## Q32.

1 – A. Immediately go and find the clinic manager, to discuss what you have heard. This is utterly unacceptable.

**Explanation:** This is the best response. Your colleague is behaving in a completely unacceptable manner, and this should be dealt with by the clinic manager.

2 – C. Knock on the door, interrupting the phone conversation, and then ask your colleague if you can have a quiet word about his behaviour.

**Explanation:** This is the second best response. Although you should take the issue straight to the clinic manager, it is also perfectly acceptable for you to discuss with your colleague about why he is behaving in this manner.

3 – D. Discuss with your other colleagues about what should be done.

**Explanation:** This is the next best response, although it's not great. The issue should be dealt with by the clinic manager.

4 – B. Ignore it. It's not your place to comment on private conversations.

**Explanation:** This is a bad response. You shouldn't just ignore the matter, as your colleague is being extremely unprofessional.

5 – E. Subtly open your colleague's door, so that everyone in the clinic can hear what he is saying.

**Explanation:** This is extremely unprofessional and will do significant harm to the clinic – the issue needs to be dealt with junior doctorally.

## Q33.

1 – B. Apologise to Jane, notify the staff, and make sure you watch them administer the medication.

**Explanation:** This is the best response to the situation. It's imperative that the staff are informed of their mistake, and that this is corrected immediately – with you watching it take place.

2 – E. Calmly approach the nursing staff, to enquire as to why this wasn't administered.

**Explanation:** This is the next best response, although it doesn't cover the seriousness of the situation. A full apology will need to be made to the patient, and an investigation will need to be made into why this medicine wasn't administered.

3 – A. Angrily confront the staff at the desk as to why this medication wasn't given.

**Explanation:** This is not a good response, you should try and be calm when confronting the staff about their error, but at the same time you do need to make it clear that this is unacceptable.

4 – C. Go straight to the Director of Nursing, to tell her that her staff are incompetent.

**Explanation:** This is a bad response. While this is a serious incident, and it's entirely possible that the Director of Nursing might need to get involved, on an initial basis the problem should be dealt with by the staff on the ward. Also, marching up to the Director's office to inform her that her staff are incompetent is very unprofessional.

5 – D. Encourage Jane to pursue legal action against the hospital.

**Explanation:** This is a terrible response. Obviously, you should not encourage the patient to take legal action against the hospital.


## Q34.

1 – B. Ask a few extra questions about the injuries, just to make sure their story makes sense.

**Explanation:** This is a good response. You are accepting their story, whilst also taking the correct precautionary measures to ensure that everything adds up. It's important to be sure that everything is okay, regardless of how it appears on the surface.

2 – E. Take a look over the girl's medical history, to check for any previous signs of abuse.

**Explanation:** This is an okay response. Again, you are taking precautionary steps to ensure that everything matches up. If there are any questionable medical reports, which might suggest a pattern of abuse, then this will become evident.

3 – D. Accept their story for now, but bring up your concerns with the head of department later in the day.

**Explanation:** This is an acceptable response. Everything appears normal, but it's good to check that you did the right thing with your head of department.

4 – C. Ask to speak to the mother in private. Accuse her of abusing her daughter.

**Explanation:** This is uncalled for, and will greatly upset the mother.

5 – A. Call social services. It's obvious they are both lying.

**Explanation:** This is an extreme form of action and completely unnecessary.

## Q35.

1 – C. Tell Nathan that his behaviour is completely unacceptable, and that you will be reporting him to senior management.

**Explanation:** This is the best response. Nathan needs to be reported. You should also make him apologise to your colleague, and comfort her, but the key thing here is to raise the fact that Nathan has behaved in an unacceptable manner.

2 – E. Tell Nathan that racism is unacceptable. Ask him to apologise to your colleague.

**Explanation:** This is the next best response. Your colleague deserves a full apology from Nathan, and it needs to be brought to attention that racism is not welcome in the workplace, or anywhere else.

3 – D. Take your colleague into a private room and attempt to comfort her over Nathan's language. Racism has no place in the workplace.

**Explanation:** This is a good response, as you are providing sustained moral support for your colleague. However, Nathan needs to be called out on his terrible behaviour.

4 – A. Tell Nathan that his behaviour is unacceptable. Ask him to give the wine back, so you can get a refund.

**Explanation:** This is not a good response. Yes you are telling him that his behaviour is unacceptable, but that's not enough. Not only does he need to apologise, but he also needs to be reported. This response makes it seem like you only really care about the gift, when there are bigger issues at hand.

5 – B. Offer to buy Nathan a better, more expensive gift.

**Explanation:** Obviously this is bad response. Nathan needs to be reported for his behaviour, not rewarded.

## Q36.

1 – A. Prior to your shift, ask Sarah to talk with you in private, in a bid to resolve your differences. This will make work much easier.

**Explanation:** This is a reasonable response. You are making a sustained effort to resolve any differences, and make the process of working together as easy as possible.

2 – E. Tell the nurse in charge that you have some personal difficulties with Sarah. Ask her if it's possible for you to swap with someone else.

**Explanation:** This is the second best solution. You are being quite polite about the differences you have with Sarah, and at the end of the day it's in the best interests of the patients for staff to collaborate together effectively. Not everyone can get along, so this is reasonable to ask. However, you should be prepared for the fact that you may have to work with Sarah, and therefore it would be better to try and resolve your differences.

3 – D. Agree to work with Sarah. Try to act as professionally as possible.

**Explanation:** This is an acceptable response. You are doing your best, and acting professionally, despite a difficult situation.

4 – B. Tell the nurse in charge that you don't want to work with Sarah. Ask her to swap you with someone else.

**Explanation:** This isn't a great response. You are being quite rude, and you should be prepared for the possibility that you'll have to work with Sarah.

5 – C. Agree to work with Sarah, but resolve to make her look as bad as possible during the shift.

**Explanation:** This is a terrible response. You would only be harming the patients by doing this, and you would be acting very unprofessionally.


## Q37.

1 – D. Ask Mr Miggins whether he wants to tell his son the news directly, or whether it's okay for you to inform his son about it.

**Explanation:** This is the best response. It comes down to doctor patient confidentiality. It's Mr Miggins's choice as to whether his son is informed or not.

2 – A. Tell Mr Miggins's son that you have got the results back, but that he would be better off speaking to his father about the results directly.

**Explanation:** This is the next best response. It's acceptable, but again it's down to Mr Miggins to decide exactly what his son is informed about – including whether you've got the results or not.

3 – B. Pass the phone straight to Mr Miggins.

**Explanation:** This is a bad response. You are being very insensitive to how Mr Miggins would be feeling at that moment.

4 – C. Tell Mr Miggins's son that you have received the results, and unfortunately it's bad news.

**Explanation:** This is a very bad response. It is not up to you to inform Mr Miggins's son about the results, not unless he gives you permission anyway.

5 – E. Announce loudly down the phone that Mr Miggins has a brain tumour, and that he doesn't have long to live.

**Explanation:** This is a terrible response, and hugely insensitive.

## Q38.

1 – D. Email Morgan and tell him that you would like to have a meeting tomorrow, to discuss his absence.

**Explanation:** This is the best response. You need to deal with this as soon as Morgan gets into work the next day, in a professional and discreet manner.

2 – E. Email Morgan and let him know in no uncertain terms that you are highly disappointed with him taking another absence.

**Explanation:** This is the next best response. This is a better option than A, because you shouldn't jump to immediate disciplinary action without getting a full account of the situation first. It could be that the two junior doctors are lying.

3 – A. Email Morgan back, informing him that as a result of his behaviour, you will be taking disciplinary action.

**Explanation:** This is the next best response, but you are jumping straight to disciplinary action without taking stock of the situation. It's imperative that you meet with Morgan first, to discuss his absence, before assessing whether disciplinary action is necessary.

4 – B. Email Morgan back, thanking him for letting you know about his absence, and tell him that you hope he gets better.

**Explanation:** This is a bad response. Morgan has behaved unacceptably, his performance is a major concern, and therefore you need to be much firmer in how you deal with him.

5 – C. Thank Morgan for his hard work over the past year. Attach a P45 form to the email.

**Explanation:** This is a very bad response. You can't fire a staff member in this manner, and in any case there needs to be a full investigation before such severe action is taken.

## Q39.

1 – B. Meet with the head of the department, to address the complaint against you.

**Explanation:** In this scenario, your priority should be your job security. It would be wise to go and see the head of department, to make sure that everything is okay.

2 – A. See if you can arrange a meeting with the woman, to try and explain exactly why you have grown a moustache.

**Explanation:** This is a reasonable explanation. However, there is a chance that it could serve to make things worse, and the woman could get more irate, so it would be better to speak with your head of department first.

3 – E. Resolve to keep your moustache beyond November. It's your choice.

**Explanation:** This is not a great option, as you are not doing anything to try and resolve the issue. Yes, it is your prerogative to keep your moustache, however you should try and reach an understanding with the patient, and with your head of department, as to why you are doing so.

4 – D. Shave your moustache immediately, find the woman and beg for forgiveness.

**Explanation:** This is a bad response. The question clearly states that you are growing a moustache for a charitable cause, and giving in to pressure so easily would undermine this.

5 – C. Ignore the complaint. Those in charge will see sense.

**Explanation:** This is the worst response. You need to take some form of action, and make a decision on what to do.

## Q40.

1 – B. Try and talk to the boy yourself, asking him to stay at the hospital and get the help that he needs.

**Explanation:** This is the best response to the situation. You are taking a reasonable and responsible approach, with the utmost consideration for the patient.

2 – D. Arrange a phone call with the patient's relatives, to get their view on the situation.

**Explanation:** This is the next best response. If possible, you should try and involve the patient's relatives in the decision.

3 – C. Tell the boy that he will unfortunately need to be sectioned under the mental health act.

**Explanation:** This is the third best response. Although it's not ideal, and this is a last resort, it's entirely possible that you might need to take this course of action.

4 – E. Tell the boy that he has broken the law by attempting to commit suicide, and will now face criminal charges.

**Explanation:** This is extremely insensitive and will only make the patient feel worse.

5 – A. Allow the boy to leave. Ultimately, it's his choice.

**Explanation:** This is by far the worst response. Based on the question, it would be entirely irresponsible for you to discharge the patient.

## Q41.

1 – B. Question the man further, querying his mood, his appetite and how he is feeling, to try and establish whether he is suicidal.

**Explanation:** This is the best response. If a patient is showing the signs of severe depression then you need to screen for suicidal ideation.

2 – C. Take the issue directly to your senior GP.

**Explanation:** Following screening for suicidal ideation, this should be directly discussed with your senior GP.

3 – E. Prescribe the man a course of anti-depressants.

**Explanation:** This is a step that should only be taken after the above steps have been fulfilled.

4 – A. You are treating the man for infection, not for depression. Ignore the issue.

**Explanation:** This is a very bad response, you should never ignore this.

5 – D. Ask the patients in the waiting room what they think you should do.

**Explanation:** This is the worst response. It's highly unprofessional and you would be breaking the doctor patient confidentiality agreement.

## Q42.

1 – D. 'The admittance team don't have access to the same results that we do, therefore they can only make a preliminary diagnosis. In any case, we'll diagnosis you ourselves.'

**Explanation:** This is the best response, as it provides the patient with an explanation for why there are differing results, and doesn't cast the admittance team in a bad light, as well as assuring the patient that he will be diagnosed in a proper and professional manner.

2 – C. 'I'm sure they just made a mistake. They don't have access to the investigation results that we do. Not to worry though sir, we'll make sure we get this sorted for you and you'll be out of here in no time at all.'

**Explanation:** This is the second best response. You are reassuring the patient about the diagnosis and making him feel at ease. However, you are also casting the admittance team in a negative light by pointing out that they made a mistake.

3 – E. 'I'm sorry for my colleague's comments sir, she's having a bad day. We'll diagnose you ourselves, so don't worry.'

**Explanation:** This is the third best response, but it's not great. You are apologising on behalf of Maria, which is good, but the patient needs a better explanation for why the results are wrong.

4 – B. 'There's only one clown in this hospital, and that's you, Maria. I can assure you sir, the admittance team are almost never wrong.'

**Explanation:** This is a negative and unhelpful response.

5 – A. 'You are so right. I can't believe how terrible they are. Only last week they admitted someone to the hospital with completely the wrong illness, and he died within 10 minutes of getting here…but don't worry I'm sure that won't happen to you sir.'

**Explanation:** This is a terrible response, which casts the hospital in a bad light, and fails to reassure the patient.

## Q43.

1 – B. Sit down with the patient and talk to him about how he is feeling, and any concerns that he has.

**Explanation:** In this scenario it's important to be compassionate towards how the patient might be feeling. As the patient is under your care, you should sit down with him and try to empathise, making him feel better about the situation.

2 – C. Apologise to the nurses and tell them that you'll have a private word with Mr Naisbeck.

**Explanation:** This is the next best response. You are making the nurses feel reassured, whilst still having a private talk with Mr Naisbeck to try and make him feel better.

3 – D. Tell Mr Naisbeck that although you understand he is feeling stressed and upset about being in hospital, he needs to try and be more polite to the staff.

**Explanation:** This is a reasonable response, but it would be better to try and take a more sympathetic approach. Instead of approaching Mr Naisbeck about the problem directly, sit down with him and have a quiet chat about how he's feeling. If things still don't improve, then you can be more direct.

4 – E. Tell the nurses to stop overreacting.

**Explanation:** This is a very bad response. The nurses don't have to put up with poor behaviour or abuse.

5 – A. Tell the patient that if his behaviour doesn't improve, you'll have him thrown out.

**Explanation:** This is very unsympathetic and a massive overreaction.

## Q44.

1 – B. Tell Stan that Dalteparin is not the correct prescription, given that Mr Bosworth has just had a spinal tap.

**Explanation:** This is the best response to the situation. It would be completely wrong to prescribe Dalteparin in this case. Given the patient has just had a spinal tap, you risk causing a blood clot.

2 – E. Query Stan over why he has prescribed Dalteparin.

**Explanation:** This is the next best response. You need to question Stan over his decision, and then make it clear to him that he's made a mistake.

3 – C. Go behind Stan's back, and prescribe Mr Bosworth with different medication instead. That way, everybody wins.

**Explanation:** This isn't great, but at least you are ensuring that the patient doesn't receive the wrong medication. You should be working with Stan though, not against him.

4 – D. Go straight to the head of medicine and tell them what Stan has just done. That will knock him off his perch.

**Explanation:** This is not a good response. You are acting out of spite, and not in the interests of the patient. Furthermore, the head of medicine doesn't need to be involved in this. You can amend the error, and correct Stan, right there and then.

5 – A. Agree with Stan. After all, he is one of the top junior doctors.

**Explanation:** This is a terrible response. You are putting the patient at risk.

## Q45.

1 – E. Walk up to Mrs Matthews and apologise on behalf of the hospital. Inform her that the junior doctors will be punished severely for this unacceptable behaviour. Ask a nurse to finish prepping the patient instead.

**Explanation:** This is the best response. You are apologising to the patient, whilst making it extremely clear that the junior doctors' behaviour is unacceptable.

2 – A. Immediately walk up to Mrs Matthews and apologise profusely on behalf of the hospital. Ask them to finish prepping the patient, and then come with you to the Chief Physician's office.

**Explanation:** This is the second best response, although it's not ideal. The junior doctors in question should not be allowed to finish prepping the patient. Furthermore, this does not need to go straight to the Chief Physician – there are other senior doctors within the hospital who are better placed to deal with this.

3 – B. Go over to Mrs Matthews and apologise on behalf of the junior doctors. Tell them to stop mucking around and finish off the preparation.

**Explanation:** This is a bad response. Yes, you are apologising, but you are also dismissing the junior doctors' behaviour as 'mucking around' when it's far more serious than that. The seriousness of their behaviour needs to be emphasised.

4 – D. Consult with the nurses over what you have just heard.

**Explanation:** This is not a good response. You need to make an immediate apology to the patient.

5 – C. Ignore it and say nothing. They could turn on you too.

**Explanation:** This is a really terrible response. You absolutely need to step in here.

## Q46.

1 – B. Tell James that you will put him in touch with the hospital specialist, who deals with organ donation issues.

**Explanation:** This is the best response to the situation. In this case, there would be a specialist team of nurses at the hospital who deal with organ donation issues.

2 – A. Tell James that the decision is down to him and the rest of his family, and that the organs won't be donated without their permission.

**Explanation:** This is the next best response to the situation. The hospital is obligated to respect the family's wishes, even if the patient was on the organ donor register.

3 – C. Tell James that although the organs won't be donated without his permission, he should think about the greater good.

**Explanation:** This is not an ideal response. Although you are respecting James's wishes, it is not your place to tell him whether or not organ donation is right/wrong.

4 – D. Tell James that since his father was on the organ donor register, the decision on whether the organs will be donated is now out of the family's hands.

**Explanation:** This is a bad response, as you are giving James incorrect information, that will serve to upset him.

5 – E. Tell James that you will donate his father's organs, whether he likes it or not.

**Explanation:** This is very insensitive and will cast the hospital in an extremely bad light.

## Q47.

1 – D. Tell the husband that you are going to act in his wife's best interests, and perform the transfusion.

**Explanation:** This is the best response to the scenario. You need to perform the transfusion, as it is in the best interests of the patient, however it is reasonable to explain this to the husband first.

2 – A. Perform the transfusion, regardless of the husband's wishes.

**Explanation:** This is the next best response. You have a duty of care to the patient –which means keeping her alive, regardless of the husband's wishes.

3 – B. Ask the husband whether he wants to be held responsible for his wife's death.

**Explanation:** There is no point in trying to guilt trip the husband into accepting the blood transfusion. You need to go through with the operation, whether he likes it or not.

4 – E. Ask the medical team to come up with some alternative solutions.

**Explanation:** This is very ineffective. The medical team has already given a unanimous decision that the patient needs a blood transfusion.

5 – C. Tell the husband that if he wants to prevent his wife from receiving blood, he needs to go and see the legal team.

**Explanation:** This is the worst response. The husband cannot legally prevent his wife from receiving blood in this situation, if it is deemed by the medical staff to be the only possible course of action. You should not even imply to the husband that it's possible to stop this from going through.

## Q48.

1 – C. Tell your friend that this is a request more suitable for his GP, and not something you can do.

**Explanation:** This is the best response to the situation. Your friend and his wife need to go and see a GP if they wish to obtain antibiotics.

2 – D. Tell your friend to leave you alone, and stop pestering you at work.

**Explanation:** This is a bit rude, but it's appropriate. Your friend should not be bothering you with requests like this at work.

3 – E. Tell your friend that if he wants antibiotics, he should visit the hospital pharmacy.

**Explanation:** This is not a good response, as the pharmacy won't give your friend antibiotics. They will simply tell him to go and see his GP – which is something that you could tell him instead.

4 – B. Ask your friend to send Julie into the hospital, so that you can assess whether she needs the antibiotics.

**Explanation:** This is a bad response. You are wasting everybody's time here, when you could just advise your friend to go and see a GP.

5 – A. Prescribe your friend the antibiotics. Wish him a good honeymoon.

**Explanation:** This is a terrible response. You can't just give your friend antibiotics, especially when they aren't even for him!

## Q49.

1 – B. Take the man to one side and try to reach a reasonable agreement, for the best interests of the patient.

**Explanation:** This is the best response. You are taking a reasonable and open-minded approach to the situation, without just assuming the worst, but still acting in the best interests of the patient.

2 – D. Proceed with the signing of the consent form as planned. Hopefully the translator doesn't have sinister intentions.

**Explanation:** This is the second best response. Yes, there is animosity between you and the new translator, but you shouldn't just assume the worst. In the event that the translator did act incorrectly then he would lose his job.

3 – A. Immediately call the translation service, and ask them to send over a different translator.

**Explanation:** This is the next best response, but it's still not great. You shouldn't jump to conclusions. If you are going to take action, without speaking to the translator first, then you should discuss it with a senior member of staff.

4 – C. Ask the patient to sign the consent form, without the help of any translation service.

**Explanation:** This is a really bad response, and highly unprofessional. The patient does not even know what she is consenting to.

5 – E. Fill in the consent form on behalf of the patient.

**Explanation:** This is the worst response. You can't just fill in the form on the patient's behalf – as this is illegal.

## Q50.

1 – A. Tell your head of department that although you understood there to be animosity between yourself and the translator, you trusted him to do his job to the best of his ability.

**Explanation:** This is the most reasonable and fair response. You are not responsible for the actions of a rogue translator, and you have a right to expect every person working within the confines of the hospital to behave with the utmost professionalism. You can also show your head of department the text that was sent.

2 – C. Tell your head of department that although you can appreciate that you should have spoken to someone about the translator prior to gaining consent, they need to take issue with the translation company, and not with you – you were simply doing your job.

**Explanation:** This is also a reasonable response. Although you were aware of animosity between yourself and the translator, you should expect every person to work with the utmost professionalism, regardless of personal feelings.

3 – B. Tell your head of department that you are not responsible for the behaviour of the translator, and that it's the hospital's fault for hiring him.

**Explanation:** This is a pretty bad response. You will only be making the situation worse here. There's also an argument that you should have reported the situation. It's not your fault, but you aren't totally blameless here.

4 – E. Tell your head of department that you take full responsibility for the translator's actions, and that you are willing to take the legal consequences for the mistake.

**Explanation:** This is a very bad response. You aren't legally responsible for this situation.

5 – D. Tell your head of department that he better find himself a good lawyer, because Mrs Aillia is not happy.

**Explanation:** This is the worst response. You are belittling your head of department, and absolving yourself of all responsibility. Very unprofessional.

## Q51.

1 – A. Call the security team to come and deal with the situation.

**Explanation:** This is the best response. The patient is behaving very aggressively, damaging hospital equipment, and needs to be restrained by someone with training. The security team are the best placed people to deal with this.

2 – E. Call the A&E department to come and fetch their escaped patient.

**Explanation:** This is a fairly bad response. Not only will it take time for members of their department to arrive, but this is something that needs to be dealt with by your department as a priority. Hospital staff are a team, so the responsibility is shared in this case, and it is your patients that the woman's behaviour is impacting.

3 – D. Try and restrain the patient yourself.

**Explanation:** This is a very bad response. Given how aggressive the woman is acting, you would be putting yourself at a significant risk. Along with this, physical restraint should only be done by someone with the correct procedural knowledge and training.

4 – B. Try to move all of the other patients in the ward, out of the room, so that the woman can be dealt with.

**Explanation:** This is not a feasible option. You are working in the emergency care unit – and it would take a large amount of manpower, time and resources to move all of the patients out of the ward, just to deal with one disruptive individual.

5 – C. Ask the nurses to fetch a sedation kit.

**Explanation:** This is the worst response, since sedation comes with significant risks and should only be a last resort. Remember too that if you want to sedate the patient, then you'll have to restrain them first.

## Q52.

1 – C. Tell Mr Clement that he is free to make his own decisions, but encourage him to involve his children in the decision-making process.

**Explanation:** This is the best response to the situation. The decision ultimately rests with Mr Clement, but it's very important to involve his family in the decision-making process.

2 – E. Encourage Janice and Paul to accept their father's decision.

**Explanation:** This is the next best response, although it's not ideal. It's important for you to try and explore why Janice and Paul feel this way, rather than simply encouraging them to be happy with their father's decision. It might be the case that they have personal reasons for wanting their father to remain in hospital, rather than going to a hospice.

3 – D. Encourage Mr Clement to accept his children's wishes.

**Explanation:** This is the third best response, but again it's not great. The decision does rest with Mr Clement, so you shouldn't encourage him to bend to other people's wishes. Yes, he should involve his family in the decision-making process, but that doesn't mean letting them make the decisions for him.

4 – A. Tell Janice and Paul that they have no say in what is done with their father.

**Explanation:** This is not a good response. It's very insensitive and will leave both children feeling extremely angry.

5 – B. Tell Mr Clement that because he is terminally ill, his children must decide what is done with him.

**Explanation:** This is the worst response. It's completely untrue, and will leave Mr Clement feeling isolated and powerless, when the decision is ultimately his.


**Q53.**

1 – B. Ask the nurses to bring you a full set of notes on the events of yesterday, so that you can determine what went wrong.

**Explanation:** This is the best course of action. Since you are undecided on how to fill in the death certificate, the first thing you should do is take a look at the hospital notes and documentation, which should provide some indication of what happened.

2 – C. Find out which members of staff were treating Mrs Dalton yesterday, to discuss the events with them.

**Explanation:** This is the next best option. If the documentation doesn't provide you with substantial clues, then you should seek out the members of staff who were in direct contact with Mrs Dalton.

3 – E. Fill in the death certificate, based on Mrs Dalton's previous symptoms.

**Explanation:** This is the third best option, but it's not particularly good. It could be that the death was down to something completely different, in which case Mrs Dalton's previous symptoms would be nothing to do with this.

4 – D. Ask one of the nurses to fill in the death certificate instead.

**Explanation:** This is not a good response. You have been asked to take responsibility, and Mrs Dalton was your patient, so you shouldn't ask the nurses to do this for you.

5 – A. Angrily blame the nurses for Mrs Dalton's death.

**Explanation:** This is the worst response. It's not fair to blame the nurses for this, and getting angry won't solve anything.


**Q54.**

1 – C. Tell the patient that you have received the blood test results back, and unfortunately she is HIV positive. Follow this up by explaining the different treatment options available to her.

**Explanation:** This is the best response. Following you telling the patient about the diagnosis, you will need to sensitively discuss a treatment plan.

2 – A. Start by reminding the patient about why you took the blood test results in the first place, before gently breaking the unfortunate news.

**Explanation:** This is the next best way to tackle the problem. It's good to explain the rationale behind your decisions, to make the patient feel comfortable about why the tests were taken, before breaking the bad news.

3 – E. Break the news to the patient in a sensitive fashion. Pre-arrange for her friends and family to visit, so that they can support her at this difficult time.

**Explanation:** This is not a good response. Although you are being sensitive to the patient, and well-meaning, it's entirely possible that the patient will be very upset or even ashamed by these test results. Therefore, you should leave her to discuss things with her family/friends. Pre-arranging for them to visit will only cause problems.

4 – D. Ask the patient whether she had unprotected sex whilst abroad.

**Explanation:** This is insensitive and blunt. In any case, if a blood test was taken then the patient would likely have been questioned beforehand.

5 – B. Tell the patient that she is HIV positive, but the hospital can cure this for her.

**Explanation:** This is clearly the worst response. Not only is it untrue, but it's very blunt and insensitive.


**Q55.**

1 – C. Go and see your consultant to discuss your colleague's behaviour. Ask your consultant whether there is any support that can be offered to your colleague.

**Explanation:** This is the best response. Although option B is good too, ultimately your colleague has left in the middle of his shift. This is a serious breach of conduct. It needs to be discussed with your consultant, so that a help plan can be put in place for your colleague.

2 – B. Text your colleague to make sure he's feeling okay. Ask him to meet with you once you've finished your shift, so that you can discuss his behaviour.

**Explanation:** This is the next best response. You are being sensitive towards your colleague's feelings, and taking intervention measures to ensure his wellbeing.

3 – D. The next time you see your colleague, resolve to offer him your full support and confidence.

**Explanation:** This is the third best response. It's okay, but it's not great. Based on your colleague's choice of words, he might not be returning to the hospital. You should endeavour to get in touch with him, or discuss the issue with a senior member of staff, as soon as possible.

4 – E. Contact your colleague's relatives, to see if they can provide any insight into his behaviour.

**Explanation:** This is a well-meaning but misplaced response. You should contact your colleague first, before getting in touch with his relatives. There could be a personal issue at home, which is causing his behaviour. In this case, it would be insensitive for you to contact his relatives directly.

5 – A. Follow after your colleague, demanding that he comes back into work.

**Explanation:** This is not a good response. Although it's true that your colleague has committed a serious breach of conduct, you are not treating him in a sensitive manner.

## Q56.

1 – B. Explain to the family that the girl is only slightly overweight, and that there are far less drastic measures of shedding pounds.

**Explanation:** This is the best response to the situation. Your findings indicate that the girl doesn't need to undergo this type of procedure. In this case, it would be for aesthetic, and there are less drastic ways of achieving her desired goal.

2 – C. Run through the advantages and disadvantages of having liposuction. Encourage the family to consider other options.

**Explanation:** This is the second best response. The patient has asked for liposuction, so you should clearly lay out the benefits and disadvantages of this, along with showing them that there are better options.

3 – E. Arrange for the girl to undergo counselling at the hospital. Tell her parents that they need to be more supportive over their child's body image.

**Explanation:** This is the third best response. Given that the girl has just tried to end her life, it would be expected that she takes part in counselling sessions. However, the comment about her parents is misplaced. It might be the case that her parents want her to have liposuction so that she feels happier about herself. We are not given any information that casts them in a negative light.

4 – A. Tell the girl that liposuction won't stop her being bullied.

**Explanation:** This is highly insensitive and inappropriate.

5 – D. Agree to the treatment. If that's what the family want, they can have it.

**Explanation:** Given the situation, the girl will not be able to have liposuction. Therefore, agreeing to perform this would be the worst response.

## Q57.

1 – A. Consult the hospital guidelines for a view on what antibiotics to prescribe.

**Explanation:** The majority of hospitals have detailed guidelines available for all staff, whether via the hospital intranet or resources in the hospital library. This should be your first port of call.

2 – E. Get in touch with your registrar, to see what they think.

**Explanation:** If option A doesn't provide you with any clues, then asking your registrar would be the next best option.

3 – C. Have a look on the junior doctoret to see what would be the best antibiotic.

**Explanation:** This is not a very reliable option, and is fairly unprofessional.

4 – B. Take a straw poll amongst your team, with the most popular antibiotic being the one that is prescribed.

**Explanation:** This is not a good option. The question has already stated that your team cannot agree on what the best antibiotic would be. Therefore, you need to explore other options.

5. D – Ask the patient what they think you should do.

**Explanation:** This is the worst option. It's highly unprofessional and will damage the patient's faith in you.

## Q58.

1 – B. Tell Phil that if he emails you written confirmation that you can request the info, then you'll do so on his behalf.

**Explanation:** This is the best response. You cannot simply give Phil the information that he is requesting, as this would be a breach of confidentiality. However, common sense should apply in this case. With written confirmation, you will be able to request the info and update him on the situation.

2 – A. Tell Phil that unfortunately you can't give him any information over the phone, as this would be a breach of confidentiality.

**Explanation:** This is the second best response, although it's not very helpful. Yes, you cannot breach confidentiality, but there are options available to Phil here, so you should provide them to him.

3 – D. Tell Phil that if he wants any information, he's going to have to visit the hospital in person.

**Explanation:** This is not a particularly good response, and will only serve to frustrate Phil.

4 – E. Tell Phil that he should not contact you about such matters in the future.

**Explanation:** You should try to demonstrate empathy and sympathy in this case. Although it's true that you are not the person whom Phil should contact about such matters, it is perfectly understandable that he is doing so, given the circumstances.

5 – C. Tell Phil that his new wife is probably not going to make it.

**Explanation:** This is hugely insensitive and inappropriate, and will make Phil feel much worse about the situation.

## Q59.

1 – C. Hand back the money to William. Tell him that his mother will receive the same care as

any other patient.

**Explanation:** This is a bit blunt, but it's factually correct, and you are making it clear that you won't take money from William.

2 – E. Inform William that it's against hospital policy to take gifts from patients.

**Explanation:** Again, this is quite blunt, but at least you are emphasising that you can't take handouts from patients. You should try and be sensitive though, reassuring William that his mother will be well looked after.

3 – D. Thank William for his kind offer, but inform him that it won't be necessary, as the staff will take the best possible care of his mother, without any payments.

**Explanation:** This is reasonable, but at the same time you should make it clear that it's not okay for doctors to take money from patients, and that William's offer is inappropriate.

4 – B. Tell William that he does not need to give you money, as his mother is already your favourite patient.

**Explanation:** While this will make William feel better, you should treat all patients with the exact same level of care and professionalism.

5 – A. Thank William for the money, and assure him that his mother will be well looked after.

**Explanation:** This is the worst response. Clearly you are in breach of the hospital code of conduct here.

## Q60.

1 – E. Ask your friend to go back outside, take off his watch and clean his wrist thoroughly. Make sure he doesn't touch anything on the way out.

**Explanation:** This is the most reasonable solution to the problem. You are being polite but firm. The question clearly states that your friend hasn't touched anything, so there isn't a major issue yet.

2 – A. Politely draw your colleague's attention to his mistake. Tell him that because he has breached the infection control policy, you will have no choice but to report him to senior management.

**Explanation:** This is an overreaction. The question clearly states that your friend hasn't touched anything. This doesn't need to go to senior management, as he has simply made an error, however it does need to be corrected with the utmost urgency.

3 – B. Tell your colleague that as a result of his error, hundreds of people could die.

**Explanation:** This is a big overreaction. Your friend hasn't touched anything, he's just made a mistake. However, at least you are emphasising the risks of the situation.

4 – D. Take your friend to one side and tell him that if he doesn't take off his watch, you'll take it off for him.

**Explanation:** This is a bad response. Although you are drawing your friend's attention to his error, you are also threatening him.

5 – C. Push the hospital emergency alarm. This is a code-red situation, and your friend must be quarantined.

**Explanation:** This is an enormous overreaction, and will cause serious problems. Your friend does not need to be quarantined.


## Q61.

1 – C. Sit down with Mrs Figgins and ask her to elaborate on her concerns.

**Explanation:** This is the best response. The issues that Mrs Figgins has raised are extremely serious, and the hospital needs to work on a resolution before she can be released.

2 – D. Arrange with the ward manager to delay Mrs Figgins's discharge, whilst these issues are dealt with.

**Explanation:** Although the question states that there is a shortage of space, Mrs Figgins is still a patient of the hospital and therefore you have a duty of care to try and resolve these issues for her, before she can be released.

3 – E. Speak to the nursing team about how Mrs Figgins's problem can be resolved.

**Explanation:** This is a passive solution, but it's still useful. You should try to take care of the issue yourself, before consulting the nursing team.

4 – B. Tell Mrs Figgins that the problems she has discussed can be resolved by an external social care team, and are nothing to do with the hospital.

**Explanation:** This is very insensitive and represents a shirking of responsibility. The problems that Mrs Figgins has discussed are to do with the hospital, because she is your patient, and is very vulnerable.

5 – A. Inform Mrs Figgins that she can stay at the hospital, but she'll have to sleep on the floor.

**Explanation:** Obviously, this is a terrible response, and completely unacceptable.


## Q62.

1 – B. Allow Ian to leave, but then approach the head matron of the paediatric ward about what you have seen.

**Explanation:** This is a difficult situation. Yes, you have clearly seen Ian taking supplies from the cupboard – which more than likely constitutes stealing, but it would be better to take the issue to the head matron than confront him on the spot. You don't know how he is going to react, especially if he has an addiction.

2 – E. Tell Ian that he needs to put the drugs back immediately, and come with you to the Chief physician's office.

**Explanation:** This is not ideal. You don't need to go to the Chief physician's office. Along with this, if you tell Ian to put the drugs back, then he'll have no reason to go with you to the office, as there's no proof of his wrongdoing (unless he owns up, which seems unlikely).

3 – A. Ask Ian to empty his pockets, and accuse him of stealing from the hospital.

**Explanation:** This falls under the same category as option B, in that it's probably not the best course of action, because confronting Ian on the spot could have risky consequences. It would be better to take this to someone more senior.

4 – C. Loudly accuse Ian of being a drug addict.

**Explanation:** This is highly unprofessional and speculative.

5 – D. Tell Ian that if he puts the drugs back, you won't tell anyone.

**Explanation:** This is the worst response. You can't simply ignore this behaviour.

## Q63.

1 – A. Wait until the next shift, when you are both working together, to confront your colleague about her behaviour. If she cannot provide a suitable explanation, then take this to a senior manager.

**Explanation:** This is the best response to the scenario. It's important for you to give your colleague a chance to explain herself, but if she can't, then you should report the issue to senior management.

2 – B. Leave the club, and call the hospital, to inform them about your colleague's behaviour. They need to be notified at once.

**Explanation:** This is the second best response, but it's still not a good one. Your colleague's behaviour is unacceptable, but there isn't an urgent need for the hospital to be notified. This is something that can be done at the start of your next shift.

3 – E. Wait until the next shift, to confront your colleague about her behaviour. Tell her that if she does it again, you'll report her.

**Explanation:** This is not a good response. Your colleague's behaviour is unacceptable. If she can't explain it then she needs to be reported now, not the next time she does it.

4 – C. Ignore it. It's nothing to do with you.

**Explanation:** You should be acting in the best interests of the hospital. Ignoring this issue represents a neglection of duty.

5 – D. Approach your colleague in the club, and tell her that if she doesn't want you to report her, she'll need to buy you a few drinks.

**Explanation:** This is the worst response. You are agreeing to look the other way, as long as it benefits you, which is totally unacceptable.

**Q64.**

1 – A. Reassure your colleague that this is something which will be taken very seriously. Immediately go to find the senior site practitioner.

**Explanation:** This is the best response. This is a very serious incident, and needs to be reported.

2 – E. Ask your colleague if she would be happy to submit a written report on what she saw. Following this, go with her to the head of medicine's office to discuss the incident.

**Explanation:** This needs to be reported, but not to the head of medicine. Your colleague will also likely need to submit a report on what she saw.

3 – C. Immediately go to registrar's office and confront him about his behaviour.

**Explanation:** Confronting the registrar directly is not advisable. Someone more senior should deal with this situation.

4 – B. Reassure your colleague that it's not her fault, and she shouldn't be embarrassed, but that the registrar can use his free time however he wishes.

**Explanation:** This is an unacceptable response. It's completely inappropriate for the registrar to be watching such material whilst at the hospital, and using the hospital resources/junior doctoret to do so.

5 – D. Ask Mr Lewishham what he thinks about the registrar watching pornography.

**Explanation:** This is the worst response. You shouldn't involve the patient in this debacle.


**Q65.**

1 – B. Tell Chad that you don't need to put up with abuse from patients. Discharge him.

**Explanation:** In this scenario the patient is being extremely rude and disrespectful towards you. While you should always try to be polite, the best response here is to discharge him and walk away.

2 – E. Tell Chad that you don't need to put up with abuse from patients. Discharge him.

**Explanation:** Don't bring yourself down to Chad's level. Unfortunately some patients are unpleasant. In this scenario, you just need to walk away.

3 – C. Tell Chad that he should start treating women with more respect, if he ever wishes to be happy.

**Explanation:** This is a reasonable response, but it would be better not to even engage Chad in conversation about this topic.

4 – D. Tell Chad that you hope his sporting career is a failure.

**Explanation:** This would be bringing yourself down to Chad's level, and being equally petty. There's no point in this, or sacrificing your professionalism for the sake of one unpleasant person.

5 – A. Tell Chad that next time he comes back to the hospital, you won't be treating him.

**Explanation:** You can't guarantee this. Again, don't sacrifice your professionalism for the sake of one nasty person. That being said, if the patient is unpleasant to you then you could speak to a senior manager and ensure that next time you aren't assigned as Chad's doctor.

## Q66.

1 – B. Speak to the head of the surgical team for that operation, and voice your concerns over your colleague's mindset.

**Explanation:** This is a tough one. Surgery is a very complex and difficult procedure. It is essential that every single member of the surgical team is in the right frame of mind to perform the operation. With this in mind, it would be best to speak to the head of surgical team – who can then perform a proper assessment over whether your colleague is in the right mental place to perform.

2 – C. Sit down with your colleague in private, and discuss how the patient's comments made her feel. Reassure her that you have the utmost confidence in her ability to take part in the operation.

**Explanation:** This is a good response, and shows a great level of care for your colleague. You are taking responsibility for the situation, and going to great lengths to comfort her and ensure that she feels valued.

3 – D. Ask the head of the surgical team to consider removing your colleague from the operation.

**Explanation:** This is not a great response. You are undermining your colleague by asking for her to be removed, when it would be better for someone to try and assess her mental state, before surgery is performed.

4 – E. Approach the patient and demand that he apologises.

**Explanation:** This is a bad response. You need to appreciate that the patient is an immature child, who probably doesn't know any better. Although his comments are hurtful, this probably isn't the best way to approach the situation.

5 – A. Ignore your concerns. Your colleague is a grown woman, she can handle it.

**Explanation:** This is the worst response. If you have doubts about your colleague's mindset heading into surgery, then you really need to voice them, because the results could be catastrophic if not.

## Q67.

1 – E. Tell the patient, in a quiet and sensitive manner, that the scan results show she won't be able to wrestle again. Book her an appointment with the counselling team.

**Explanation:** This is the best response to the scenario. You are being sensitive and respectful towards the impact that this news could have on the patient. Given how upsetting this could be, it also makes sense to book her an appointment with the counselling team.

2 – B. Sit down with the patient, in a quiet and sensitive manner, to discuss her options moving forward. Ask her whether she has any friends/relatives whom she wants to discuss things with.

**Explanation:** This is a good response. You are being very sensitive to how the patient is feeling, and it's great that you are talking through potential options with her.

3 – A. Sit down with the patient, and inform her that the scan results give her very little hope of wrestling again in the future.

**Explanation:** This is not the best response, because it comes across as very blunt. However, at least you are being open and honest.

4 – D. Ask a junior doctor to break the news. You have better things to do.

**Explanation:** This is a pretty bad response. You need to take responsibility for your own patient.

5 – C. Inform the patient that while the scan results are extremely negative, you have hope that she'll be able to wrestle again in the future.

**Explanation:** This is the worst response. The question clearly states that she will not be able to wrestle again. You are giving her false hope, and could actually be endangering the patient if she decides to try and get back into the sport.

## Q68.

1 – B. Gather a few of your other colleagues together, and sit down with the pair as a group, to discuss how things can be improved moving forward.

**Explanation:** This is the best solution, and is the most sensitive. If you and your colleagues can show the pair that their behaviour is causing more harm than good, then this might give them an incentive to change.

2 – A. Take both of your colleagues to one side, and inform them that their relationship is having a disruptive influence on the treatment of patients within the ward.

**Explanation:** This is the next best response. You are being very frank and honest, but this might be something that is necessary given the circumstances. You can't allow them to disrupt things any further.

3 – C. Go to the head of medicine, and ask for the pair to be placed in different sectors moving forward.

**Explanation:** This is an overreaction. You do not need to get someone so senior involved in something so petty.

4 – E. Ignore it and say nothing.

**Explanation:** This is obviously not a good response. You shouldn't allow your colleagues to continue disrupting things.

5 – D. Try to take advantage of their recent breakup, by dating your male colleague yourself. That way, there will be no more arguments.

**Explanation:** This will only lead to more arguments and problems, between all three of you.

## Q69.

1 – E. Tell your colleague that as a result of his behaviour, you will have no choice but to report him to the police.

**Explanation:** The UK has strict laws surrounding 'revenge pornography'. Your colleague is clearly in breach of this law, and therefore you have full rights to report him to the police.

2 – D. Tell your colleague that he has broken the law by sharing these images, and that he needs to hand himself in to the police.

**Explanation:** It's better for you to just go straight to the police directly, however if possible you should also inform your colleague about why you are doing so.

3 – C. Go to a senior doctor and ask them what they believe the best course of action would be.

**Explanation:** This is a reasonable approach. Although your colleague has broken the law, the hospital will also need to launch a disciplinary enquiry, and also possibly provide support for the individual whose images have been shared around.

4 – B. Go to his ex-partner and explain to her what your colleague has done.

**Explanation:** This is an okay response. Here, you are informing your colleague's ex partner about his behaviour – as she certainly has a right to know. However, it could be argued that it would better for you to take action first, before explaining to her about the situation and what has occurred. It's likely that there will be significant embarrassment and distress on her end upon discovering what has happened.

5 – A. Immediately confront your colleague and tell him that he needs to stop sharing the images around.

**Explanation:** This simply isn't enough. Your colleague not only needs to stop sharing the images, but they need to be deleted, and he needs to be reported for his behaviour.

## Q70.

1 – A. Treat Johnny under the mental health act.

**Explanation:** In this circumstance, with psychiatric assessment not listed as an option, the best course of action would be to treat Johnny under the mental health act. This would likely be a natural follow up to any psychiatric review of Johnny and his behaviour.

2 – D. Ask the nurses whether they think it's worth treating Johnny under the mental capacity act.

**Explanation:** This is a waste of time. Johnny does not need to be treated under the mental capacity act, as he is clearly in control of his own thoughts and actions.

3 – B. Tell Johnny that if he won't cooperate, you will need to enforce cannulation.

**Explanation:** This is a bad response. Cannulation is an action that needs to be performed with explicit consent from the patient.

4 – E. Inform Johnny's mother that if her son doesn't cooperate, there could be criminal charges levelled against her.

**Explanation:** This is a very bad response, and is likely to distress Johnny's mother even further. It's also untrue.

5 – C. Discharge Johnny. There's nothing you can do if he won't cooperate.

**Explanation:** This is a terrible response. Given the seriousness of the situation, you can't just let Johnny leave.

## Q71.

1 – D. Approach a senior member of staff from outside of the ward for guidance on how you should deal with this. Ideally, this should be your educational supervisor.

**Explanation:** This is the best response. The question clearly states that you feel your learning has been impacted and you aren't progressing as a result of your colleagues' behaviour. Therefore, the best person to talk to about this issue would be your educational supervisor.

2 – C. Ask your colleagues from other departments in the hospital for advice on what to do.

**Explanation:** This is an okay response. It might be the case that your colleagues have experienced something similar, or know of someone whom you can contact to resolve this issue.

3 – A. Try and organise a sit-down meeting with your senior colleagues. Accuse them of bullying and harassment, and inform them that they are a disgrace to the profession.

**Explanation:** This is not a great response, as you are probably going to make the situation worse, but at least you are highlighting how upset you are at your colleagues' behaviour.

4 – B. Next time someone makes a patronising comment, call them out in front of the patients.

**Explanation:** This will not resolve the issue. If anything, it will make the staff look unprofessional in front of the patients, by bickering.

5 – E. Ignore it, and resolve to prove to the senior doctors in the ward that you have what it takes to survive.

**Explanation:** Bullying is extremely serious, and not something that should be taken lightly. You should not just ignore it.

## Q72.

1 – E. Tell the senior doctor that certain members of your team did not perform to their best, but for this the entire team must share the responsibility.

**Explanation:** This is a reasonable response. You are emphasising the reasons for why things went wrong, but also showing that you accept the idea of 'team responsibility', rather than blaming individuals.

2 – B. Tell the senior doctor that no one person is to blame for the entire problem, and that all members of the team must share the responsibility equally.

**Explanation:** This is a good response, but it doesn't really emphasise exactly what went wrong. However, it does show team ethic and responsibility, which is good.

3 – D. Tell the senior doctor that every person in the team must share the blame equally for what occurred, but certain members were in the midst of personal issues while dealing with the patient.

**Explanation:** This is not a great response. If you noticed that other members of the team were allowing their personal circumstances to impact their medical practice, then it is your responsibility to do something about this.

4 – C. Tell the senior doctor that although you did your very best with this patient, other members of the team let you down.

**Explanation:** This is a bad response. You are shirking responsibility, and blaming others.

5 – A. Inform the senior doctor that it's all Chris's fault, and that he was to blame for all of the mistakes that occurred when dealing with this patient.

**Explanation:** This is the worst response. You are completely absolving yourself of blame, and pinning it onto one individual.


## Q73.

1 – E. Tell Gregg that he could be subject to criminal prosecution if he fails to notify his partner about his condition, in advance of having intercourse with her.

**Explanation:** This is the best response. It's extremely important for you to emphasise the seriousness of the situation. In this instance, you are appealing to the patient's selfish side, by showing them that if they don't tell their partner, then they could be prosecuted.

2 – A. Inform Gregg that if he does not notify his partner, as a doctor you have a legal responsibility to notify her yourself.

**Explanation:** This is the second best response. If Gregg doesn't tell his partner, then as the doctor you must do so.

3 – C. Tell Gregg that he has a moral responsibility to notify his partner, but not a legal responsibility.

**Explanation:** This is untrue. Gregg does have a legal responsibility, and could be prosecuted for failing to inform his partner. However, at least in this option you are appealing to Gregg to tell his partner.

4 – D. Tell Gregg that even though he has HIV, there's a good chance he can be cured.

**Explanation:** This is a lie, and therefore constitutes a very bad response.

5 – B. Tell Gregg that he won't need to inform his partner, just as long as he starts using sexual protection.

**Explanation:** Again, this is untrue. Gregg does need to inform his partner.

## Q74.

1 – A. Encourage Pauline to speak to some of the other nurses, and then take the issue to senior management.

**Explanation:** This is the best response. Ultimately, Pauline and the other nurses need to take responsibility for dealing with this issue themselves – by taking it to senior management – as they are the ones being impacted by it. However, you should fully encourage them to act, as it is unacceptable for Graham to be acting this way towards other members of staff.

2 – E. Speak to the other nurses about how they feel on the issue.

**Explanation:** This is the next best response. It would be a good idea to discuss the issue with the other nurses, to establish how they have been impacted by this behaviour.

3 – C. Find a member of senior management, with whom you can discuss the issue.

**Explanation:** This is an okay response, but you are involving yourself in a situation which isn't anything to do with you. Yes, it's great that you are taking responsibility for the issue and standing up for other members of staff, but they need to speak to senior management about the issue themselves. The only perspective you have is what you've heard and seen.

4 – D. Confront Graham about his behaviour. Accuse him of being disrespectful towards the nurses.

**Explanation:** This is not a good response. You are not in a position to confront Graham. You need to speak to the other nurses first, and following that this needs to be discussed with senior management.

5 – B. Tell Pauline that she shouldn't have interrupted Graham.

**Explanation:** This is the worst response. You are belittling Pauline, and will make her feel much worse.

## Q75.

1 – A. Call the consultant to explain the situation, and tell him that you feel you would only be harming the patients by coming into work in this state.

**Explanation:** This is the best response to the situation. You should be honest with the consultant about the situation, even if it means risking your job.

2 – D. Call the consultant to explain the situation, and offer to work extra time over the next few days to make up for it.

**Explanation:** This is the next best response. You are being honest with the consultant, whilst still offering a solution to the problem, even if that solution isn't ideal.

3 – C. Call your friend working at the hospital, and ask her to try to cover your shift, whilst you take a quick nap.

**Explanation:** This is not a good response, and you are putting unreasonable demands on your friend. However, at least you are trying to find an adequate solution to the situation.

4 – E. Call the consultant, but lie telling him that you are stuck in traffic. Take a quick nap for a few hours.

**Explanation:** This is a very bad response. You are lying to the consultant.

5 – B. Try and wake yourself up with a coffee, and go into work.

**Explanation:** In this response, you are putting the patients at risk. This is therefore the worst option.


## Q76.

1 – B. Speak to your consultant and explain to her what has just happened. Ask her for permission to go home.

**Explanation:** This is the best response. You need to take patient safety into consideration. If you do have a virus of some sort, or even food poisoning, then it's really important for you to remove yourself from the premises.

2 – E. Speak to one of the nurses and ask them whether it's okay for you to leave.

**Explanation:** This is not ideal. You need to speak to someone who can actually give you permission to leave, such as your consultant or a senior member of staff.

3 – A. Pack your things and leave without telling anyone. They'll manage without you just fine.

**Explanation:** This could be extremely disruptive and cause lots of problems in the hospital. You need to speak to someone before you go.

4 – D. Continue working for an hour, to see if the sickness wears off. If not, ask for permission to go home.

**Explanation:** As mentioned, your primary concern here should be patient safety. Working for an extra hour is not an effective solution, and could lead to you infecting patients. Therefore, this is a very bad response.

5 – C. Take a paracetamol from the medicinal cupboard and continue with your shift.

**Explanation:** This is a bad response. You can't just continue, as you are clearly very sick, and pose a risk to the patients.

## Q77.

1 – C. Sympathise with Miranda and implore her to go into more detail about how she is feeling.

**Explanation:** This is the best response. There are a huge number of pressures that come from working in modern medicine, and it is not uncommon for junior doctors to feel overwhelmed. In this case, you should be sympathetic, and provide her with someone to talk to.

2 – B. Tell Miranda that she needs to have a talk with her consultant about how she feels. Offer to go with her for support, if she would prefer.

**Explanation:** This is the next best response. However, you don't really need to go with Miranda to speak to her consultant. It would be better and more professional for her to have a sit-down chat with him, by herself.

3 – D. Speak to a senior doctor about Miranda's troubles.

**Explanation:** This is not a great response, although it's not terrible. This likely won't solve much, as there probably is very little that an unrelated senior doctor can do to resolve things, but they could provide you with some additional avenues for support.

4 – E. Go and speak to Miranda's consultant by yourself.

**Explanation:** This wouldn't be the right course of action. While Miranda is clearly distressed, she needs to go and see the consultant herself. You going on her behalf will not resolve things.

5 – A. Tell Miranda that she needs to get a grip of herself if she wants to succeed in medicine.

**Explanation:** This is extremely insensitive and will only upset Miranda more.

## Q78.

1 – D. Take a calm and persuasive approach, to try and get the patient to return to his bed.

**Explanation:** This is the best solution to the problem. Your first priority should be to persuade the patient to calm down, and the best way to do this is to try and take a calm and measured approach, without inciting further panic.

2 – A. Immediately call security. They are the best placed people to deal with this, and restrain the patient, if necessary.

**Explanation:** This is the next best response. It is imperative that the patient is not able to leave the ward. Given his behaviour, he presents a serious risk to other patients and members of staff.

3 – B. Run to the nurse's aid, to check whether she is okay after being punched.

**Explanation:** This is a reasonable approach, but your first priority needs to be the patient, and getting him to calm down, before you can assist the fallen nurse.

4 – C. Shout and yell at the patient to get back in his bed.

**Explanation:** This is not a good response. It is likely to make the patient even more irate, and cause panic in the ward.

5 – E. Try to tackle the patient, physically, yourself.

**Explanation:** You are not correctly trained to do this, and this could lead to harm being inflicted on either yourself or the patient.

## Q79.

1 – A. Tell the man that unfortunately you have no choice but to call the police.

**Explanation:** In this situation, you would have no choice but to call the police. This does not represent a breach of confidentiality, as doctors are still bound by law.

2 – B. Call up the department who are in charge of junior doctorational patient issues, and ask them to send a representative down to discuss the issue.

**Explanation:** This would be the next best response. This department would be well placed to deal with such an individual, especially considering he speaks very poor English. Either way, the police will need to be contacted.

3 – D. Go to the front desk and ask the nurse in charge what should be done.

**Explanation:** This is not really a great solution, but the nurse would immediately advise you to take either Option A or Option B.

4 – E. Pass the patient over to another colleague.

**Explanation:** This is a poor solution. You need to deal with this issue yourself.

5 – C. Tell the man that he needs to leave the hospital within the next 10 minutes, or you'll call the police.

**Explanation:** This is the worst solution. You are bound by law to report this issue to the legal authorities.

## Q80.

1 – B. Tell Maureen that she needs to speak to the head of the surgical team, and tell him that she's too tired to participate in the operation.

**Explanation:** This is the best resolution to the problem. You can clearly see from Maureen's choice of words that she is not in a fit state to perform the operation. You need to find a replacement.

2 – E. Ask Maureen to come with you to the head of the surgical team, so that you can explain why she won't be participating.

**Explanation:** This is the next best response, although it's a little strange for you to explain it on her behalf. At least in this response you are ensuring that Maureen, in her current state, does not participate.

3 – D. Tell Maureen that she can go back to sleep. You'll find a suitable replacement for her.

**Explanation:** Maureen needs to explain to the head of the surgical team that she cannot take part.

4 – A. Ask Maureen whether she feels capable of performing the operation.

**Explanation:** This is polite, but at the same time Maureen's choice of words clearly indicates that she is not able to perform this operation. Asking her this is just a waste of time. Even if she says yes, you won't be able to have confidence in her.

5 – C. Tell Maureen that the operation is taking place in 10 minutes, so she'd better wake herself up before then.

**Explanation:** This is unacceptable. If Maureen is feeling 'too tired', then she is not in a fit state to perform surgery and a replacement needs to be found.

## Q81.

1 – D. Sympathise with Rebecca, and encourage her to try and be brave with patients in future. Offer to help her out with her next patient.

**Explanation:** This is a really good response. You are being supportive and encouraging, whilst offering to go the extra mile to help out a new member of staff.

2 – B. Tell Rebecca that this is a serious problem, and she needs to speak to her clinical supervisor in order to try and resolve it.

**Explanation:** This is the next best solution. This is a big issue, bedside manner is extremely important, and doctors must be able to communicate with their patients. In this case, Rebecca's clinical supervisor would be well placed to help her with this issue.

3 – C. Tell Rebecca that she needs to try and overcome her fear of people if she is to succeed as a doctor.

**Explanation:** While this is true, you could try and be a bit more sensitive towards how Rebecca is feeling, and offer her tips on how to overcome this.

4 – E. Tell Rebecca that if she doesn't improve her patient skills, she is liable to be fired from the hospital.

**Explanation:** Again, while this is true, it's quite insensitive and doesn't really serve to help Rebecca with the problem. If anything, this will just make her feel worse.

5 – A. Tell Rebecca that if she dislikes working with people, she's probably in the wrong career.

**Explanation:** This is very insensitive and unhelpful. You aren't resolving anything here, or offering any solution.

## Q82.

1 – B. Correct the nurse. Tell her that Aaron is allowed to stay, but he must remain at the back

of the room and not behave disruptively.

**Explanation:** This is the best response. Relatives are allowed to stay in the room during resuscitation attempts/CPR, provided they are not causing a disruption or getting in the way.

2 – D. Tell Aaron that he can stay in the room, and ask a member of the ward staff to stand next to him and explain what is happening.

**Explanation:** This is the next best response. Assigning a member of staff to explain to Aaron what is happening, will hopefully mitigate some of the stress from the situation for him.

3 – E. Tell the nurse that she is wrong to try and make Aaron leave. He can stay, but he must remain completely silent during the process.

**Explanation:** This is correct, although asking Aaron to remain completely silent is a bit much. It's important to make sure he's not disruptive, but you also need to take into account the distress of the situation.

4 – C. Tell Aaron that he is allowed to stay, but he must be prepared for the worst.

**Explanation:** This is reasonable, but at the same time it's not going to make Aaron feel better, nor will it help his state of mind. This could lead him to become more upset and disruptive.

5 – A. Tell Aaron that he needs to leave the room immediately, or you will call security to escort him out.

**Explanation:** This is incorrect. As stated, relatives are allowed to remain in the room, provided they are not disruptive.

## Q83.

1 – B. Speak to your supervising consultant about the issue. They are well placed to give you advice.

**Explanation:** This is the best response to the scenario. Your supervising consultant is the best person to give you advice on handling this issue, and may speak to other members of staff to try and resolve it.

2 – E. Try and make yourself available for as many jobs as possible in future. If you can prove to the doctors what you are capable of, then this could be resolved.

**Explanation:** This is a positive and pragmatic resolution to the problem. You are taking action to better yourself and prove that you are capable of great things.

3 – D. Try and make an appointment with the Chief Physician, to see what can be done to resolve this.

**Explanation:** This is not a good response. Involving someone so senior in what is, contextually, a minor issue, is quite inappropriate. There are many people who are much better placed to deal with this.

4 – A. Approach the doctor who asked you to make him a tea, and question him over whether he thinks you are fit to work here.

**Explanation:** This is a slightly odd way to tackle the problem, and won't really resolve anything.

5 – C. Accept that there is a bedding in period for junior doctors in hospitals, and that it will take time before the doctors in the unit can trust you.

**Explanation:** The question states that you have been at the hospital for several weeks now, and don't feel as if you are making any progress. There is clearly an issue here, which needs to be resolved as soon as possible.

## Q84.

1 – C. Speak to the consultant and inform her that unfortunately you have three other projects on the go at the moment. However, if she would be willing to extend the deadline, then you could get it completed for next week.

**Explanation:** In this case, honesty is the best policy. The consultant will appreciate you being open with her. There is no point in you taking on this project if you can't complete it to the best of your ability, and the other projects that were already in place should take priority. In this case, you are also giving her the extra option of you doing it next week, which shows commitment and enthusiasm for the task.

2 – D. Tell the consultant that you won't be able to take part in the project, as you have other projects to complete.

**Explanation:** As mentioned, honesty is the best policy here. The consultant will appreciate this.

3 – E. Ask the consultant whether you should give her task priority over the other three projects.

**Explanation:** It is up to you to manage your workload. Once you tell the consultant that you have three other projects, she'll likely give the task to someone else, so it's better to just be open with her.

4 – B. Get in touch with all of the other project supervisors, explaining to them that you need to give this new project priority, as it will impress the consultant.

**Explanation:** This is not a good response. The other project supervisors will be extremely offended, and this will reflect badly on you.

5 – A. Ignore the other projects, in order to make sure this one is finished. You could really advance your career if this goes well.

**Explanation:** This is the worst response. The other projects need to take priority over this new task.

## Q85.

1 – A. Tell him that he needs to go and see his supervising consultant, to discuss the impact that his exhaustion could have on patient wellbeing.

**Explanation:** This is the best response. It's essential in this case to consider patient safety. If the doctor is exhausted, then they can't perform to the best of their ability, and this could have an impact on patients.

2 – D. Tell him that he needs to go and see his supervising consultant, to discuss the impact that his workload is having on his personal life.

**Explanation:** Working in the medical profession is really difficult, and it's true that it will have an impact on your social/personal life, however it's never okay for this to become detrimental. In this case, the junior doctor's personal problems should be a big concern.

3 – E. Tell him that he needs to go and see his supervising consultant, to discuss working different shift patterns.

**Explanation:** In this case, it does not seem as if the shift patterns are the problem. The doctor is struggling to manage his workload. He is scheduled to finish his shifts at a reasonable time, but is unable to do so.

4 – B. Tell him that he needs to go and see his supervising consultant, to discuss the fact that he is working past his expected timeframe, on some occasions.

**Explanation:** This is an okay response, but at the same time it is very normal for doctors to work past their expected timeframe. The difference in this case is that the doctor in question is working past their expected timeframe on many occasions, and this is having a detrimental impact on their life.

5 – C. Tell him that he should avoid going to see his supervising consultant, because his inability to manage the workload could reflect poorly on his performance.

**Explanation:** This is very poor advice. The doctor needs to go and see his consultant as soon as possible, to deal with this issue.

## Q86.

1 – B. Inform Abigail that the hospital would never publish information such as this without gaining her full consent beforehand.

**Explanation:** This is the best explanation. You are reassuring the patient that her information will not be shared publicly.

2 – C. Tell Abigail that although her case won't be published, she should do the right thing and inform her girlfriend.

**Explanation:** This is the next best response. You are reassuring the patient that her information will not be shared publicly, whilst still encouraging her to do the right thing morally.

3 – D. Encourage Abigail to speak to the hospital legal department, who can give better advice on the publication of such material.

**Explanation:** This is an okay response, but as a doctor you should be aware of the guidelines surrounding the publication of such material, meaning that you can also advise the patient on how the hospital will handle this.

4 – E. Ask Abigail whether she would pursue legal action, if the hospital published her case without her permission.

**Explanation:** This isn't a very good response. It would be much better to just tell the patient that the hospital won't publish the case without her permission.

5 – A. Inform Abigail that she has no choice in whether her case is published in a research paper.

**Explanation:** This is incorrect, and will greatly upset the patient.


## Q87.

1 – C. Tell Michelle that Mrs Harley is her patient, and that she will need to take responsibility for treating her.

**Explanation:** This is the best response to the situation. Michelle needs to take responsibility for Mrs Harley, who is her patient for the evening.

2 – A. Tell Michelle that you will try to find another doctor to treat Mrs Harley, before you leave.

**Explanation:** This is the next best response. Although you would be ensuring that there is a doctor available to treat Mrs Harley, you are giving them extra responsibility, which could detract from their own patients. The responsibility here rests with Michelle.

3 – D. Tell Michelle that she needs to speak to the Chief Physician, if she doesn't want to treat Mrs Harley.

**Explanation:** This isn't a great response. This isn't an issue for someone that high up to deal with.

4 – B. Agree with Michelle. Stay at the hospital so that you can treat Mrs Harley.

**Explanation:** This is a bad response. You have completed your shift, plus extra time. You should not have to stay just because Michelle is too busy.

5 – E. Leave a note on Mrs Harley's bed, then go home. Hopefully another doctor will see it and take action.

**Explanation:** This is the worst response. You can't just ignore the situation, as this could endanger the patient.


## Q88.

1 – B. Go and find a senior colleague, who can review Martin's condition before he is discharged.

**Explanation:** This is a good response. The best thing to do here would be to consult a senior doctor, who can assess whether Martin is fit to leave.

2 – D. Call Dr Blake and ask her whether she agreed to discharge Martin.

**Explanation:** This is the next best response. If a senior colleague is not available, then it would be a good idea to call Dr Blake directly, to question her over the veracity of Martin's claim.

3 – C. Explain to Martin that you don't have the power to discharge patients, so he will just have to wait until Dr Blake arrives at the hospital.

**Explanation:** Although this will upset the patient, it is the next safest course of action. You cannot allow Martin to leave based on his claim alone.

4 – A. Discharge Martin, so that he can have the dinner date with his wife.

**Explanation:** This is not a good response. At the very least, you will need to perform an assessment on Martin before he is discharged.

5 – E. Allow Martin to leave without signing a discharge form.

**Explanation:** This is the worst response. It's essential that a discharge form is signed.


**Q89.**

1 – E. Tell Dr Chaudry that you have never done this procedure before, so it would be too risky for you to do so now.

**Explanation:** This is the best response to the scenario. You should not perform this procedure without the proper training, as you would be putting the patient at risk.

2 – D. Ask another colleague to perform the procedure instead of you.

**Explanation:** This is the next best response. You need to realise that there is no benefit to doing something which you aren't trained for, only a risk, and therefore it would be better to get another colleague to perform the procedure. However, you should try and observe them whilst they do so, so that you can learn for the future.

3 – C. Take Dr Chaudry to one side and ask him for advice on the best way to perform the procedure.

**Explanation:** This is not a great response. Yes, Dr Chaudry can give you tips on how to perform the procedure, but you need practical assistance. Verbal tips alone will not help the situation.

4 – A. Agree to perform the procedure, while Dr Chaudry deals with the patient upstairs.

**Explanation:** This is a bad response. You are putting the patient at risk.

5 – B. Inform the patient that although you've never done this procedure before, you'll give it your best shot.

**Explanation:** This is the worst response. Not only are you putting the patient at risk, but you will make them feel extremely nervous about you performing the procedure.

**Q90.**

1 – A. Apologise to the family, and assure them that you will personally ensure that the scan is done properly this time.

**Explanation:** This is a good response. You are apologising for the mistake that has been made, and reassuring them that it won't happen again.

2 – D. Apologise to the family, and carefully lay out the procedure for making a formal complaint.

**Explanation:** This is an okay response. You are apologising on behalf of the hospital. Ideally you don't want them to make a formal complaint, but it is necessary protocol to show them how this is done.

3 – B. Tell the family that mistakes happen, and they will just have to accept that you need another scan.

**Explanation:** This is not a good response. You need to apologise, and you are being quite blunt and insensitive. However, other than that, what you are saying here is factual.

4 – C. Tell the family that this is the fault of the relevant department, and not anything to do with you.

**Explanation:** Here you are shirking the responsibility. While it wasn't you that performed the scan, you should apologise on behalf of the hospital.

5 – E. Apologise to the family, and offer to do the next scan yourself.

**Explanation:** This is the worst response. You do not work in the department which produces the scans, so you would be giving the family false information.

**Q91.**

1 – A. Leave Craig to his own devices. Return to the consultant and tell him about what happened.

**Explanation:** This is the best response. As mentioned, you don't really have time to talk through the issue with Craig, so it's acceptable to just return to the consultant and inform him of the situation.

2 – B. Try and convince Craig to join you on rounds. Tell him that you will need to report this behaviour if not.

**Explanation:** This is the second-best response. The consultant has given you a window of just 5 minutes to find Craig. This means that you can't afford to hang around arguing with him. You should do your best to persuade him, but if he doesn't come then just go back and report it to the consultant.

3 – D. Sit down with Craig and question him over his lack of interest in medical rounds.

**Explanation:** This is not a great response. Although it might seem good, this will be very time consuming, and you've only a 5 minute window.

4 – E. Ask Craig about what his top score on the game is. Challenge him to a match.

**Explanation:** This is obviously a very bad response. You are encouraging Craig to continue his bad behaviour, and avoiding medical rounds yourself.

5 – C. Go back to the consultant, and tell him that you couldn't find Craig.

**Explanation:** This is the worst response. You are lying to the consultant.


**Q92.**

1 – B. Approach your colleagues and encourage them to speak to the consultant if they disagree with his decision making.

**Explanation:** This is the best response. Your colleague's clearly have an issue, and it's important that they develop their relationship with the consultant to the point where they can trust, or question, his decisions.

2 – E. Ask your colleagues what could be done to make them feel more confident about raising their opinion during rounds.

**Explanation:** This is a really good response. As mentioned, it's important that your colleagues feel confident enough to raise their views during rounds.

3 – D. Approach the consultant and tell him that a few of your colleagues are unsure about his decision-making.

**Explanation:** This is not a great response, but at least you are making the consultant aware of the discord surrounding his decision.

4 – C. Approach your colleagues and inform them that you will have no choice but to report this conversation to the consultant.

**Explanation:** This is not a good response. The way this answer is worded, makes it seem as if you are informing on your colleagues, rather than trying to help the situation.

5 – A. Say nothing. This issue has nothing to do with you.

**Explanation:** It's important that this issue is resolved, so that everyone in the group can be confident in the decision making of the consultant.


**Q93.**

1 – C. Tell Dr Barnes that he needs to treat you with more respect. Inform him that Mr Hibbs could die if he is prescribed with this type of drug.

**Explanation:** This is a good response. Dr Barnes is completely out of line here in the manner that he is speaking to you, and he needs to be informed about his mistake with the patient.

2 – B. Ask Dr Barnes to take a look at the patient history, to show him why he's wrong.

**Explanation:** This is also a good response. Encouraging Dr Barnes to look at the patient history will show him the error of his ways. However, you should also call him out on his disrespectful language.

3 – D. Ask one of the other doctors to explain to Dr Barnes why he is wrong.

**Explanation:** This is an okay response, but this is something that you could do yourself instead.

4 – E. Inform Dr Barnes that you are indeed, a big shot. Tell him that if he prescribes Mr Hibbs with the drugs, he will be risking his career.

**Explanation:** This is not a great response. Although it's good that you are giving Dr Barnes a reason to change his mind, you are being arrogant about it. Along with this, he needs to change his mind for the wellbeing of the patient, not just because it could impact his career.

5 – A. Immediately apologise and agree with Dr Barnes. You spoke out of turn here.

**Explanation:** This is a terrible response. You will be putting the patient at risk.


**Q94.**

1 – A. Consult with the surgical team. Ask them to send round a representative, who can ensure that Earl understands everything about the operation, before he goes into theatre.

**Explanation:** This is the best response. The hospital has a responsibility to ensure that all patients have a full and proper understanding of any risks involved, prior to attending surgery. In this case, it is clear that Earl is lacking essential knowledge about the operation, and therefore this needs to be given to him before anything else can happen.

2 – D. Tell Earl that it would be a good idea for him to speak to a specialist within the next 24 hours.

**Explanation:** This is not a great response. You should be helping Earl to find a specialist within the hospital, not just advising him to speak to someone. However, at least you are telling him that he should speak to an expert about the surgery.

3 – B. Try and explain the risks involved in the surgery to Earl yourself.

**Explanation:** This isn't good. You aren't a member of the surgical team, so it would be unwise for you to try and explain the risks involved. It would be much better for someone with expertise to provide Earl with this information.

4 – E. Ask Earl why he signed the consent form without proper understanding of the situation.

**Explanation:** This is quite insensitive. It's possible that the person in charge of explaining the surgery did not do a good enough job. It's unfair to blame the patient in this circumstance.

5 – C. Ignore the situation. Earl has signed a consent form, so it doesn't matter.

**Explanation:** As mentioned, the hospital has an obligation to provide its patients with essential information on topics such as this.


**Q95.**

1 – A. Inform the nurse that your patient has a greater need for the room than Mrs Fleming.

**Explanation:** This is a good response. In this circumstance, based on the question, your patient has a greater medical and social need for the private room than Mrs Fleming. Therefore, if possible, your patient should be given the private room.

2 – B. Enquire with the nurse about why Mrs Fleming needs a private room.

**Explanation:** This is a reasonable response. It would be good to ensure that you fully understand Mrs Fleming's circumstances, before you move her from the room.

3 – D. Speak to the nurse about your patient's request. If she does not agree with you, take the issue to someone more senior.

**Explanation:** This isn't great, although it could be necessary. Ideally you would resolve this situation with the relevant lower level staff, before moving it higher.

4 – C. Return to your patient and inform him that unfortunately there are no private rooms available.

**Explanation:** This is a very sensitive situation, and you would be greatly upsetting the patient here, especially when they have a greater need for the room than Mrs Fleming.

5 – E. Confront Mrs Fleming, asking her to leave the private room immediately.

**Explanation:** This is a very bad response, and will cause a number of problems. You are being very unprofessional and rude to Mrs Fleming, who is still a patient at the hospital.


**Q96.**

1 – B. Give Chris the benefit of the doubt. Send a polite response back, asking the department why your request has been rejected, and what you can improve to ensure it gets accepted.

**Explanation:** This is the best response. Even if Chris doesn't like you, you shouldn't just assume that this is why your request has been rejected.

2 – E. Go down to the radiology department and ask them about the case. Try and speak to another staff member than Chris, if possible.

**Explanation:** This is an okay response, but at the same time you don't need to go directly to the department. They might be extremely busy, and won't have time to deal with direct requests such as this.

3 – D. Speak to your clinical consultant about why the department rejected your request.

**Explanation:** This is not really a good response. Apart from advising you on how to improve the quality of your requests, your consultant can't do much here.

4 – A. Send a response back, accusing Chris of letting his personal feelings get in the way of good practice.

**Explanation:** This is unprofessional. As mentioned, you should give Chris the benefit of the doubt in this situation.

5 – C. Go down to the radiology department and angrily confront Chris. If he won't listen to reason, it's time to get physical.

**Explanation:** This is the worst response. Violence is never the answer.

### Q97.

1 – C. Encourage Mr Barkley to be open and honest with his family about the circumstances surrounding his illness.

**Explanation:** This is a good response. As a doctor, you should encourage Mr Barkley to share the news with his family, so that they can deal with the emotional consequences together.

2 – D. Ask Mr Barkley whether he wants you to inform his family, to make it easier for him.

**Explanation:** In this circumstance, this is a reasonable request. The patient has just received a terminal diagnosis. As his doctor, it would be proper for you to try and take the pressure off, by giving him this option.

3 – B. Encourage Mr Barkley to participate in counselling sessions, so that he can come to terms with his illness, and be honest with his family.

**Explanation:** Although counselling sessions could be useful in this case, the question specifically states that Mr Barkley does not have long to live, so there would be questionable benefit to this.

4 – E. Inform Mr Barkley that he cannot stay at the hospital unless he is honest with his family.

**Explanation:** This is completely incorrect and will upset the patient even more.

5 – A. Tell Mr Barkley that he is acting against the law, by failing to inform his family of the circumstances surrounding his illness.

**Explanation:** This is false, and will lead to great upset for the patient, who certainly doesn't need to be threatened with legal action at the current time.

### Q98.

1 – D. Speak to the relevant ward consultant about the issue.

**Explanation:** The best solution to this issue would be to discuss the issue with Cassie, to try and resolve it amicably. You have already tried to do this, and it didn't work, so now you need to involve someone senior. In this case, the best person to deal with it would be the relevant ward consultant.

2 – A. Ask Cassie if she would be happy to meet with you and your educational supervisor, to discuss the recent issues.

**Explanation:** This is an okay solution but if you don't share the same educational supervisor then you are not really helping things. Your supervisor can deal with your issues, but they aren't in a position to help Cassie.

3 – E. Ask your other colleagues whether they have had any issues with Cassie and her workload.

**Explanation:** This is a reasonable solution, although it doesn't really solve much. At least here you are establishing whether this is a problem that is impacting others, or whether it's just affecting you.

4 – C. Offer to help Cassie with the extra research projects that she is taking on.

**Explanation:** This is not helpful. You need Cassie to put more work into other tasks, not the other way around.

5 – B. Tell Cassie that she is being highly unprofessional, and should consider resigning from the hospital.

**Explanation:** This is the worst option. You are being unprofessional and unhelpful here.


## Q99.

1 – B. Tell Sue that you will take her to see her mother, right away.

**Explanation:** This is the best response. You have no right to tell Sue about the diagnosis, especially since the patient has specifically requested that she tell her daughter herself.

2 – E. Ask another member of the team to escort Sue to her mother.

**Explanation:** If you are not available to escort Sue to see her mother, another member of staff will suffice.

3 – C. Tell Sue that she will need to book an appointment to see her mother.

**Explanation:** This is incorrect. You don't need to make an appointment to see relatives in the hospital, unless the circumstances are incredibly specific.

4 – D. Sit Sue down in a quiet room, and inform her that her mother has been diagnosed with a serious illness.

**Explanation:** This is a very bad response. Although you aren't giving Sue the full diagnosis, you are certainly breaking doctor patient confidentiality here, and going back on the agreement between yourself and Mrs Andrews

5 – A. Tell Sue that her mother has been diagnosed with bowel cancer.

**Explanation:** This is the worst option. You are breaking the doctor patient confidentiality agreement.


## Q100.

1 – A. Speak to Sarah once she leaves the staff room, to clarify what you have just heard. Ask her to come with you to see a senior member of the nursing staff.

**Explanation:** This is the best solution. You have just witnessed a nurse admitting to a serious breach of the rules. You need to report this, and Sarah is also a witness to these comments.

2 – C. Confront Mandy about her comments. Tell her that she is behaving unacceptably.

**Explanation:** This is the next best solution, although it's arguably not enough. You need to make sure that someone senior hears about this. Mandy's behaviour cannot be allowed to continue.

3 – E. Poke your head round the door and remind Mandy of why disinfectant, and wearing gloves, is important.

**Explanation:** This is similar to option C, it's just not enough. You need to take a strong stance on this.

4 – B. Walk into the staff room and berate Mandy for her comments. Call her unprofessional and disgusting.

**Explanation:** This is not a good response. You are inflaming the situation, and acting unprofessionally yourself.

5 – D. Resolve not to wash your hands next time you walk into the Emergency Care Unit.

**Explanation:** This is obviously the worst response. You will be causing more problems here, and becoming part of the issue yourself.

**Q101.**

1 – B. Tell the manager that Matthew won't be discharged for at least a week, and that you won't accept his money.

**Explanation:** This is a good response. You are being firm and clear on the medical guidelines, as well as adhering to hospital policy by not taking money from the man.

2 – C. Ask the manager to have a quiet chat with you, so that you can discuss the seriousness of his player's situation.

**Explanation:** This is a good response, as you are being sensitive to the manager's feelings and ensuring that when Matthew is eventually discharged, the seriousness of his injury is taken into account.

3 – E. Inform the manager that you support a rival team, so there's no chance of you discharging Matthew.

**Explanation:** This is a bad response. You are doing the right thing, but for the wrong reasons. On top of this, you will make the manager upset and angry.

4 – D. Tell the manager that you are willing to discharge Matthew, but only on the condition that he doesn't play football for a month.

**Explanation:** This is a bad way to deal with the situation. The question clearly states that Matthew won't be ready for discharge for at least a week, if not longer.

5 – A. Tell the manager that if he wants you to discharge his player, it will take a lot more than £500.

**Explanation:** This is a very bad response. You are taking money for a service that's against medical guidelines.

## Q102.

1 – A. Find a senior colleague and bring the error to their attention. Ask them whether a different drug would be more suitable.

**Explanation:** This is definitely the best response in this scenario. A senior doctor should have a good idea on how to approach this situation.

2 – C. Text your consultant, to enquire about the mistake.

**Explanation:** This is a good response, as you should try to contact the consultant, but texting isn't very urgent. If you are going to contact the consultant, you should call him.

3 – E. Tell the patient that there's been a mix up, and ask for him to be patient whilst you resolve the medication issue.

**Explanation:** This is not great. You will be damaging the patient's faith in the medical staff by telling him this. You just need to amend the issue yourself.

4 – B. Visit your consultant at his home to discuss the issue.

**Explanation:** This is very inappropriate and over the top.

5 – D. Do nothing. The consultant must have prescribed this for a reason.

**Explanation:** This is the worst response. You can't just allow the patient to take medication that could harm him.

## Q103.

1 – D. Take the man to one side and inform him that if he does not calm down, you will have to ask him to leave.

**Explanation:** This is a good, reasonable response. The man is not acting violently, so you don't need to call security yet, however he is being disruptive and causing problems – so it is more than fair to give him a warning prior to any other action being taken.

2 – A. Call security to escort the man from the premises.

**Explanation:** This isn't the best call, but given the circumstances you would be justified in calling security. The man is being extremely disruptive. If you are concerned that there will be a threat of violence, then you have the right to ask him to leave. However, a warning should suffice first.

3 – C. Ask the man to go outside, and come back when he has calmed down.

**Explanation:** This isn't a good response. The man is intoxicated, so asking him to go outside and calm down isn't going to help.

4 – B. Ask the other patients in the waiting room whether the man's behaviour is upsetting them.

**Explanation:** This is unnecessary. The question clearly states that the man's behaviour is upsetting some of the other patients.

5 – E. Try to treat the man as quickly as possible, so that he can leave.

**Explanation:** This is unfair on the other patients. This man does not deserve to be seen before them.

## Q104.

1 – B. Go to your educational supervisor and admit that you made a mistake. Ask her what your next step should be.

**Explanation:** This is a good response. Your supervisor will be in a good position to tell you how you should act, and may advise you to go and see the patient directly to explain the situation.

2 – E. Consult with the legal team about what your next steps should be.

**Explanation:** At some point, you are going to have to explain yourself to the patient and apologise sincerely for the mistake. However, before you do so it would be good to speak to the legal team. They will be able to tell you how you should approach the situation, and what type of things you should avoid saying.

3 – A. Approach the patient and admit that her bout of sickness was down to your error. Apologise profusely, and tell her that it won't happen again.

**Explanation:** This is the natural next step, following seeking out the opinion of someone senior. Mistakes happen, even in the medical profession. The best thing you can do is make sure that you are sincerely apologetic to the patient, and try to rebuild her confidence in your care.

4 – C. Say nothing. Hopefully nobody will ever find out.

**Explanation:** Obviously, this is not a good response. You should be open and honest with your colleagues and with patients.

5 – D. Resign. Hopefully this way you can avoid a potential lawsuit.

**Explanation:** This is the worst option, and represents a disproportionate response to the situation.

## Q105.

1 – E. Inform the doctor that if he doesn't stop with this behaviour, you will report him to senior management.

**Explanation:** This is a good response. No person should be subject to such behaviour, which could easily be construed as bullying.

2 – C. Ask the doctor to clarify the reasons why he feels you are a poor doctor.

**Explanation:** This is an acceptable response, as it shows that you are looking for tips on how to improve. That being said, you shouldn't allow the doctor to speak to you like this.

3 – B. Ask the doctor what you can do to convince him that you are capable and competent.

**Explanation:** This doctor is behaving extremely unprofessionally. The problem with this response is that it seems as if you are trying to gain his approval, when really you should be telling him about how unacceptable his behaviour is.

4 – A. Inform the doctor that his behaviour is extremely unprofessional, and that he's the one who should be let go.

**Explanation:** It's good to tell the doctor that he's being unprofessional, but the last part of this response simply brings you down to his level. It's childish and unnecessary.

5 – D. Agree with the doctor. Resign immediately.

**Explanation:** This is the worst response. You are simply giving up.

## Q106.

1 – D. Give the patient two pills. Wait until the next day, to have a serious talk with the patient's father. Make the nursing team aware of what has just occurred.

**Explanation:** In this situation, it is clear that you need to have a very serious chat with the patient's father. This can wait until the next day, but until then it's very important that the nurses keep a close eye on the patient.

2 – B. Give the patient two pills, and leave the rest of the medication with the nursing team.

**Explanation:** This is an okay response, but you do need to make sure you speak to the patient's father. At least here you are administering the correct medication, and ensuring there are no mishaps overnight.

3 – A. Tell the patient that he is to take two pills, and two pills only. Then go home.

**Explanation:** This is not really a good solution. It's quite vague as to what is being done with the rest of the medication (it would unwise to leave it with the patient).

4 – C. Once you leave work, call the patient's father and demand that he explain himself.

**Explanation:** This is an overreaction. It might be the case that the patient's father has made a simple mistake. You can wait until tomorrow to speak to him.

5 – E. Call the police, to report the patient's father.

**Explanation:** This is a major overreaction, and will lead to significant problems.

## Q107.

1 – B. Have a quiet chat with the girl, to try and explain why the nurse call button is so important, and must only be used on the most special of occasions.

**Explanation:** This is a good, professional response. You need to take into account the age of the patient. She clearly does not understand that her behaviour is wrong, so you need to take a sensitive approach to showing her this.

2 – D. Call the patient's parents, and ask if they can come in to have a quick word about her behaviour.

**Explanation:** This is a good response, and would be a follow on if option B doesn't work. Obviously, the patient's parents are the best placed people to deal with her behaviour.

3 – E. Tell the nurses that they need to be more sympathetic towards the child's behaviour.

**Explanation:** This isn't a good response. Yes, the patient is very young, but the nurses shouldn't have to put up with abuse.

4 – C. Tell the nurses that the next time the button is pushed without good reason, they have permission to remove it altogether.

**Explanation:** This is very over the top. You need to talk with the girl about her behaviour, and call her parents, before such drastic measures are enforced.

5 – A. March up to the girl and call her a spoilt little brat. Tell her that the next time she pushes the button without reason, there will be serious consequences.

**Explanation:** This is completely inappropriate and unacceptable.


## Q108.

1 – B. Ask the woman to calm down. Inform her that mild discomfort is a normal symptom following such an operation, but promise to examine Sophie's elbow anyway.

**Explanation:** This is a reasonable response. You are calming the angry individual, making it clear that this is a normal circumstance (as far as you can tell), but also assuring the patient that you will look into it.

2 – A. Assure the woman that you will take the utmost care of Sophie, and will now take steps to examine her elbow.

**Explanation:** This is the next best course of action. However, you should assure her that, on the face of it, the mild discomfort is totally normal.

3 – E. Tell Sophie's girlfriend that you will have a discussion with the surgical team, and get back to her.

**Explanation:** This is okay, but it would be better to cite the patient notes, and then examine Sophie yourself.

4 – C. Tell the woman that since Sophie is still experiencing elbow pain, she'll probably need to go back in for repeat surgery.

**Explanation:** This is untrue, and will make the situation significantly worse.

5 – D. Call security and ask them to escort Sophie's girlfriend out of the hospital.

**Explanation:** This is extremely unnecessary, and shows a lack of sympathy and understanding for the patient and her loved one's perspective.

**Q109.**

1 – C. Tell Melissa that this is something she should discuss with her educational supervisor, but that she has your full support.

**Explanation:** This is a good response. It's great to show Melissa that she has your support, but this is something that should ideally be dealt with by her educational supervisor, who can provide her with suitable advice.

2 – B. Tell Melissa that she has your full support in this issue, but that this could cause safety issues for patients.

**Explanation:** This is also a good response. You are reassuring Melissa that she has your full support, but also emphasising why the problem needs to be dealt with.

3 – A. Sympathise with Melissa, but reinforce that this is a serious issue which she will need to deal with.

**Explanation:** This is similar to option B, but option B is better because it tells Melissa exactly why it's a serious issue.

4 – E. Tell Melissa that you will raise her concerns with a senior member of staff.

**Explanation:** This isn't very effective. It's good that you are taking action, but ideally you should be encouraging Melissa to resolve the matter herself.

5 – D. Tell Melissa that unfortunately her dyslexia will likely mean that she has to resign.

**Explanation:** This is very insensitive, and untrue. Although dyslexia is an issue, it is not a barrier to becoming a doctor.

**Q110.**

1 – E. Take your colleague aside for a one-to-one chat, and inform him that you have noticed him struggling, even if nobody else has. Encourage him to go and see a senior manager about the situation.

**Explanation:** This is the best response. You can't just ignore this situation, because ultimately it could cause a risk to patients. However, in this case it would be better for your colleague to recognise his own mistakes and try to fix them – which is why encouraging him to go and see a senior manager is the best option.

2 – C. Do your best to help out your colleague. Maybe he's just going through a temporary struggle.

**Explanation:** This is reasonable. If nobody else will listen to you, then you should take a proactive approach and try to help your colleague better his performance.

3 – D. See if you can arrange a meeting with a senior consultant to discuss the issue.

**Explanation:** This is okay, but it's a little bit unnecessary. You don't need to go and see someone about this, it would be better to encourage your colleague to see someone himself.

4 – B. Pass off your concerns as nothing. If nobody else can see it, then maybe it's just you.

**Explanation:** As mentioned, it's important for you to act in this scenario. Your colleague's ineptitude could present a risk for patients.

5 – A. Quietly start gathering video evidence of your colleague's ineptitude. Plan to show the video on the projector screen at the next big meeting.

**Explanation:** This is a terrible response. You will humiliate your colleague, and it will make you look extremely unprofessional.


**Q111.**

1 – B. Seek out a senior member of staff, explain the situation, and ask for permission to leave.

**Explanation:** This is the most reasonable response to the situation. You cannot be expected to stay at the hospital given such terrible personal circumstances.

2 – E. Explain to your colleague that she is being quite insensitive, and that you need to leave immediately.

**Explanation:** This is the next best response. The reason that this is better than option D, is that in this situation it is obviously not your priority to find someone who can cover your shift. You should go to a senior member of staff to inform them, but they will then provide suitable cover. You need to leave and see your family as soon as possible.

3 – D. Tell your colleague that you need to leave, but first try to find someone who can cover your shift.

**Explanation:** As explained above, this is going above and beyond what would be expected of you in this circumstance.

4 – C. Tell your colleague that she is wrong. Leave immediately.

**Explanation:** Nobody could blame you for leaving right away in these circumstances, but you need to take into account that you are working in a busy A&E department, so it would be a good idea to inform a senior manager first – so that cover can be arranged.

5 – A. Agree with your colleague and stay at the hospital. The wellbeing of patients must come first.

**Explanation:** This is the worst response. Under these circumstances, your job should come second.


**Q112.**

1 – A. Approach Melvin and inform him about Henry's behaviour. He has a right to know about the rumours going around.

**Explanation:** This is a reasonable approach. Melvin certainly deserves to know if people are gossiping in this manner, as anyone would. Try and put yourself in his position.

2 – D. Ask your other colleagues to stop engaging with Henry in malicious behaviour. If

everyone else stops, then he will have to as well.

**Explanation:** This is a responsible approach. This is a very childish situation. It would be better if everyone started acting professional.

3 – B. Ignore the situation. You have better things to do than deal with childish gossip.

**Explanation:** This isn't a great response, because it could lead to conflict in the workplace, but at the same time it's not a bad thing to just put yourself above this situation and stay professional.

4 – C. Go to a senior manager and report the situation.

**Explanation:** As mentioned, this is a very silly and childish situation. It's not something that you need to involve a senior manager in, as it can be dealt with junior doctorally.

5 – E. Spread rumours yourself, to try and stop Henry.

**Explanation:** This is really childish and you would be sinking down to Henry's level.


## Q113.

1 – C. See if you can get in touch with the doctor from the previous shift, to establish his reasons for refusing to prescribe a laxative.

**Explanation:** This is the best response to the situation. Getting in touch with the previous doctor could provide you with essential background info, which will cast a light on exactly why a laxative wasn't given.

2 – D. Do a full assessment of the patient yourself, and if you deem it appropriate, prescribe a laxative.

**Explanation:** If you can't get in touch with the previous doctor, then you would be authorised to make your own assessment of the situation.

3 – E. Ask the nurses whether there was a specific reason why the patient couldn't be given a laxative.

**Explanation:** This is an okay response, but it's entirely possible that the previous doctor did not discuss the reason for refusing a laxative with the nurses.

4 – A. Tell the patient that, because of her previous doctor's refusal to do so, you will also be unable to prescribe her with a laxative.

**Explanation:** This is incorrect. The patient is under your care now, so you have the prerogative to perform your own assessment on whether a laxative would be suitable.

5 – B. Tell the patient that she'll need to hold her bowels for at least another 24 hours if she wants a laxative.

**Explanation:** This is very insensitive and will make the patient feel extremely upset.

## Q114.

1 – C. Ask Michael to please try and calm down. Inform him that you are extremely sorry on behalf of the hospital, but that there appears to have been a mix-up with the discharge dates.

**Explanation:** This is the most reasonable response to the situation. You are being very clear about what has happened, whilst also offering Michael a sincere apology. You are also being firm about Michael's behaviour, which is unacceptable.

2 – A. Inform Michael that there has been a mistake with the discharge dates, and that Sally won't be released until 4 days from now.

**Explanation:** This isn't a good response. The hospital has messed up here, and in doing so they have caused Michael and Sally a huge amount of inconvenience. You need to apologise, at the very least.

3 – D. Tell Michael that he needs to try and calm down. Ask him to come back once he has stopped yelling, so that you can discuss the discharge dates.

**Explanation:** This won't help the situation. You should ask Michael to try and calm down, but the rest of this answer will only make him angrier.

4 – B. Find the junior doctor responsible for the error, and get him to explain himself to Michael.

**Explanation:** This won't help either. Although it might placate Michael to shout at the person who actually made the mistake, the poor junior doctor who made the error will be getting hauled up right in front of a very angry patient. This will be very humiliating.

5 – E. Tell Michael that if he does not stop shouting at you, you'll be forced to get physical.

**Explanation:** Obviously, this is a pretty terrible response.

## Q115.

1 – D. Sit down with Neil to explore the reasons why the family don't feel comfortable with having a post-mortem.

**Explanation:** In this case, the most sensitive thing to do would be to talk to Neil about the reason why his family isn't comfortable with having a post-mortem.

2 – E. Ask the consultant to speak with the family again, but emphasise to him that he needs to avoid putting pressure on them.

**Explanation:** This is the next best course of action. The consultant may not have been aware that he was putting pressure on the family, so it would be good for him to have another meeting with them, but with a different mindset this time around. As mentioned, you both disagree on the reasons for why the patient died, but since he is the consultant you should still have some respect for his opinion.

3 – B. Tell Neil that you will have a word with the consultant, and the post-mortem will be cancelled for the time being.

**Explanation:** This is also reasonable, but at the same time it doesn't solve much. If the family isn't comfortable with it, then the post-mortem needs to be cancelled full stop.

4 – C. Confront the consultant and accuse him of acting unprofessionally in these circumstances.

**Explanation:** This is not a great response. It might be the case that the consultant did not realise how he was behaving, in which case it would be better to take a less combative approach when dealing with him.

5 – A. Tell Neil that since the family have already consented, there's nothing you can do to stop the post-mortem from going ahead.

**Explanation:** This is a bad response. It will make the family very upset, and it's also not true.

## Q116.

1 – C. Quietly ask Osman whether he is feeling okay.

**Explanation:** This is the best initial response. Before you do anything, you should try to speak to Osman, to determine how he's feeling. It's important that you do this in a sensitive fashion. If he denies that he's ill then you can decide on the next best step.

2 – D. Take the consultant to one side and explain to him your concerns about Osman's condition.

**Explanation:** This is the next best step. You should try to talk to Osman first, sensitively, but if this isn't possible for some reason then you should speak to the consultant in charge of the rounds.

3 – B. Politely excuse yourself, take Osman to one side, and demand he has something to eat.

**Explanation:** This is pretty rude and insensitive. It's good that you are talking directly to Osman, but demanding that he has something to eat will not help things.

4 – A. Immediately draw the consultant's attention to Osman's condition. Ask someone to fetch Osman a glass of water.

**Explanation:** This is not a good response. You will likely make Osman very uncomfortable, as you are drawing attention to his condition in front of everybody, and you are being insensitive to the needs of his religion.

5 – E. Loudly declare that Osman is putting patients at risk by refusing to have a drink.

**Explanation:** This is really rude and unprofessional.

## Q117.

1 – B. Immediately approach the nurses and tell them that Remy has an allergy to doxycycline.

**Explanation:** This is the best approach. You need to take immediate action to prevent this medicine from being administered, and harming the patient.

2 – C. Question the nurses over why they are prescribing Remy with doxycycline.

**Explanation:** This is the next best response, although it would be better to take immediate action and just stop the nurses altogether.

3 – E. Take the doxycycline from the nurses, and inform them Remy is allergic to both this, and penicillin.

**Explanation:** This would be good, except there is no evidence in the question that Remy is allergic to penicillin.

4 – D. Allow the nurses to administer the medicine, but question the consultant over it next time you see him.

**Explanation:** This is obviously a terrible response, and will harm the patient.

5 – A. Let Remy take the medicine. It will serve him right for being a whiney little cry baby.

**Explanation:** This is obviously the worst response. It doesn't matter how unpleasant a patient is, you must always act with the utmost professionalism. You have a duty of care to Remy.


## Q118.

1 – A. Try and arrange a meeting with Bradley, so that you can discuss the issue. Question him on whether he's aware that his behaviour is contradictory to hospital rules.

**Explanation:** This is the best response. It might be the case that Bradley doesn't realise he's breaking the rules. Before you decide the next step, it would be a good idea to talk to him about it.

2 – C. Arrange a meeting with Bradley. Suggest to him that there are better ways to make money, that don't involve circumventing the hospital's rules.

**Explanation:** This is a reasonable response. The best course of action here is to try and persuade Bradley that he should stop doing what he is doing. If this fails, then you can take it higher.

3 – B. Go straight to senior management. This is completely unacceptable behaviour.

**Explanation:** At the end of the day, Bradley is breaking the hospital rules, so you wouldn't be doing the wrong thing by reporting him. However, before you do report him, it would be a good idea to actually speak to Bradley first to establish whether he is aware that he's breaking the rules, and to find out if he's intending to stop.

4 – E. Ask your educational consultant on whether you should report this issue.

**Explanation:** This isn't really anything to do with your educational consultant.

5 – D. Meet with Bradley, to discuss joining him in this profitable venture.

**Explanation:** This is the worst response. You are encouraging Bradley to continue breaking the rules, and breaking the rules yourself.

**Q119.**

1 – C. Tell Gus that he can't go back to work straight after passing out. Ask a nurse to escort him to one of the hospital beds.

**Explanation:** This is the best response, as it is the safest. In this situation, you should treat your colleague as you would a patient. Given that he has just passed out, there appears to be a medical issue, and it needs to be dealt with.

2 – D. Inform a senior doctor on the ward about what has just occurred.

**Explanation:** This is the next best solution. Action needs to be taken. If you are unsure of what should be done, then the next best solution would be to ask a senior doctor about it.

3 – A. Ask Gus whether he is sure that this is the right thing to do.

**Explanation:** This isn't a great response. You need to take action yourself here, since Gus has already declared that he wants to get back to work.

4 – E. Tell Gus he needs to rest for a period of at least five minutes, before he returns to work.

**Explanation:** This is a bad response. Gus needs to be checked by a doctor. Passing out is a serious issue, it's not something that can be resolved by a quick five minute rest.

5 – B. Allow Gus to go back to work, but inform all of his patients that he has just passed out.

**Explanation:** This is clearly the worst response. Not only are you allowing Gus to return, unsafely, to the workplace, but you will also distress his patients.

**Q120.**

1 – B. Find Kevin and confront him about what you have found. Ask him if he understood the concept of 'original content'.

**Explanation:** This is the best response. It's quite aggressive, and you could be a little bit more reasonable initially, but you should definitely speak to Kevin first, before you take any other action.

2 – A. Go straight to the consultant and inform him that Kevin cheated on this task.

**Explanation:** This is an okay response, although it's not great. Again, you should speak to Kevin first. Following that, it would be best to arrange a meeting with the consultant where you can discuss your concerns, rather than marching straight to his office and declaring that Kevin cheated.

3 – E. Find the consultant and inform him that Kevin doesn't deserve to take part in the research seminar.

**Explanation:** This is similar to option A, but slightly worse.

4 – C. Gather the other members of the group project together, excluding Kevin, and submit a formal complaint to the head of medicine.

**Explanation:** This isn't an issue for the head of medicine to deal with.

5 – D. Do nothing. Kevin simply outsmarted you all.

**Explanation:** This is the worst response. You shouldn't allow Kevin to just get away with this.


## Q121.

1 – E. See if you can get in touch with the replacement doctor directly, to explain the situation.

**Explanation:** This is a good response. You are going to reasonable lengths to make sure that patient receives the all-important results tonight, as would be expected of a doctor in your position.

2 – C. Call the hospital, and ask them to get the new doctor to look up the results, using the hospital system. Apologise for the error.

**Explanation:** In the event that you can't contact the doctor, you would need to get in touch with the hospital directly, who can then pass this information over.

3 – B. Drive back to the hospital to provide the staff with the necessary paperwork. Apologise for the error.

**Explanation:** This is a good response, but you don't need to do this. You can call the hospital instead, to save time.

4 – A. Wait until tomorrow, to provide Mr Fernandez with the results.

**Explanation:** This is not ideal, as you should give Mr Fernandez the results as soon as possible, but it's still preferential to Option D…

5 – D. Text your friend, who works in the hospital canteen, asking him to provide Mr Fernandez with the test results.

**Explanation:** This is a terrible idea. Your friend works in the canteen, so it's unlikely that he's had any medical training, or that he understands anything about the test results or what they mean.


## Q122.

1 – A. Approach Jade and gently inform her that unfortunately she's made another mistake with her paperwork. Tell her that she will need to speak with a senior manager about this.

**Explanation:** This is the best approach. You are taking a sensitive approach to the issue, directly approaching Jade and informing her of the severity of the situation. You should take into account that Jade could be very upset by this news, so it's important to try and be gentle in your approach.

2 – C. Approach Jade and inform her that as a result of her error, she will need to see a senior manager.

**Explanation:** This is an okay response, as it's factual, but it's also very blunt. This approach is likely to upset Jade.

3 – B. Speak to a senior doctor and inform them that Jade has made another error. Encourage them to sack her.

**Explanation:** This is a bad response. You should speak to Jade about the error first, before a senior doctor is informed. Encouraging the doctor to sack her is extremely unprofessional.

4 – E. Inform Jade that the hospital operates on a '3 strikes and you're out' policy. Tell her that she needs to leave immediately.

**Explanation:** This is a terrible response. You don't have the authority to make decisions like this, and the information you are giving Jade is untrue.

5 – D. Correct the error and don't say anything. Jade is improving, you can cut her some slack.

**Explanation:** This is the worst response. Your hospital has rules in place for a reason. Yes, Jade is attending further training, but you can't just write off another error as nothing. Mistakes like this could put patients at risk.


## Q123.

1 – D. Contact your colleague, informing him that you will be reporting the post to a senior manager.

**Explanation:** This is the best response. You need to report this post. Not only is it breaking the doctor patient confidentiality agreement, but your colleague is also threatening violence against a patient. Even if he is joking in relation to the last point, this could be seen by others and taken literally, which will reflect extremely badly on the hospital. You should inform your colleague that you are reporting him first though, out of courtesy.

2 – B. Speak to a consultant about the post, and what should be done.

**Explanation:** This is the next best response. As mentioned above, this is a serious situation, and it needs to be reported.

3 – A. Contact your colleague, and tell him that he really needs to remove the social media post.

**Explanation:** This is not great, simply because it's not enough. You aren't being clear enough here – your colleague has committed a serious breach of conduct.

4 – E. Message your colleague, informing him that appendicitis is actually really painful.

**Explanation:** This is not useful. You aren't dealing with the major issue here, which is that your colleague has behaved unacceptably.

5 – C. Reply to the post, stating that you found it amusing.

**Explanation:** This is unprofessional, and makes you look extremely bad. You need to emphasise how bad this behaviour is, not condone it.

**Q124.**

1 – B. Consult the patient notes, to discover who is treating the woman. Promise to raise the issue with her current doctor and then get back to her.

**Explanation:** This is a reasonable and professional response. Even if you are not treating the woman yourself, you are still a member of the hospital team and therefore you need to treat the patient with respect and courtesy.

2 – E. Tell the woman that you will speak to the surgical team and see what they can do.

**Explanation:** This is not a great response. Yes, you will placate the patient, but if the surgery has been postponed then it's for a reason, and it's very unlikely there is anything you can say to the surgery team that would change this.

3 – C. Ask the woman what surgery she needs.

**Explanation:** This is unprofessional and will damage the patient's faith in hospital staff.

4 – A. Inform the woman that she is not your patient, and therefore she needs to find someone else to deal with the problem.

**Explanation:** This is a very bad response. In this situation, provided you have time, you should do your best to at least find a doctor who can help the patient.

5 – D. Take the woman down to the legal department, so that she can pursue a formal complaint.

**Explanation:** This is a terrible response. You shouldn't be encouraging the woman to take action against the hospital, it would be better to just try and resolve the issue for her.


**Q125.**

1 – C. Tell Miles that the hospital rules forbid you from attending.

**Explanation:** This is the best response. You are being honest with Miles, although you should still thank him for the invite.

2 – E. Thank Miles for the invite, but inform him that you will be busy working that day.

**Explanation:** You aren't being completely honest with Miles here, but it's an acceptable cover excuse nonetheless, and doesn't hurt his feelings.

3 – D. Thank Miles for his invite, but tell him that you don't want to attend.

**Explanation:** This is fairly rude and will upset the patient, who clearly feels that he has a good rapport with you.

4 – B. Berate Miles for asking you to risk your job in such a manner.

**Explanation:** This is not a good response and will upset the patient. He is not to know about hospital policy.

5 – A. Inform Miles that there's nothing you would rather do less, than attend his party.

**Explanation:** This is extremely rude and unprofessional. You will greatly upset the patient.

## Q126.

1 – B. Tell Brian that you will arrange for someone to replace him during the operation. Encourage him to cooperate with the police.

**Explanation:** This is the best response. You are taking a sensible and reasonable approach to the situation. Informing Brian that you'll find someone else to replace him will put him in a better frame of mind, and hopefully will ensure that he focuses on dealing with the incident at hand, rather than worrying about the surgery.

2 – D. Tell Brian that he needs to face the consequences of his actions, and that you will tell the head surgeon about what has happened.

**Explanation:** This is the next best response, and is also perfectly acceptable. In a situation as serious as this, it's better to encourage your friend to work with the legal authorities, to resolve his issue.

3 – E. Pass the phone over to the lead surgeon to deal with this issue.

**Explanation:** This isn't great, although it's not terrible. It's just very likely that the lead surgeon will inform Brian that he'll find a replacement, and then tell him to cooperate with the police, which is exactly what you do in option B.

4 – A. Inform Brian that you will speak to the head surgeon and ask him to delay the operation, whilst Brian deals with the police.

**Explanation:** This is not a good response. Yes, the operation might need to be delayed slightly whilst you find a replacement, but this implies that Brian might be able to avoid going to the police station, and make it to the hospital. Quite frankly, that is just not going to happen.

5 – C. Agree to talk with the police officer, and try to persuade him about why Brian is needed at the surgery.

**Explanation:** Brian has committed a very serious offence. There is nothing you could say to the policeman that would change this, and nor should you try.

## Q127.

1 – B. Encourage your colleague to sit down with his education consultant and discuss these issues in depth.

**Explanation:** This is definitely the best solution. In this case, it is the responsibility of your colleague's education consultant to deal with issues such as this. Likewise, it is the responsibility of your colleague to raise the matter with someone higher, if he does not feel that the standards are up to scratch.

2 – E. Ask your colleague why he thinks another hospital would provide a better standard of teaching than this one.

**Explanation:** This is a little bit of an odd response. It's not good, although it's not terrible. It might be the case that your colleague is misinformed over how hospitals are actually run. That's not to say that he shouldn't expect high standards, but it would be useful to know what he thinks other hospitals do better.

3 – A. Inform your colleague that in your opinion, the hospital has very high standards, and great teaching.

**Explanation:** This isn't very helpful. It's great that you are standing up for the hospital, but at the same time just stating your opinion isn't going to help. You need to consider your colleague's point of view and why he is feeling this way.

4 – C. Tell your colleague that he is being ungrateful, and needs to change his attitude.

**Explanation:** This response is bad. It will make your colleague angry, and shows a lack of sensitivity for how he is feeling.

5 – D. Ask your colleague whether he would consider himself an arrogant person.

**Explanation:** This is pretty much the same as option C, except here you are being outright insulting.

**Q128.**

1 – D. Inform Kayla that the reason for putting the time and date on records is so that every single doctor for a patient can see how the patient has been treated, whilst at the hospital.

**Explanation:** This is the best response. There are other reasons for why putting the time and date on patient records is important, but the primary reason is so that doctors can consult with this record, and provide the best possible level of continuous care to a patient.

2 – E. Inform Kayla that the reason for putting the time and date on records is so that if a doctor makes a mistake, the hospital can point out when and by whom the mistake was made, thus ensuring the right person is fired.

**Explanation:** This is misinformed, but somewhat right. It's important to see which doctor has made the mistake and when they made it, but not so that they can be sacked. Putting the time and date on records ensures that doctors take accountability, and can amend their own mistakes in future, if necessary.

3 – C. Inform Kayla that the primary reason for putting the time and date on records is for hospital protection against potential lawsuits.

**Explanation:** Again, this is misinformed and represents a misinterpretation of why hospitals use this system. Using a time and date system is useful, because it allows the hospital to correspond with legal authorities should the need arise. It may well have some use in protecting a hospital against lawsuits, but this is not the primary reason.

4 – B. Tell Kayla not to ask you stupid questions.

**Explanation:** This is really rude and unhelpful.

5 – A. Ask Kayla how she even gained employment at the hospital, if she has to ask such a

question.

**Explanation:** This is the worst response. It's incredibly rude and will make Kayla feel upset.

## Q129.

1 – E. Tell Kelsie that although you are always happy to offer guidance, she needs to speak to her education consultant if she wants extra help.

**Explanation:** This is a reasonable response. You are being polite and sensitive, whilst also making it clear that this behaviour pattern is unacceptable.

2 – D. Tell Kelsie that she needs to try and take some more responsibility for her own patients.

**Explanation:** This is acceptable, although you could be a little bit more sensitive in the way that you tell her.

3 – C. Tell Kelsie that although you are always happy to help her, this behaviour cannot continue if she wishes to be a successful doctor.

**Explanation:** This isn't great, although it's not far from the truth. Rather than bringing Kelsie's future career into it, you should try to focus on who can provide her with the proper support.

4 – B. Carry on as you are. It's great to help out your colleagues.

**Explanation:** This is unhelpful. The question clearly emphasises that this is having a negative impact on your own work.

5 – A. Pull Kelsie to one side and inform her that, as from this moment, you will be unable to assist her with any medical matters.

**Explanation:** This is a bad response. You will make Kelsie feel upset and confused. You should always be looking to help out your colleagues if you can, although not to the detriment of your own work.

## Q130.

1 – C. Go and speak to Ruben. Inform him that his comments are totally unacceptable.

**Explanation:** This is the first thing that needs to be done. Your initial priority should be to stop Ruben from behaving in this manner, before he is dealt with by someone senior.

2 – D. Once you have finished with your patient, go and tell a senior doctor about what has just happened.

**Explanation:** This is the next thing that you would do. Ruben's behaviour represents a serious breach of conduct, and it needs to be reported. It is very likely that your patient, at the very least, will submit a formal complaint. Ruben's patient could also complain.

3 – E. Once you have finished with your patient, inform Ruben that there could be serious consequences for his behaviour.

**Explanation:** This is okay, but the wording isn't great. You don't need to tell Ruben that there 'could' be serious consequences, because there will be serious consequences. In an event like this, Ruben will at the very least need to explain himself to senior hospital management, and the case could also be referred to the GMC.

4 – B. Apologise sincerely to the patient, and assure him that Ruben is just having a bad day.

**Explanation:** This isn't good enough. You should apologise to the patient, but Ruben's behaviour cannot be excused.

5 – A. Go and shut Ruben's door, so that nobody else can hear his inappropriate remarks.

**Explanation:** Again, this is nowhere near good enough. Ruben's patient will still be witness to his terrible behaviour.

**Q131.**

1 – B. Approach the nurse in question and ask her to try and keep the noise down.

**Explanation:** This is the best response. You are being reasonable. It might be the case that the nurse has not noticed that Joel is awake, or that she's disturbing anyone, so your first course of action should be a polite and considered approach.

2 – C. Wait until the next day, and then go and see the ward manager to enquire about whether Joel can move to a new location on the ward.

**Explanation:** This is a reasonable response. However, it would be better to just point out that there is a noise problem with that bed in particular. You could move Joel to a new bed, but if this is an ongoing problem then future patients could be impacted too.

3 – A. Ask Joel whether the noise from the nurse station is bothering him.

**Explanation:** This is an okay response, but if you think that the nurse is being too noisy then you should say something, regardless of how it's impacting your patient.

4 – D. Do nothing. It's bad luck that Joel's bed is next to the nurse station, but that's life.

**Explanation:** This is a very bad response. It's not 'bad luck' that any patient has ended up in this bed, it represents a mistake from the hospital. You need to say something.

5 – E. Wait until the nurse has finished talking on the phone, and then unplug it when nobody is looking. That will stop the noise.

**Explanation:** This is by far the worst response. The nurse station plays an extremely important role in patient-to-doctor coordination, and unplugging the phone removes an essential form of communication. You could be endangering the lives of patients by doing this.

**Q132.**

1 – A. Apologise sincerely to Lauren for the problems that she has been having. Inform her that if she is willing to wait for a few minutes, you will go and find out whether it's possible to move her to another ward.

**Explanation:** This is a great response. The patient is clearly very upset, so you should do your best to help find a resolution to her problem, and apologise on behalf of the hospital – who have clearly allowed this to become an issue.

2 – B. Tell Lauren that you are happy to discharge her, but will need to conduct a short medical assessment first.

**Explanation:** The patient record indicates that Lauren could be considered for early release. If you perform a medical assessment, and are suitably assured that Lauren will be okay, then you can discharge her from the hospital.

3 – E. Tell Lauren that you'll have her moved to another ward immediately.

**Explanation:** This is an okay response, but you can't guarantee that this is possible.

4 – C. Tell Lauren that she is not due for discharge for another three days. Inform her that she'll have to stay put.

**Explanation:** This is not a good response. You will only further upset the patient, as you aren't attempting to help with the issue.

5 – D. Tell Lauren that it would be a good idea for her to purchase some noise-cancelling headphones.

**Explanation:** This isn't helpful at all. It will only make the patient feel angrier.


**Q133.**

1 – D. Tell Barbara that you weren't aware of any wrongdoing, but will do your utmost to improve your patient handling skills.

**Explanation:** This is a good response. You are highlighting that you weren't aware of the errors, but also showing a recognition of your mistakes and a willingness to better yourself.

2 – C. Tell Barbara that you weren't aware of any wrongdoing, but that you are happy to apologise to the patients in person.

**Explanation:** This is an okay response. It's great that you are showing an acceptance of your mistakes, and a willingness to take responsibility.

3 – A. Tell Barbara that you are very confused by the comments about your behaviour. Ask her if there has been a case of mistaken identity.

**Explanation:** This is a poor response. You are failing to accept your errors, and using a very bad excuse.

4 – E. Ask Barbara for tips on how to avoid being spotted, the next time you do something wrong.

**Explanation:** This is very bad. You are showing the senior consultant that you only care about making mistakes if you get caught.

5 – B. Tell Barbara that you are shocked and appalled by these comments about your behaviour, especially coming from someone as incompetent as her.

**Explanation:** This is the worst response. You are openly insulting a senior member of staff, and refusing to take responsibility for your actions.

### Q134.

1 – C. Tell the consultant that you don't feel comfortable performing this. Ask him to give you another demonstration.

**Explanation:** Performing a procedure that you aren't comfortable or confident with, is likely to harm the patient. Therefore, it is better to be honest with the consultant, whilst asking him for further tips.

2 – A. Be honest with the consultant and inform him that you still don't feel comfortable performing this procedure.

**Explanation:** As mentioned, you should try and be honest with the consultant, although it would better to take a proactive approach and ask him to show you how it's done.

3 – D. Ask someone else in the group to do it, whilst you watch.

**Explanation:** This is not great, because the consultant has asked you specifically to do the procedure.

4 – E. Start crying. Hopefully the consultant will feel sorry for you.

**Explanation:** This is a very poor response. Crocodile tears will not solve your problem.

5 – B. Try and perform the procedure to the best of your ability.

**Explanation:** Patient safety should be the number one concern. If you don't have any clue of how to do the procedure, then you shouldn't even attempt it. Yes, everyone has to learn at some point, but if you really don't have any idea then it's not the right move to attempt this.

### Q135.

1 – C. Try and get in touch with the Foundation Programme Director, to inform them about the lack of communication from Amanda.

**Explanation:** This is the best response. The Foundation Programme Director is the best placed person to deal with this. They also need to be informed, especially if it turns out that Amanda is taking the same attitude to her other FY1s.

2 – E. Speak to one of the senior doctors on the ward, about arranging an appointment with Amanda.

**Explanation:** It's likely that one of the senior doctors will have had some contact with Amanda. Therefore, it's reasonable to ask them for help in this instance.

3 – D. Send Amanda an email titled URGENT REQUEST PLEASE RESPOND IMMEDIATELY. She will surely at least open this.

**Explanation:** The question clearly states that Amanda has not responded to any of the emails that you've already sent her. Therefore, there's no point sending another one.

4 – B. Leave an angry note on Amanda's door, stating that you believe she is unprofessional and rude.

**Explanation:** This is not a good response. The question clearly states that you have already got off to a bad start with Amanda, and this will only make things worse.

5 – A. Wait for Amanda to contact you. She's clearly very busy.

**Explanation:** It's extremely important that junior doctors can speak to their educational and clinical supervisors, to discuss important issues. Amanda doesn't seem to be making any effort to get in touch, which is a serious matter. You need to take action here.

## Q136.

1 – A. Take the consultant to one side and question him about the smell.

**Explanation:** This is the most polite, professional response. If you suspect that your colleague has been drinking, then you need to take immediate action.

2 – E. Take the consultant to one side and inform him that he stinks of alcohol.

**Explanation:** This is really rude but it's still the second best option. You need to speak up about the issue.

3 – B. Wait until the consultation is finished, and then question your colleagues about whether they have noticed the smell.

**Explanation:** This is not a good response. You shouldn't wait until the consultation is finished. If the consultant has been drinking then he cannot be relied upon to make good judgement calls.

4 – C. Ask the consultant, in front of the patient, why he smells of alcohol.

**Explanation:** This is a very bad response, and will damage the patient's faith in the hospital staff.

5 – D. Do nothing. It's not your place to question a senior member of staff.

**Explanation:** This is a very bad response. Even if your colleague is not showing physical signs of alcohol consumption, the smell alone should be enough to make you act.

## Q137.

1 – B. Stand up for your colleague. Inform Dr Green that he is in breach of hospital guidelines.

**Explanation:** This is the best response. Washing hands between seeing patients is an established Infection Control policy, and refusing to do this represents a serious breach of safety.

2 – E. Tell Dr Green that his behaviour is out of line, and that he should apologise to Emma.

**Explanation:** This is a reasonable response. Regardless of how senior he is, Dr Green has no right to address your colleague like this, and you should speak up to assert that.

3 – D. Refuse to take part in the rest of the round, until Dr Green washes his hands and apologises to Emma.

**Explanation:** This is very unhelpful. However, at least you are taking action against Dr Green's poor behaviour. He cannot be allowed to conduct the rounds, and examine patients, without adhering to safety protocol.

4 – C. Tell Emma that if she ever wants to get promoted, she needs to treat Dr Green with more respect.

**Explanation:** This is a bad response. You are implying that personal promotions and agreeing with senior figures is more important than doing the right thing by the patients.

5 – A. Concur with Dr Green. Inform Emma that she is rude and disrespectful.

**Explanation:** This is the worst response. You are insulting your colleague, who will now feel even worse about the situation, when she is in the right.

## Q138.

1 – A. Apologise for the inconvenience caused, but make it clear that dogs are not allowed in the main hospital building.

**Explanation:** This is the best possible response. It's good to be sympathetic, but at the end of the day the hospital rules are there for a reason. She cannot bring the dog into the main building.

2 – E. Tell Eileen's daughter that she will need to come back without the dog, if she wishes to see her mother.

**Explanation:** This is quite blunt, and could upset Eileen's daughter, but it's also a factual relay of the rules. This is what will need to happen.

3 – D. Enquire with a senior doctor as to whether the dog can enter the main hospital building.

**Explanation:** This is a bad response. You already know the rules, so why waste time asking a senior doctor?

4 – B. Tell Eileen's daughter that she can bring the dog upstairs, but it must be kept on a leash.

**Explanation:** This is a very bad response. You are breaking the hospital rules, and could be putting patients' safety at risk.

5 – C. Call the police and have Eileen's daughter arrested.

**Explanation:** This is an absurd overreaction and completely unnecessary. There are no grounds for this.

## Q139.

1 – D. Tell Mr Ingram that you will speak to the relevant person, and try to find him a new bed for the night.

**Explanation:** This is the most reasonable response to the scenario. The hospital has a duty of care. If Mr Ingram's carer is not available until the morning then the best option would be for the hospital to take care of him until then.

2 – E. Ask the nurses to find out if there are any available beds in which Mr Ingram can stay.

**Explanation:** This is an okay response, but Mr Ingram is still your patient, so you should try and take responsibility for dealing with this issue yourself – not just passing it over to the nurses.

3 – C. Ask Mr Ingram if an alternative carer can be arranged.

**Explanation:** This is a poor response. Although it might seem like a reasonable request, you need to think about Mr Ingram's position. He is an elderly man, with no loved ones, who has just been released from hospital. Putting the responsibility on him to return home and then arrange for a new carer himself, is a little unfair. What happens if he returns home and an alternative carer can't be arranged?

4 – A. Tell Mr Ingram that his personal problems are no concern of the hospital. Ask him to leave.

**Explanation:** This is a really unprofessional and insensitive response. Mr Ingram's personal issues are a concern of the hospital in this case, because he is your patient.

5 – B. Tell Mr Ingram that if he doesn't want to leave by himself, you can ask security to escort him out.

**Explanation:** This is a terrible response. You don't need to call security on a defenceless elderly man.


## Q140.

1 – A. Immediately seek out Eileen, and assure her that you did not give any consent for Rhotunda to sign your name on this email. Tell her that she has your full support.

**Explanation:** This is the best response. You are taking immediate action, and giving your supervisor your full support. Ultimately it is her responsibility to deal with this situation, but it will help her to know that you did not consent.

2 – D. See if you can arrange a meeting with the head physician to discuss Rhotunda's comments.

**Explanation:** This isn't the best response, but if you feel strongly about your supervisor's position then it would be reasonable for you to act. However, ultimately the responsibility for doing this should rest with your supervisor herself.

3 – B. Contact Rhotunda and inform her that you strongly disagree with her opinion.

**Explanation:** This is a fairly poor response. If you are going to contact Rhotunda, then you should first of all be questioning her over why she used your name as a consenter without permission.

4 – E. Seek legal advice. Your name has been used without permission.

**Explanation:** Yes, your name has been used without permission, but it's just an email. There are more effective ways to deal with this situation.

5 – C. Do nothing. If that's how the rest of the FY1s feel, then who are you to argue?

**Explanation:** This is a very poor response. In this situation, you should definitely take action.

## Q141.

1 – B. Politely ask Benjamin's parents if he could stop filming. Explain that you aren't very comfortable appearing on film.

**Explanation:** This is a reasonable response. You are being polite and respectful. The patient has the right to film you, but you are raising a well-put objection to this, without being aggressive. Raising the issue with Benjamin's parents first, is also a good idea.

2 – D. Tell Benjamin that you would appreciate it if he didn't film during your consultation.

**Explanation:** This is also an okay response, but you are more likely to gain a positive outcome if you speak to Benjamin's parents.

3 – E. Ignore it. He's just a child.

**Explanation:** If you don't feel comfortable being filmed then you should say something, or even speak to a senior colleague about it, but ignoring it in this case is a better solution than A or C, both of which could cause serious problems.

4 – A. Tell Benjamin that you do not consent to being filmed, and therefore legally he must delete the footage.

**Explanation:** This is not true. Patients have a right to record consultations with their doctor, as it is their own personal information.

5 – C. Take Benjamin's mobile phone from him and delete the footage yourself.

**Explanation:** This is an aggressive action, which could cause serious problems.

## Q142.

1 – A. Walk over and inform the junior doctor that he will need to delete the footage immediately.

**Explanation:** GMC guidelines in this case are clear. Doctors need to ask for permission before making a visual or audio recording of patients. In this case, Benjamin and his family have not given their consent for this to happen.

2 – C. Ask the junior doctor to step outside and calm down, whilst you apologise to the family

for his behaviour.

**Explanation:** This is the next best response. You are apologising on behalf of the junior doctor, who has acted irrationally.

3 – B. Ask a senior doctor for advice on what to do.

**Explanation:** This is an okay response, but it would be better to take responsibility for the situation yourself.

4 – E. Ask Benjamin's family whether they are happy for the footage to appear on the junior doctoret.

**Explanation:** This is a truly terrible response, and will only serve to make the family more angry and upset. They clearly haven't given their consent, so their answer here is obvious.

5 – D. Tell the junior doctor that he has no legal requirement to delete the footage, as he was being filmed first.

**Explanation:** This is not true. It will make the family even more angry and upset. You are giving the junior doctor bad legal advice. He needs to delete the footage.


**Q143.**

1 – A. Agree to the family's wishes. A post-mortem cannot take place if consent from the patient's relatives is withheld.

**Explanation:** This is the best response. The post-mortem cannot be done if the family doesn't give permission.

2 – E. Ask the family whether they would consent to a post-mortem, if it could be conducted within the 48 hour period.

**Explanation:** The question states that it is not possible for the post-mortem to take place within the 48-hour window. Therefore, this is not a viable option, and you would be wasting time.

3 – D. Sit down with the family and explain that their religious views are a load of nonsense. Urge them to consider the post-mortem.

**Explanation:** This is very offensive, insensitive and ignorant. You will be making the situation far worse.

4 – C. Tell your consultant that although the family haven't consented to the post-mortem, you think it would be a good idea to go through with it anyway.

**Explanation:** The only saving grace of this response is that your consultant will surely tell you that the post-mortem can't be done without permission. You will come across as extremely unprofessional.

5 – B. Ignore the family's request. In this instance, a post-mortem would be extremely beneficial, and could help save the lives of future patients.

**Explanation:** This is the worst response. Legally, you can't have the post-mortem without the consent of the patient's family.

## Q144.

1 – B. Agree to fetch a senior doctor. Resolve to argue your case after the man has spoken to them.

**Explanation:** This is the most reasonable response. The question states that the man is becoming increasingly irate. In these circumstances, the best thing to do would be to fetch a senior doctor who can deal with him.

2 – C. Inform the man that you are confused and upset by his comments. Assure him that you have not meant to cause any offence.

**Explanation:** This is a good response. You are being polite and respectful, and assuring the man that there has been a misunderstanding. Hopefully this will calm him down.

3 – A. Ask the man what exactly you have said that has offended him so badly.

**Explanation:** This is an okay response, if a little blunt. In this situation you would be entitled to ask what you have done wrong, if you aren't aware of what you've said that was deemed offensive.

4 – E. Inform the man, telling him that he could ruin your career with such accusations.

**Explanation:** Situations like this are extremely difficult. If you feel that you haven't behaved in the manner that you are being accused of, then it would be easy to panic and get emotional. However, this will only make things worse. As the question states, the man is becoming irate. You need to fetch a senior doctor to defuse this situation.

5 – D. Tell the man that he could ruin your career with such accusations.

**Explanation:** This is the worst response. The man has made an extremely serious accusation. Even though you do not agree with it, or do not understand it, it needs to be followed up on.

## Q145.

1 – B. Find a senior doctor and ask them to assist you with the patient. Explain to the patient that you would like your colleague's advice on this issue.

**Explanation:** This is the best solution. If you can't find the specialist then you should seek out the help of a senior doctor. Asking them to assist you with the patient is a good idea, as it means that you will be learning at the same time. Finally, you are also taking a sensitive approach to explaining to the patient what exactly you are doing.

2 – E. Find a senior doctor, and ask them if they would be able to deal with this patient instead of you.

**Explanation:** This is the next best response. You need to realise your own limitations. If you aren't the right person to deal with a patient, whether that's because of a lack of experience or some other reason, then you should take responsibility for finding someone who can deal with them.

3 – D. Ask the nurses whether they can find a doctor who is more suitable to treating this type of patient.

**Explanation:** This is the third best response. The nursing team should be able to assist you with this, but it would be better for you to take responsibility.

4 – C. Tell the patient that you aren't confident enough to deal with him, and that you'll be right back when you find someone else who can.

**Explanation:** This is a terrible response. You will greatly damage the patient's faith in the hospital staff.

5 – A. Deal with the patient as best as you can. Keep him overnight in the hospital, so that the specialist can deal with him when she's available.

**Explanation:** Although you are taking responsibility here, the question states that you don't feel confident in your ability to treat this patient. Therefore, by just treating him to the best of your ability, you are taking a big risk. If you miss something crucial then you could be putting the patient's life in jeopardy. You need to find someone senior to deal with this situation.

## Q146.

1 – B. Ask your colleague to speak to her educational supervisor about how she feels. Encourage her to do what makes her happy.

**Explanation:** This is the best response. Your colleague's educational supervisor is the best placed person to deal with this issue. They are there to offer support, and will be experienced in handling such matters.

2 – E. Tell your colleague that she has your full support, and that you are always available if she needs someone to talk to.

**Explanation:** This is a sensitive and thoughtful response, which provides your friend with the knowledge that she has someone there to support her.

3 – D. Ask your colleague to speak to the ward consultant about this issue.

**Explanation:** This isn't ideal. Your ward consultant might be willing to talk with your colleague about the issue, but her educational consultant would be a better option.

4 – C. Tell your colleague that she is selfish for losing interest in medicine, and clearly doesn't care about saving lives.

**Explanation:** This is a very bad response. You are insulting your colleague, which is likely to make her more upset.

5 – A. Tell your colleague that if she is losing interest in medicine, the best thing would be to resign immediately.

**Explanation:** This is the worst response. You are encouraging your colleague to just give up, which is extremely unhelpful. That's the opposite of what you should be doing!

### Q147.

1 – A. Ask Tim to come and sit down with you in a quiet room, so that you can discuss the situation and his options moving forward.

**Explanation:** This is the best response. You are being sensitive and respectful of the fact that Tim has received some terrible news, and therefore is reacting emotionally. Given that Tim has just punched the wall, potentially injuring himself, the best option would be to take him out of the room and try to calm him down in a private setting.

2 – C. Tell Tim that you will give him and his mother some privacy.

**Explanation:** This is also a good response. Obviously, Tim is reacting very emotionally to the news, as many people would. In this case, it might be best to let him and his mother talk about how they are feeling in a private space.

3 – D. Offer to bring Tim a hot beverage, in the hopes that it will comfort him.

**Explanation:** This isn't great. At least you are giving him and his mother some privacy, but a hot beverage is hardly going to help.

4 – E. Assure Tim that the doctors at the hospital have done their very best to save his mother.

**Explanation:** This is not great. You need to understand that Tim is reacting emotionally to the situation, so being defensive isn't going to help.

5 – B. Tell Tim that if he does not calm down then you will be forced to call security, who will escort him from the building.

**Explanation:** This is obviously the worst response. You are being completely insensitive to Tim's feelings and the impact that this news could have on him. You will also hugely upset the patient, from watching her son get escorted from the building.

### Q148.

1 – B. Inform the patient's parents that their son isn't eating hospital food. Tell them that this is a serious problem which could significantly hinder his recovery.

**Explanation:** This is the best response. In this situation, your first port of call would be the patient's parents. If they cannot successfully intervene then you would need to take other measures, but the parents are the most reasonable choice for first stage intervention. In this response, you are clearly explaining why this is a big problem.

2 – E. Sit down with the patient and try to talk to him about why he won't eat the hospital food.

**Explanation:** You are the patient's doctor, so taking a sensitive and responsible approach to amending the problem is highly recommend in this situation. If the patient's parents can't convince him, then you should make a sustained effort to do so yourself.

3 – C. Ask the patient's parents to have a serious chat with their son about his behaviour.

**Explanation:** This is reasonable, but at the same time you need to emphasise the implications of the scenario to the parents.

4 – D. Ask the patient's parents whether they could bring in a burger from the local fast food restaurant for their son.

**Explanation:** This is not a good response. You are giving the parents an unprofessional and unreasonable request. Fast food is probably not the best option here for a sick patient.

5 – A. Tell the patient's parents that they will need to ask their son to eat, or else…

**Explanation:** This is the worst response. You are threatening the patient's parents!

## Q149.

1 – E. Speak to the consultant on the ward, and explain to him what has just happened.

**Explanation:** This is the best response. The consultant should have a good idea of what to do in this scenario.

2 – A. Go to the nurse desk and ask them if they can provide you with a full report on Darren's activity for the day.

**Explanation:** This is reasonably helpful. The nurses should be able to provide you with a report on Darren's activity. However, given his behaviour, it might be possible that he didn't get much done today – which is why the consultant would be a better person to speak to.

3 – B. Go and see your educational supervisor and ask them what you should do.

**Explanation:** This is a reasonable response but it doesn't accomplish much. Your educational supervisor is unlikely to be of too much help here, although they might give you some useful advice on what you should do next.

4 – C. Hang around with your colleagues for the rest of your shift, helping them out with their patients.

**Explanation:** This isn't a good response. This means that the patients whom you are supposed to be dealing with, will be neglected.

5 – D. Chase after Darren and ask him whether he has resigned.

**Explanation:** This is an irrelevant action which will resolve nothing. Your priority should be in finding out what patients you need to deal with for the remainder of your shift.

## Q150.

1 – C. Ask Mark for a quiet chat. Tell him that he needs to be more considerate towards the feelings of his colleagues.

**Explanation:** This is the best approach. It might be the case that Mark doesn't realise he is upsetting your colleagues, so having a quiet talk with him first is the best option.

2 – A. Take Amanda to one side and ask her whether she feels hurt by Mark's comment.

**Explanation:** This isn't a great solution. You've already been informed that your colleagues, in general, are offended by Mark's jokes. Even if Amanda tells you that she isn't upset by this incident, you still need to speak to Mark about the issue.

3 – B. Approach Mark and inform him that his jokes are not very funny.

**Explanation:** This isn't ideal. You are being very blunt about the situation. Simply telling Mark that his jokes aren't funny isn't going to help, you need to explain why this behaviour must stop.

4 – E. Tell Mark that the hospital is no place for humour.

**Explanation:** This isn't true. The problem here isn't with humour, it's with the fact that Mark's jokes are inappropriate and insensitive.

5 – D. Go and see the Chief Physician about Mark's behaviour.

**Explanation:** This is a minor issue. You don't need to waste the Chief Physician's time, when it could be easily be dealt with by yourself or another senior colleague.

# PRACTICE QUESTIONS
# SECTION 2

In the below questions, you will be given a scenario, and then asked to choose the 3 most appropriate answer options. There are 150 questions in total, and you can find the answers to these at the end of the section. In our answer options, we have placed the three best options in rank order. Although you will not need to rank the answers in the actual test, we encourage you to try this for the practice test – as it will help you to think more clearly about why you've chosen each option.

---

**Q1.** You have just started your shift for the day. Handover goes extremely smoothly. You will be taking over from a doctor named Fran. Fran informs you that she is in an extremely bad mood, and seems happy to be leaving. You will see Fran tomorrow, during your next shift.

Your first patient is a 70 year old man named Mr Edwards. Mr Edwards says the following:

**Mr Edwards:** *'Thank god you are here. My last doctor was awful. She was so rough with me, and when I informed her about this, she snapped at me.'*

**Take a look at the below answers, and then choose the three best options.**

A – Immediately go and inform a senior colleague about Fran's poor behaviour.

B – Tell the patient that if he doesn't want doctors to snap at him, then he should stop moaning.

C – Apologise sincerely to the patient. Promise to have a word with Fran about her behaviour.

D – Tell the patient that Fran was clearly having a bad day.

E – Assure the patient that you will speak to Fran about the issue.

F – Call Fran at her house, to demand an explanation.

G – Wait until the next time you see Fran to speak to her. Tell her that she is unprofessional.

H – Tell the patient that a full investigation will be made into Fran's deplorable behaviour.

| 1 | 2 | 3 |
|---|---|---|
|   |   |   |

---

**Q2.** Today, one of your patients has been diagnosed with terminal cancer. The patient in question is devastated. Just before you are about to go home, at the end of your shift, the patient approaches you and asks you to inform his family about the diagnosis later that evening. You inform him that you'll make sure this gets done.

During handover, you inform the doctor who is replacing you about the situation. His name is Andrew. Andrew assures you that he will inform the family about the diagnosis, in a sensitive and compassionate manner. You then go home.

When you come in the next day, the family of the patient approaches you. The man's wife asks whether you have any news on her husband's condition, and whether he will be out of hospital and on the road to recovery soon.

**Take a look at the below answers, and then choose the three best options.**

A – Go and find Andrew to discover why he didn't give the family the news.

B – Immediately take the family into a quiet room and gently break the news.

C – Inform the family that Andrew was meant to discuss this with them yesterday.

D – Take the family to see Andrew. Announce that he has something to tell them.

E – Tell the family that they need to speak to the patient to find out about his condition.

F – Tell the family that you will consult with the hospital specialist, to find out their loved one's chances of survival.

G – Ask the family whether they were here yesterday night.

H – Tell the family that you've got some bad news. Ask them to take a seat first.

| 1 | 2 | 3 |
|---|---|---|
|   |   |   |

**Q3.** One of your patients is ready for discharge from the hospital. His name is Derick. The patient has been under the hospital's care for a few weeks now, but luckily has made a full recovery. Just before the patient leaves, he approaches you:

**Derick:** *'I just wanted to let you know, I'm really disappointed in the quality of care that I've received at this hospital. I'm not going to make a formal complaint, but I wasn't at all impressed by how things are run around here.'*

**Take a look at the below answers, and then choose the three best options.**

A – Tell Derick that since he's about to be discharged, his thoughts on the hospital are irrelevant.

B – Encourage Derick to make a formal complaint.

C – Ask Derick if he would be willing to sit down with you and have a talk about what he didn't like.

D – Ask Derick if he would be willing to speak with a senior member of staff about these issues.

E – Ask Derick to provide you with detailed feedback on what he thinks could be improved.

F – Apologise to Derick about this. Tell him that you will personally make a sustained attempt to improve the hospital's standards in future.

G – Apologise to Derick. Inform him that next time he comes into the hospital, things will be better.

H – Ask Derick to name the members of staff who he felt didn't perform to a good enough standard.

| 1 | 2 | 3 |
|---|---|---|
|   |   |   |

> **Q4.** You are working in the paediatric ward on Monday evening. You are speaking to a young girl and her parents. Suddenly, from behind you, there are raised voices. Another one of your patients, a young boy named Stuart, is arguing with his parents.
>
> **Stuart:** *'I want those football boots and I want them NOW!'*
>
> **Stuart's mother:** *'Well you can't have them. Your birthday is 3 months away. Now shut up!'*
>
> **Stuart:** *'That's so unfair. I want them, I want them, I WANT THEM!'*
>
> The family's argument is beginning to disturb other patients in the ward. There are lots of young children sleeping.

**Take a look at the below answers, and then choose the three best options.**

A – Approach the family and ask them to try and keep the noise down, because there are patients sleeping.

B – Approach the family and ask them to have their disagreement somewhere else, because there are sleeping patients.

C – Approach Stuart's parents and inform them that they should buy him the football boots.

D – Approach Stuart and tell him that he can't have the football boots, so he needs to be quiet.

E – Tell Stuart that you will buy him the football boots if he quietens down.

F – Approach the family and tell them that they need to lower their voices, because they are disturbing the other patients.

G – Go and find a senior doctor, who will be able to tell the family to quieten down.

H – Tell the family that if they don't lower their voices, you may have to ask them to leave the ward.

| 1 | 2 | 3 |
|---|---|---|
|   |   |   |

> **Q5.** You've been working in the emergency care unit for a few weeks now, as an FY1. Although things started well, in the last few weeks you feel as if you are being given less and less work to do. It does not feel as if the senior doctors in the ward trust in your ability to perform basic tasks, and you now find yourself performing more admin work than actual clinical work. Although you have raised this concern with a senior doctor, he was quite dismissive.

**Take a look at the below answers, and then choose the three best options.**

A – Go and find your clinical supervisor, to discuss what the next course of action should be.

B – Consider making a formal complaint against the hospital.

C – See if you can get in touch with the Foundation Programme Director. He should be able to advise you on the next steps.

D – Speak to your educational supervisor about how you can persuade the doctors to trust you.

E – Do nothing.

F – Ask the senior doctors in the ward to attend a meeting with you, where you can voice your concerns.

G – Speak to a different senior doctor about the issue.

H – See if you can be transferred to an alternative unit.

| 1 | 2 | 3 |
|---|---|---|
|   |   |   |

**Q6.** You are working in the A&E department on a busy Thursday night. A woman comes into the department, complaining that she has shut her finger in the door, and needs you to release the pressure. Her finger is a very nasty shade of purple. The woman then informs you that she has failed to pay the hospital car parking fare, because she has only just arrived in the UK, and could not understand the instructions on the machine. She asks if you can help her to avoid getting a car parking fine.

**Take a look at the below answers, and then choose the three best options.**

A – Tell the woman that you will be unable to treat her until she pays the car parking fare.

B – Tell the woman that once you have treated her, she needs to go and speak to the hospital reception desk, who will help her to pay the car parking fare.

C – Tell the woman that once you have treated her, you will come out with her and show her how the machine operates.

D – Ask the woman to go and speak to the reception desk, before returning here for treatment.

E – Tell the woman that you'll treat her first, before finding someone who can resolve the car parking fare issue for her.

F – Tell the woman that although you are happy to treat her, you cannot help her with the car parking issue.

G – Call the police.

H – Tell the woman that there's no need to worry about the fare. Following treatment, ask someone to show her where she can resolve this issue.

| 1 | 2 | 3 |
|---|---|---|
|   |   |   |

**Q7.** One of your patients is on the liver transplant list. During the evening shift, his son David approaches you:

**David:** *'Hi Doctor. Is there any news on my Dad? Is he likely to get a new liver soon?'*

Based on earlier discussions with your consultant, you are aware that David's father is not particularly high on the list, so it will be a while before he receives a new liver. He does not require an emergency transplant.

**Take a look at the below answers, and then choose the three best options.**

A – Inform David that it's unlikely his father will receive a liver anytime soon.

B – Reassure David that his father will be getting a liver very soon.

C – Tell David that because his father has only just been put on the list, and is not listed as an emergency transplant, there will be a lengthy wait.

D – Ask David to come with you to see the head of surgery, who can explain things better.

E – Tell David that you will inform him as soon as a new liver becomes available.

F – Reassure David that his father isn't an emergency case, and therefore he shouldn't worry.

G – Ask David whether he'd like to go out for a drink sometime.

H – Tell David that you will keep him informed on the status of the liver transplant list, but that there could be a long wait.

| 1 | 2 | 3 |
|---|---|---|
|   |   |   |

**Q8.** One of your patients approaches you in the middle of the night. She seems extremely frightened. She claims to have seen a hooded man walking around the ward whilst you were out of the room, and believes that he was carrying a long, sharp object.

The patient in question has a history of hallucinations, and is being treated for severe psychosis. This is not the first time that the patient has claimed to have seen something like this, and it has always been a fabrication.

**Take a look at the below answers, and then choose the three best options.**

A – Call the nurses over to sedate the patient, and get her back into bed.

B – Sit the patient down on her bed, and inform her that lying is wrong.

C – Tell the patient that this is a serious issue. Sit her down and ask her a few more questions about what she saw.

D – Immediately contact hospital security, asking them to review the CCTV of the ward, as a matter of urgent priority.

E – Ask the other patients if they have spotted anything.

F – Ask the nurses whether they have spotted anything.

G – Inform the patient that the ward is the safest place possible for her. Assure her that it's completely secure here.

H – Contact the other wards in the hospital, to see if they have any patients missing.

| 1 | 2 | 3 |
|---|---|---|
|   |   |   |

**Q9.** You are an FY1, working in the paediatric ward. You have just started your morning shift, when an angry woman approaches you. You recognise her as the mother of one of your patients, Joseph. Joseph is a young boy, who is recovering from a bicycle accident.

**Joseph's mother:** *'Oi, I want a word with you! What the hell have you done to my son?'*

**You:** *'Hi, Mrs Mullins. I'm very sorry but I'm not sure what you are referring to. Please could you explain?'*

**Joseph's mother:** *'Last night you, his doctor, showed him how to watch a horror movie on his laptop. The movie was rated 18! We've come in today and he's scared witless. I want to make a formal complaint about the hospital.'*

You were not working last night. The doctor looking after Joseph was a junior doctor, named Paul.

**Take a look at the below answers, and then choose the three best options.**

A – Apologise sincerely to Joseph's mother. Inform her that you were not working last night, but that you will launch a full investigation into this situation and how it occurred.

B – Ask Joseph's mother to come with you to see your educational supervisor, who can deal with this issue.

C – Apologise to Joseph's mother. Inform her of how she can go about making a formal complaint.

D – Tell Joseph's mother that you weren't working last night.

E – Ask Joseph's mother the name of the horror movie that her son watched.

F – Go and find Paul. Encourage him to apologise to Joseph and his mother.

G – Apologise sincerely to Joseph's mother. Ask her to come with you to see a senior member of staff, who can deal with this situation appropriately.

H – Tell Joseph's mother that the doctor responsible for this is named Paul. Point out where she can find him.

| 1 | 2 | 3 |
|---|---|---|
|   |   |   |

> **Q10.** You have been working on surgical rotation for a while now. Today you are discussing a patient named Mrs Wilkins, with your consultant surgeon. Mrs Wilkins is suffering from severe abdominal pain, and the consultant also suspects that she is suffering from an iron deficiency. Following your discussion, the consultant asks you to send Mrs Wilkins downstairs, so that she can get an MRI scan. You are confused as to why he has ordered this test.

**Take a look at the below answers, and then choose the three best options.**

A – Get the test done, and deliver the results to the consultant.

B – Tell the consultant that you don't think this is the appropriate thing to do. Call him an idiot.

C – Ask the consultant to clarify why he has ordered an MRI scan. Ask him whether he has been drinking.

D – Get the MRI scan done. Once you get the results, ask the consultant to clarify why he ordered this test.

E – Ask the consultant to explain the rationale behind ordering an MRI scan.

F – Tell the consultant that you think there are better options than an MRI scan. Explain to him why you think this.

G – Refuse to order an MRI scan.

H – Ask another doctor about why Mrs Wilkins needs an MRI scan.

| 1 | 2 | 3 |
|---|---|---|
|   |   |   |

> **Q11.** You have just started your morning shift, when one of your colleagues approaches you. He looks extremely tired, and there are large bags under his eyes. Your colleague informs you that he was up all night playing video games, so he has only had one hour of sleep. He also claims that he spent significant amounts of money online gambling, and now can't afford to pay his bills this week.

**Take a look at the below answers, and then choose the three best options.**

A – Inform your colleague that he has acted extremely unprofessionally. Ask him whether he considers himself to be suffering from video game addiction.

B – Tell your colleague that the best person to speak to here would be his clinical supervisor.

C – Advise your colleague that he cannot treat patients after one hour of sleep. Urge him to speak to a senior doctor and go home.

D – Tell your colleague that you will loan him the money to help him pay the bills for this week.

E – Ask your colleague whether he has had any big wins.

F – Tell your colleague that he must speak to a senior doctor about this issue.

G – Tell your colleague that his financial problems are none of your concern.

H – Inform your colleague that he needs to put patient safety as his number one priority.

| 1 | 2 | 3 |
|---|---|---|
|   |   |   |

---

**Q12.** When you arrive for your shift on Wednesday, one of the nurses approaches you. She informs you that a patient's family have issued a complaint against you. They are saying that the information you supplied them with yesterday, about their relative, was highly confusing. The family feel that you deliberately misled them. They are currently on the top floor of the hospital, in their relative's private room.

**Take a look at the below answers, and then choose the three best options.**

A – Pass on a message from the nurse to the family, informing them that as a result of their complaint, their relative will no longer be treated by this hospital.

B – Immediately go and see the family. Apologise to them for any confusion yesterday, and assure them that you had only the best intentions for their relative.

C – Go upstairs and meet with the family. Tell them that if they are willing to withdraw their complaint, you will be more open and honest with them about their relative's medical information.

D – Meet with the family upstairs. Tell them that you did not mean to confuse them, and are happy to answer any questions that they might have about their relative's medical information.

E – Meet with the family. Ask them what it was that they were confused about yesterday.

F – Speak to the patient once his family has left. Ask him why they issued a complaint.

G – Ask the patient whether he feels unhappy with the treatment that he has received.

H – Meet with the family upstairs. Inform them that they are being quite ungrateful, given the hard work you've put into caring for their relative. Ask them to leave the hospital immediately.

| 1 | 2 | 3 |
|---|---|---|
|   |   |   |

**Q13.** You are an FY1 working in the spinal care unit. Over the past few weeks, a woman named Mrs Long has been in the ward, receiving treatment. Mrs Long is not your patient, and was being treated by one of the senior doctors. Unfortunately, today that doctor is off sick, and therefore you have been asked to include Mrs Long in your list. When you arrive at Mrs Long's bed, her family are visiting. This is the first time that they've come to see her. After introducing themselves, the family asks you to give a full breakdown of Mrs Long's condition and explain how the hospital are planning to deal with it, step-by-step, from this point onwards. Since you are a new doctor, you are very unfamiliar with Mrs Long's condition. When you inform the family that it would better for them to speak to a senior doctor about this, they become irate. Mrs Long's son begins to shout at you:

*'Wow, you don't even know anything about my mum's condition. You call yourself a doctor? You're a disgrace. YOU'RE A DISGRACE!'*

**Take a look at the below answers, and then choose the three best options.**

A – Tell Mrs Long's son that you will not accept being spoken to in this manner.

B – Tell the family that from now on, if they wish to contact you, they'll have to do so through the hospital legal department.

C – Tell the family that you do not appreciate being spoken to in this manner, and that a senior doctor would be able to provide them with a much better range of information.

D – Explain to the family that you do not appreciate being spoken to in such a manner. Tell them that you will find a senior doctor to deal with their query.

E – Apologise to the family. Admit that you are still new to the job and learning as you go.

F – Assure the family that although you are a capable doctor, you have only just been given this case, and therefore a senior doctor would be better placed to deal with their query.

G – Call security and have them escort Mrs Long's son from the building.

H – Walk away from the situation. Someone else can deal with it.

| 1 | 2 | 3 |
|---|---|---|
|   |   |   |

**Q14.** You are sitting in the canteen, when a disagreement breaks out between two members of staff. One of the people involved is called Nathan, and he seems very angry:

**Nathan:** *'That's mine, give it back!'*

**Hector:** *'No it's not, I'm telling you I only just bought this muffin. You're just jealous because it was the last one.'*

**Nathan:** *'I've had enough of you. This is the last straw.'*

Nathan stands up and grabs Hector by his shirt collar. You immediately stand up to intervene. In response, Nathan pushes you away, and then spits in your face.

**Take a look at the below answers, and then choose the three best options.**

A – Punch Nathan in the face.

B – Tell Nathan that he has committed a criminal offence. Ask Hector to come with you, so that you can report this to a senior manager.

C – Tell Nathan that such behaviour is totally unacceptable.

D – Tell Nathan that you are going to report this behaviour to someone senior.

E – Apologise to Nathan. You should never have got involved in the first place.

F – Quietly explain to Nathan that what he has just done is out of line. Ask him to apologise.

G – Ask Hector if he would be prepared to testify about this incident in court.

H – Leave the canteen immediately. Discuss with your educational supervisor about how you should react, and whether it's worth pursuing legal action.

| 1 | 2 | 3 |
|---|---|---|
|   |   |   |

**Q15.** One of your patients calls you over. He complains that the ward consultant stinks of alcohol, and is slurring his words. He feels that the consultant presents a serious threat to patient safety if he is allowed to continue working on the ward today.

Upon speaking to the consultant, you are unable to verify this information. You do not think that he smells of alcohol, and he seems to be completely competent in his thoughts and speech.

**Take a look at the below answers, and then choose the three best options.**

A – Tell the consultant about what the patient said. Ask him to have a chat with the patient, to alleviate his concerns.

B – Ask the consultant to take a blood test, to determine whether he is practising whilst under the influence of alcohol.

C – Tell the consultant that some of the patients have complained about the way he smells.

D – Inform the consultant that he needs to speak to the patient in question, as a matter of urgency.

E – Go back to the patient and inform him that he was mistaken about the consultant.

F – Speak to another doctor and ask them to sniff the consultant, to see if they can notice anything peculiar.

G – Take the consultant into a quiet room and ask him whether he has been working whilst under the influence of alcohol.

H – Go to the head physician and demand that the consultant is relieved of his duties.

| 1 | 2 | 3 |
|---|---|---|
|   |   |   |

**Q16.** You are working on the paediatric ward. A father has brought his young daughter into the ward. The girl, Emma, is 10 years old and is suffering from intense stomach pains. She is extremely distressed. Whenever you try to examine Emma she reacts angrily, kicks you, and bites you:

**Emma:** *'It hurts so much! Don't touch me. Go away, go away!'*

**Emma's father:** *'Please, Emma. Let the doctor take a look!'*

**Emma:** *'No!'*

**Take a look at the below answers, and then choose the three best options.**

A – Tell Emma's father that if his daughter does not calm down, you will be unable to treat her.

B – Tell Emma that if she can try to calm down and let you examine her, you can help make her stomach pain go away.

C – Ask Emma why she doesn't want to let you treat her.

D – Ask Emma's father to assist, whilst you restrain his daughter.

E – Order one of the nurses to fetch a straightjacket.

F – Tell Emma to stop being a little brat.

G – Ask one of the nurses to help you examine Emma.

H – Ask Emma's father to assist you with examining his daughter.

| 1 | 2 | 3 |
|---|---|---|
|   |   |   |

**Q17.** You are on your lunch break, with another member of staff – named Jonathon. Jonathon has only just taken his break, whereas you have only half an hour left. Whilst the two of you are eating, a nurse rushes into the canteen. She seems extremely distressed. She runs up to the table and addresses Jonathon:

'Dr Ford, we really need you to come quick. Mr Wiggins, your patient, is in a terrible state. His heart rate has rocketed, he looks extremely pale and he says that he is feeling sick to his stomach.'

In response, Jonathon tells her to find someone else to deal with it, because he is eating.

**Take a look at the below answers, and then choose the three best options.**

A – Agree with Jonathon. He's on his lunchbreak, it wouldn't be fair to disturb him.

B – Tell Jonathon that his patient should come before his lunch.

C – Advise Jonathon that although he is not obligated to go and deal with the patient, he probably should do it, just to be safe.

D – Tell Jonathon that if he doesn't deal with the patient, he could lose his job.

E – Tell Jonathon that if he leaves the canteen now, you'll eat the rest of his sandwich.

F – Tell the nurse that there are plenty of other doctors who can deal with this matter.

G – Explain to Jonathon that he will need to put his break on hold whilst he deals with the patient.

H – Ask Jonathon to consider whether his sandwich is more important than the patient's life.

| 1 | 2 | 3 |
|---|---|---|
|   |   |   |

**Q18.** You are just starting your shift in the emergency care unit. As you approach one of your patients, you notice that he is reading a hospital labelled form. Upon enquiring about the form, you realise that it's a patient report – but not for this patient. The form is for another patient, named Mr Andrews, and contains all of the details of his treatment. It seems that the last doctor to treat your patient accidentally left the form by the bed. You are aware that the doctor is working on another ward right now.

**Take a look at the below answers, and then choose the three best options.**

A – Take the form away from the patient, and put it back where it's meant to be.

B – Go and find Mr Andrews. Inform him that there has been a serious incident.

C – Take the form away from the patient, and find the previous doctor. Encourage him to tell senior management about this issue.

D – Warn your patient that if he tells anyone about this, there will be serious consequences.

E – Take the form away, and bring this incident to the attention of a senior member of staff.

F – Ask the patient how much of the form he has read.

G – Take the form away from the patient. Ask him not to speak about this to anyone.

H – Put the form back in its place. Find the previous doctor and inform him that he has made a serious error.

| 1 | 2 | 3 |
|---|---|---|
|   |   |   |

**Q19.** An elderly patient has been admitted into your care. The man is named Winston. Winston suffers from Asperger's Syndrome. He has informed the nursing staff that he does not like to be touched and finds physical contact extremely uncomfortable, and has specifically requested that the staff avoid psychically intrusive diagnostic techniques.

Your consultant feels that the only way to diagnose Winston's problems is to conduct a series of procedures which would involve touching the patient, in a way that the patient is likely to find intrusive and uncomfortable.

**Take a look at the below answers, and then choose the three best options.**

A – Speak to the consultant about whether there are any other ways of diagnosing, that won't risk significantly distressing the patient.

B – Sit down with Winston and explain to him that in order for the staff to diagnose him properly, there is a chance you might have to conduct some procedures that he'll find distressing.

C – Tell the consultant to go ahead with the procedures, regardless of how Winston feels. In this case, the patient's medical wellbeing must come first and foremost.

D – Try to persuade Winston that the necessary procedures are for his own good, regardless of if he doesn't like it.

E – Explain to the consultant that because Winston has specifically requested you avoid such procedures, you will need to find alternative solutions.

F – Speak to Winston and accuse him of wasting the hospital staff's time.

G – Sit down with the patient and explain to him what procedures would need to be done, in order to diagnose him. Tell him that he has no obligation to consent to these if he doesn't wish to.

H – Tell Winston that there is no way for the hospital to treat him, if he doesn't consent to the intrusive diagnostic procedures.

| 1 | 2 | 3 |
|---|---|---|
|   |   |   |

**Q20.** You are an FY1, who has just joined a new hospital. Last night, a complaint was made by a patient, in regards to another junior doctor who has been working at the hospital for much longer than you. The patient believes that the junior doctor made an error. The consultant approaches you this morning, and informs you that he would like you to go and speak to the patient about the issue, to try and convince them that the hospital was not responsible for the error.

When you arrive at the patient's bed, they inform you that they are thinking of making a legal complaint.

**Take a look at the below answers, and then choose the three best options.**

A – Go back to the consultant and inform him of what the patient has said. Ask him not to involve you in situations like this in future.

B – Confess to the patient that you have no idea why the consultant asked you to speak to them, as you've really only just arrived here.

C – Tell the patient that if they want to make a legal complaint, they should go right ahead, because the hospital has done nothing wrong.

D – Tell the consultant that the patient has threatened legal action. Inform him that although you are always willing to help, you don't believe you should have been put in this situation.

E – Go and find your educational supervisor. Express your concerns over being put in this position.

F – Beg the patient to reconsider.

G – Tell the consultant that the patient has threatened legal action. Inform him that you felt it was highly unfair to put you, as an FY1, into this situation.

H – Tell the consultant that if he ever asks you to do something like this again, the patient won't be the only one taking legal action…

| 1 | 2 | 3 |
|---|---|---|
|   |   |   |

**Q21.** You are working in the intensive care unit. One of the patients in a ward is a professional racing car driver, who is very famous. The man is considered an junior doctorational celebrity. Following a racing accident, he is comatose. On Monday, as you are finishing your shift, you notice another FY1 coming into the ward followed by a group of people. The FY1 is named James:

**James:** 'Alright guys, there he is, there's the WORLD-FAMOUS racing driver Gary McFadden. Make sure to tag me in any photos!'

Immediately, the group of people pull out their cameras and start taking pictures of the patient.

**Take a look at the below answers, and then choose the three best options.**

A – Pull out your camera and join in. After all, he is world-famous!

B – Immediately approach the group of people and inform them that they need to leave the hospital. Demand that they stop taking photos.

C – Quietly take James to one side and inform him that his behaviour is extremely unprofessional.

D – Demand that the group of people leave the hospital. Tell James that you are taking this straight to senior management.

E – Call hospital security and ask them to escort James and his friends out of the hospital. Make sure that their cameras are confiscated.

F – Immediately inform a senior manager about the situation.

G – Go and see your educational supervisor about this issue.

H – Ask your colleagues about whether this is acceptable behaviour.

| 1 | 2 | 3 |
|---|---|---|
|   |   |   |

**Q22.** You are an FY1. Over the past few weeks, you have noticed that one of the consultants is using extremely bad language when speaking to female members of staff. There seems to be a recurring pattern to this behaviour – whenever a patient is deteriorating, or things are going wrong, the consultant gets very angry and abusive. Although none of the nurses have complained, and nobody has spoken to him about it, a few of your colleagues have commented that they can't believe the consultant is getting away with such poor behaviour.

**Take a look at the below answers, and then choose the three best options.**

A – Go and see the consultant yourself. Tell him that he has been bullying female members of staff for too long now, and needs to stop.

B – Speak to the female members of staff, to see if they want you to step in on their behalf.

C – Walk up to the consultant's door, and loudly announce that his reign of terror is over. You will be the hero of the hospital!

D – Speak to a senior member of staff, explaining the situation. Inform them that you feel something should be done.

E – Make an appointment with the consultant to voice your concerns.

F – Ask a senior member of staff to go and speak to the consultant directly.

G – Inform your colleagues that you would like to speak to the consultant about his behaviour, but you don't feel senior enough to do so.

H – Do nothing. It's not your problem.

| 1 | 2 | 3 |
|---|---|---|
|   |   |   |

**Q23.** You are an FY1 working in the surgical ward. You and your colleague, who is a senior doctor, are discussing a patient. You are very new to the hospital. Here is the conversation that you have:

**Senior doctor:** *'What are your thoughts on this patient?'*

**You:** *'Well…in this case I would suggest that our first action is to run a blood test.'*

**Senior doctor:** *'Good try, but that's wrong. The patient should have a CT scan first, before we run any blood tests.'*

Later on, during surgical ward rounds, the consultant asks you why you have failed to run a blood test on the patient. He seems quite angry.

**Take a look at the below answers, and then choose the three best options.**

A – Inform the consultant that you wanted to run a blood test initially, but the senior doctor said this shouldn't be done.

B – Immediately blame the senior doctor. Inform the consultant that it's him he should be angry at, and not you.

C – Tell the consultant that in this case, you deferred to the opinion of the senior doctor. Inform him that you wanted to run a blood test, and said a CT scan would be a terrible idea.

D – Ask the consultant to meet with you after rounds, to discuss the issue in private.

E – Go and find the senior doctor. Make him admit his mistake to the consultant.

F – Apologise wholeheartedly for the error. Beg the consultant not to fire you.

G – Tell the consultant that your initial idea was to run a blood test, but then you changed your mind.

H – Ask the consultant to speak to the senior doctor about this, as it was his idea not to run a blood test.

| 1 | 2 | 3 |
|---|---|---|
|   |   |   |

**Q24.** You are scheduled to meet with your educational supervisor, for your two-weekly progress meeting. His name is Haroon. When the time arrives, you knock on his door. After a short pause, Haroon opens the door and informs you that unfortunately he's just too busy to see you today, but asks if you would be able to reschedule for tomorrow. Through the door, you can see his computer screen. On Haroon's screen is a popular online gambling game, where virtual crabs race against each other.

**Take a look at the below answers, and then choose the three best options.**

A – Inform Haroon that you can see his screen through the door, and he doesn't look too busy to be meeting with you.

B – Tell Haroon that crab racing is a serious vice. Recommend that he seeks counselling for this addiction.

C – Inform Haroon that you are happy to meet with him tomorrow, but ask him to explain the reasons why he cannot make the meeting today.

D – Agree to meet with Haroon tomorrow. Wish him luck in his races.

E – Ask a senior doctor to conduct your two-weekly progress meeting instead.

F – Go straight to the Foundation Programme Director. This is totally unacceptable.

G – Question Haroon over why the meeting can't take place now.

H – Ask Haroon whether the games on his screen are the reason for him being busy, or whether he's doing something else in the background.

| 1 | 2 | 3 |
|---|---|---|
|   |   |   |

**Q25.** The senior doctors at your hospital are really unhappy with the general performance of junior doctors. They have approached the Foundation Programme Director, and asked whether it would be possible for the FY1s to take an exam, to show who really needs to step up and work harder. The exam will take place in one month's time, and will require a large amount of study to prepare for.

When the time comes, all of the FY1s sit down to take the exam. In the middle of your exam, one of your colleagues gets up, leaving his exam paper on the desk and comes and sits down next to you:

**Steve:** *'Alright, mate?'*

**You:** *'We're in the middle of an exam, what are you doing?!'*

**Steve:** *'I know but I'm bored.'*

**Take a look at the below answers, and then choose the three best options.**

A – Immediately raise your hand and gain the attention of the exam invigilator.

B – Demand that Steve leaves you alone, and gets back to his exam.

C – Tell Steve that you are bored too.

D – Ask Steve whether he has the answer to question 6.

E – Don't engage Steve in conversation. Ignore him and continue working on your paper.

F – Walk to the front of the room and inform the invigilator that Steve is behaving unacceptably.

G – The next time the invigilator comes around, ask him to remove Steve from the room.

H – Loudly ask Steve to leave you alone.

| 1 | 2 | 3 |
|---|---|---|
|   |   |   |

---

**Q26.** You could not get the attention of the invigilator, who is dealing with another colleague – named Wendy, who is disabled. Wendy is very distressed and the invigilator is trying to calm her down. As a result, you choose option E. After another minute of trying to talk to you, and being ignored, Steve gets frustrated. He stands up, takes your exam paper away from you, and tears it in two. He then returns to his seat, acting like nothing has happened.

Nobody else in the room seems to have noticed what has happened. The invigilator is still dealing with Wendy.

**Take a look at the below answers, and then choose the three best options.**

A – Go over to Steve and demand that he explains his poor behaviour.

B – Interrupt the invigilator, and inform him of what has just happened.

C – Rip Steve's exam paper up.

D – Ask Steve to come with you to see a senior doctor, to explain what just happened.

E – Wait for the invigilator to finish dealing with Wendy, before approaching them and explaining the situation.

F – Ask another colleague to act as a witness for what just happened.

G – Try and complete the exam on the torn strips of paper.

H – Loudly express your dismay at what Steve has just done.

| 1 | 2 | 3 |
|---|---|---|
|   |   |   |

---

**Q27.** You are an FY1 working in the paediatric ward, on a patient named Neil. Neil is 14-years-old. His parents are away on holiday at the moment, although they are contactable by phone. Your consultant has advised you that, in order to diagnose Neil, a physical examination will need to be performed. Although Neil has consented to this examination, he reacts poorly upon your attempt, and insults you – using a homophobic remark. Upon you expressing your concern over the remark, Neil defiantly repeats it.

None of your other colleagues have witnessed this incident.

**Take a look at the below answers, and then choose the three best options.**

A – Tell Neil that his behaviour is utterly unacceptable.

B – Tell Neil that he will need to explain his comments to a senior member of staff.

C – Inform Neil that such remarks are not appreciated, and that he should have a higher level of tolerance.

D – Continue treating Neil without any further comment. Call his parents following the procedure, to express your concerns.

E – Try and explain to Neil why his comments are wrong. Following the procedure, call his parents, to express your concerns.

F – Ask Neil how he would like it if you insulted him.

G – Explain to Neil that if he does not want you to perform the procedure, then you can fetch a senior member of staff instead.

H – Ask Neil to explain to you what he means by those comments, before elaborating to him on why they are wrong.

| 1 | 2 | 3 |
|---|---|---|
|   |   |   |

**Q28.** You are dealing with a very young patient, named Bethany. Bethany is 11-years-old. Although Bethany is ready to be discharged, she does not seem happy. Upon consulting with Bethany, she informs you that she wants to end her life, and that she doesn't feel happy to return home. She claims that her parents' constant fighting is making her life miserable.

Bethany's parents do not seem to be aware of how she is feeling, and appear happy to be bringing her home.

**Take a look at the below answers, and then choose the three best options.**

A – Tell Bethany that she can stay at the hospital for as long as she wants.

B – Sit down with Bethany's parents and tell them of what she has said. Ask them to try and get along for the benefit of their daughter.

C – Keep Bethany at the hospital until her parents can resolve their differences.

D – Ask Bethany's parents if they would be willing to take part in joint-counselling sessions with their daughter.

E – Sit down with Bethany's parents and inform them that Bethany will need to stay at the hospital whilst this issue is addressed.

F – Tell Bethany to keep her personal problems to herself.

G – Ask Bethany to speak to her parents about the issue.

H – Tell Bethany that you will look into this issue, and that she can stay at the hospital whilst you do.

| 1 | 2 | 3 |
|---|---|---|
|   |   |   |

**Q29.** One of your colleagues has been struggling with the hospital workload as of late, and his educational supervisor has advised him that he needs to study more if he wants to be successful as a doctor. Upon entering the staff room, you find him reading from an exercise book that he purchased online. The book in question is on the hospital 'ban list' of reading materials, as the hospital believes it contains incorrect information that could harm patients.

**Take a look at the below answers, and then choose the three best options.**

A – Immediately leave the staff room and report your colleague to a member of senior management.

B – Ask your colleague whether he is aware that the book is on the hospital ban list.

C – Ask your colleague to stop reading that book, and come with you to see a senior member of staff.

D – Advise your colleague that the book in question is on the hospital ban list.

E – Ignore it. What's the worst that could happen?

F – Tell your colleague that taking advice from that book could be harmful to patients.

G – Take the book away from your colleague and throw it into the bin.

H – Tell your colleague that he has broken the hospital rules and must now be punished.

| 1 | 2 | 3 |
|---|---|---|
|   |   |   |

**Q30.** You are an FY1 working the night shift. In the middle of your shift, you are bleeped by a nurse, asking you to attend to a patient upstairs in the emergency care unit. The patient in question, who is named Mrs Matthews, informs you that she is in extreme pain. She says that her stomach is in agony. Mrs Matthews was admitted to the hospital for treatment of gangrene in her right leg.

The nurse demands to know what you are going to do about this. You do not have a clue about what the best approach is.

**Take a look at the below answers, and then choose the three best options.**

A – Inform Mrs Matthews that because she came in for an issue with her right leg, you cannot treat her for stomach pains.

B – Immediately find a senior doctor, to ask them for advice on how to proceed.

C – Ask Mrs Matthews whether she would be happy for you to find a senior doctor, who can treat her.

D – Tell the nurse that you are a new doctor, so she should go easier on you.

E – Ask Mrs Matthews whether she would like to be sedated.

F – Ask the nurse to find a senior doctor, whilst you conduct a physical examination of Mrs Matthews.

G – Tell Mrs Matthews, in no uncertain terms, that she needs to deal with the pain.

H – Loudly speculate on whether Mrs Matthews will survive the night.

| 1 | 2 | 3 |
|---|---|---|
|   |   |   |

**Q31.** You have been working at your current hospital for a number of months now. In the past few weeks, you have noticed some strange occurrences coming from the radiology department. It seems as if the only results to come out as scheduled from the department, are for male patients. Even when female patients have had scans, they are being delayed by several days at a time, with male scan results being released at a much quicker rate.

Several of your other colleagues have commented on this too. They believe that Dr Taylor, the head of radiology, is giving priority to male patients over female.

**Take a look at the below answers, and then choose the three best options.**

A – Gather a group together and go down to the radiology department. Demand that Dr Taylor resigns.

B – See if you can get in touch with Dr Taylor, to discuss the situation.

C – Speak to your educational supervisor about the situation.

D – Ask your clinical supervisor whether there is any medical reason that she could think of, for why female results are being delayed.

E – Email Dr Taylor, asking him to explain why there is such an obvious disparity between the release of male and female scan results.

F – Express your concerns to a senior member of staff.

G – Take a look at recent patient records, to establish whether there is a definite disparity. Go down to the radiology lab to discuss the results.

H – Email Dr Taylor, asking him to meet with you outside of the hospital, so that you can discuss the situation.

| 1 | 2 | 3 |
|---|---|---|
|   |   |   |

> **Q32.** Two of your colleagues are getting married in a week's time. However, two days before the wedding, one party sits you down and informs you that she isn't ready to get married. She tells you that she's been having doubts about the wedding for a long time, and doesn't think she can go through with it. She is worried that if she calls off the wedding, it will have a detrimental impact on the professional relationship with her husband.

**Take a look at the below answers, and then choose the three best options.**

A – Sympathise with your colleague. Inform her that she needs to be honest with her partner about her doubts.

B – Tell your colleague that she is selfish, unfit to practice medicine, and doesn't deserve to maintain a good professional relationship with her partner.

C – Ask your colleague why she has approached you with this issue. Tell her that you aren't interested in her personal problems.

D – Tell your colleague that she needs to discuss this issue with her partner. Encourage her to try and maintain a good professional relationship with him.

E – Tell your colleague that you are pleased the wedding's off, because you are interested in her partner.

F – Encourage your colleague to speak to a senior member of staff about this issue.

G – Tell your colleague that this is an issue which needs to be resolved between herself and her partner. Offer her your full support.

H – Immediately go and tell your colleague's partner what she said.

| 1 | 2 | 3 |
|---|---|---|
|   |   |   |

> **Q33.** On Friday, you overhear a conversation between one of your colleagues and his patient:
>
> **Hakim:** *'You see Mr Jacobs over there? He's just been diagnosed with cancer.'*
>
> **Mr Gregg:** *'Oh no, that's terrible. I'm so sorry for him.'*
>
> **Hakim:** *'On top of that, he's also got worms!'*

**Take a look at the below answers, and then choose the three best options.**

A – Immediately approach Hakim and inform him that he is in breach of the doctor patient confidentiality agreement.

B – Ask Hakim that he will need to come with you, to see a senior doctor about this behaviour.

C – Tell Mr Jacobs that Hakim has disclosed his personal information, and must now be held accountable.

D – Ask Mr Jacobs to come with you to the legal department, so that this can be reported.

E – Inform Hakim that his behaviour is totally unacceptable.

F – Tell Mr Jacobs that everyone in the hospital knows about his embarrassing problem.

G – Do nothing. Hakim can say whatever he wants.

H – Inform Mr Gregg that he could now be liable for a lawsuit.

| 1 | 2 | 3 |
|---|---|---|
|   |   |   |

**Q34.** You are just starting your shift for the day. Yesterday was a bad day for you. You are suffering from personal problems at home and your mood has not been as good. Although you have tried to put on a professional front at work, you are aware that you were a little bit snappy with one of your elderly patients – Mrs Strong, and she seemed upset when you left.

**Take a look at the below answers, and then choose the three best options.**

A – Ask the nurses whether there have been any complaints against you. If not, ignore the issue.

B – Ask one of the nurses to apologise to Mrs Strong on your behalf.

C – Seek out Mrs Strong and apologise for being short with her on the previous day.

D – Go and see a senior member of staff. Inform them that you have acted unprofessionally.

E – Seek out Mrs Strong and beg her not to take legal action against you.

F – Speak to Mrs Strong and explain that you were having a bad day yesterday.

G – Inform Mrs Strong that she annoyed you yesterday, and should apologise.

H – Tell Mrs Strong that yesterday was a one off, and assure her it won't happen again.

| 1 | 2 | 3 |
|---|---|---|
|   |   |   |

**Q35.** One of your colleagues approaches you, he is quite distressed. He informs you that he has misplaced the scan results for one of his patients, and is too scared to ask the radiology department for a replacement. He claims that this is the third time in two weeks that he has misplaced patient scans, and the head of radiology has already warned him about his lack of organisation. Your colleague begs you to go and ask the radiology department to provide the results again, on his behalf. Your hospital does not share scan results via a computer system, for security reasons.

**Take a look at the below answers, and then choose the three best options.**

A – Inform your colleague that he needs to take responsibility for his mistake, and ask the department to provide the results again.

B – Tell your colleague that unfortunately he will need to man up and admit his mistake to the head of radiology.

C – Encourage your colleague to make up some positive results to give to the patient. They won't improve physically, but at least they'll be happy.

D – Go to the head of radiology and apologise on behalf of your colleague.

E – Inform your colleague that he has committed a grave error, and could now lose his job.

F – Tell your colleague that he needs to explain why he's lost the scan results to the patient.

G – Suggest to your colleague that he sends an email to the radiology department, apologising for the error.

H – Tell your colleague that he needs to improve his organisational skills if he is to continue working in the medical profession.

| 1 | 2 | 3 |
|---|---|---|
|   |   |   |

**Q36.** Over the past week, there has been a serious investigation into an alleged bullying incident amongst the staff at the hospital. One of your colleagues, Kirsty, claims that two other junior doctors – named Paul and Melissa, have subjected her to bullying, over a period of 2-3 months. You have never got along with Paul and Melissa, who have always been fairly unpleasant to you, but you have never witnessed any bullying behaviour from them towards Kirsty.

Today, the senior doctor in charge of dealing with this incident has called you into his office. He claims that Kirsty said you witnessed the bullying, and has asked you to give a statement.

**Take a look at the below answers, and then choose the three best options.**

A – Inform the senior doctor that Paul and Melissa are well-known bullies at the hospital, and should be reprimanded.

B – Give the doctor a full account of how you saw Paul and Melissa punch and kick Kirsty, whilst in the staffroom.

C – Tell the doctor that you have not seen Paul and Melissa bullying Kirsty, and therefore cannot pass comment.

D – Tell the doctor that Kirsty is lying, and that you haven't seen any bullying take place.

E – Tell the doctor that although you don't get along with Paul and Melissa, you haven't seen negative behaviour from them towards Kirsty.

F – Inform the doctor that although Paul and Melissa are both fairly unpleasant people, you haven't witnessed any bullying.

G – Tell the doctor that Kirsty must be mistaken, because you haven't witnessed any bullying.

H – Tell the doctor that you consider bullying to be extremely serious, and would have reported it immediately if you'd seen it taking place.

| 1 | 2 | 3 |
|---|---|---|
|   |   |   |

**Q37.** One of your patients is shortly due to be discharged. His name is Charles. However, he is extremely angry, as he cannot find his phone. Charles is refusing to leave until this is located, and is causing quite a scene. He claims that he left his phone on his hospital food-tray last night, and when he woke up both the tray and the phone were gone. Charles is becoming more and more irate, and he is threatening physical retribution towards staff members.

Whilst the staff look for the phone, one of the nurses approaches you. Her name is Melinda.

**Melinda:** *'Dr Smith…I think I've made a really big mistake. I assumed Charles has finished with his food last night, so I took the tray and poured the contents into the bin. I think his phone might have been on that tray…'*

**Take a look at the below answers, and then choose the three best options.**

A – Immediately go and tell Charles about what Melinda has done.

B – Tell Melinda that she will need to be honest about this error, but should speak to a senior doctor first about how to approach the patient.

C – Tell Melinda that she could face legal consequences for this.

D – Ask Melinda to come with you to see a senior doctor.

E – Encourage Melinda to speak with Charles about the issue.

F – Tell Melinda not to say anything.

G – Tell Melinda that the best approach in this situation would be to find the nursing sister, and inform her about the mistake.

H – Tell Melinda that she needs to speak to the nursing sister immediately.

| 1 | 2 | 3 |
|---|---|---|
|   |   |   |

**Q38.** Your hospital has a very strict policy on animals within the premises. The policy states that no animals of any kind are allowed within the hospital grounds, with the exception of guide dogs.

You are an FY1. On Saturday night, you are working in the A&E department. During your break, a patient comes into the waiting room. He is blind, and walks with the aid of both a stick and a guide dog. The dog appears well trained and obedient. As soon as the man walks into the waiting room, one of the nurses approaches him and says the following:

**Nurse:** *'We don't allow dogs in here, sir. Get that filthy animal out of this hospital, or you won't be seen.'*

**Take a look at the below answers, and then choose the three best options.**

A – Approach the nurse and inform her that she is correct. Ask the man to leave immediately.

B – Approach the nurse and inform her that guide dogs are permitted within hospital grounds.

C – Tell the nurse that she needs to be more respectful towards the patient, and that guide dogs are allowed in the hospital.

D – Speak to the nurse and inform her that although dogs aren't permitted, she needs to be more polite to patients.

E – Apologise to the patient on the nurse's behalf. Inform him that disciplinary measures will be taken against her.

F – Go and find a senior doctor to inform him about what has just happened.

G – Apologise to the patient on behalf of the hospital. Inform the nurse that she is mistaken, and guide dogs are allowed.

H – Inform the man that he has broken hospital rules by entering the premises with a dog. Call the police.

| 1 | 2 | 3 |
|---|---|---|
|   |   |   |

**Q39.** You are good friends with a man named Matt, who works in the hospital admin department. Matt specialises in dealing with hospital website issues. Your hospital website is currently undergoing a dramatic revamp, and the new site will be unveiled next week. Matt has been a key player in the revamp of the website. On Tuesday, he confesses to you that he's had enough of working at the hospital, and in one final act of revenge, will be sabotaging the launch of the new website. He plans to replace every single page on the website, with a picture of cats. Matt informs you that he's been working on the sabotage for several months now, and has coded misinformation into the HTML of the website.

**Take a look at the below answers, and then choose the three best options.**

A – Inform Matt that he would be acting highly irresponsibly by doing this. Encourage him to think about the greater good.

B – Encourage Matt to sabotage the website. It will be really funny.

C – Go straight to Matt's boss and inform him of the situation. This type of behaviour is unacceptable.

D – Tell Matt that if he doesn't go back on his plans, you will be forced to intervene by telling his boss.

E – Inform Matt that this type of behaviour is reckless and could put the general public at risk.

F – Beg Matt not to go through with his dastardly plan.

G – Ask your fellow medical colleagues what you should do.

H – Tell Matt that if he doesn't want to work at the hospital, he should quit, without putting other people at risk.

| 1 | 2 | 3 |
|---|---|---|
|   |   |   |

**Q40.** Over the past few weeks, many of your colleagues have complained that an individual named Barry McFadden has been harassing them on social media. The individual in question is clearly writing from a fake social media profile, and seems to be spreading lots of lies and petty gossip amongst the hospital FY1 community. Although your colleagues have been encouraged to ignore this person, they are getting more and more wound up by Barry's behaviour, which could accurately be described as 'trolling'. Barry's behaviour continues to escalate, leaving racist and extremist remarks on many of your colleagues' pages.

On Monday, you are sitting in the staff room with your colleague, when he goes out to use the bathroom. You notice that he has left his phone on the table, still logged in to his social media profile. He is signed in as Barry McFadden, the person who has been harassing your colleagues.

**Take a look at the below answers, and then choose the three best options.**

A – Wait until your colleague returns from his break and then confront him about the situation.

B – Take your colleague's phone to a senior member of staff.

C – Go and tell the rest of the hospital FY1s about who Barry McFadden really is.

D – Go and see a senior member of staff. Inform them of what you saw.

E – When your colleague returns, point out that he left his social media profile signed in.

F – Go and speak to your educational supervisor about what you saw.

G – Inform your colleague that you noticed he was signed in to an alternative social media profile. Question him over the identity of Barry McFadden.

H – Tell your colleague that you know he is Barry McFadden. Inform him that you will make a profile too, to join in on the fun.

| 1 | 2 | 3 |
|---|---|---|
|   |   |   |

---

**Q41.** One of your patients is ready for discharge. The man's name is Mr Noble. Just before he leaves the hospital, Mr Noble turns to you and says:

**Mr Noble:** *'Just so you know, I'm going to be leaving a terrible review of this hospital. I can't believe some of the things that go on here. Just last night I went upstairs and NONE of the toilets had been cleaned...in a hospital! It was absolutely disgusting in there, and then I went back in this morning and still nothing had been done. Where the hell are all your cleaning staff?'*

You are aware that the hospital is currently suffering from a severe lack of cleaning staff, and are considering outsourcing as a matter of urgency.

**Take a look at the below answers, and then choose the three best options.**

A – Apologise sincerely to the patient and inform him that the hospital is suffering from a shortage of staff at this time. Inform him that you are doing everything possible to amend this.

B – Tell the patient that if he thought the toilet was so dirty, he should have reported it. Inform him that you can't wait to see the back of him.

C – Tell the patient that the hospital toilets are no concern of yours.

D – Tell the patient that you are very sorry for this situation. Ask him if he would be willing to speak with a senior member of staff to try and resolve this issue.

E – Ask the patient to consider the great standard of care he has received, when writing his review.

F – Ask the patient whether there is anything you can do to improve his opinion of the hospital.

G – Remind the patient that if he writes defamatory comments about the hospital online, he will need to justify these remarks in court.

H – Encourage the patient to contact the local newspaper with his thoughts.

| 1 | 2 | 3 |
|---|---|---|
|   |   |   |

---

**Q42.** You have just started your shift at the hospital for the day. One of your patients is a 30-year-old man, named Kevin. Kevin has previously been treated by a colleague named Dr Square. Dr Square is now on holiday for 2 weeks, and so Kevin is now your patient. Today you are meeting him for the first time. Upon introducing yourself as his new doctor, Kevin reacts quite badly:

*'Who the hell are you? I don't want to be treated by you. The only doctor who can treat ME is Dr Square. He's my doctor and I want to speak to him right now!'*

**Take a look at the below answers, and then choose the three best options.**

A – Inform Kevin that he is being extremely rude, and will not be treated until he's more polite.

B – Tell Kevin that Dr Square is on holiday, and therefore is not available to treat him.

C – Try and assure Kevin that you are more than capable of treating him, and that you are a fully trained and qualified doctor.

D – Tell Kevin that Dr Square is on holiday, so he will need to try and accept the idea of being treated by someone else.

E – Tell Kevin that you will try and convince Dr Square to return from holiday, so that he can come and treat him.

F – Ask Kevin whether he would feel more comfortable being treated by a senior member of staff, than by you.

G – Tell Kevin that if he doesn't want to be treated by you, then he'd better pack his things and leave the hospital.

H – Tell Kevin that you'll return in one hour's time. If he hasn't changed his mind by then, he can leave.

| 1 | 2 | 3 |
|---|---|---|
|   |   |   |

**Q43.** You are treating a patient for a suspected lung condition. The woman in question is having difficulty breathing. After an initial assessment, your consultant informs you that he suspects the woman is suffering from asbestosis. Further tests confirm this. Based on your questioning, it appears that the woman may have developed this after working in an unsafe environment.

Later that evening, a man approaches you in the hospital. He claims to be a friend of the woman, and offers you £5000 to change your diagnosis of her. After further questioning, it emerges that the man is the woman's boss.

**Take a look at the below answers, and then choose the three best options.**

A – Inform the man that you won't accept his money, and that the diagnosis is clear.

B – Inform the patient that her boss has offered you money to change the diagnosis.

C – Inform the patient that her boss has offered you money, and that as a result she no longer has asbestosis.

D – Tell the man that if the woman has contracted asbestosis as a result of her working conditions, his company could be held liable.

E – Tell the man that the woman's working conditions are responsible for her illness, and therefore he needs to have a serious think about how he treats his employees.

F – Tell the man that you won't accept this offer, and that your patient's safety comes first.

Inform him that you will need to take a record of this conversation.

G – Accept the generous offer. The woman will be treated anyway, so everybody wins.

H – Inform the man that you won't accept his offer under any circumstances, and that you will be informing the patient about this occurrence.

| 1 | 2 | 3 |
|---|---|---|
|  |  |  |

**Q44.** You are just about to finish your shift at the hospital, when you notice a man sitting behind the nurse's desk, using the computer. There are no other nurses in the immediate vicinity. You have never seen this man before. He is not wearing any kind of hospital uniform, nor does he have a visitor's badge, and appears to be browsing through patient records.

When you confront the man, he tells you that he is just conducting some standard maintenance work.

**Take a look at the below answers, and then choose the three best options.**

A – Immediately call security to deal with this situation.

B – Go and find one of the nurses, to verify the man's claim.

C – Go home. It's not your problem.

D – Ask the man why he is not wearing a visitor's badge.

E – Tell the man that he needs to step away from the computer immediately.

F – Go and speak to your educational supervisor about the issue.

G – Inform the man that he is in breach of the hospital code of conduct.

H – Tell the man that he needs to leave. Ask a fellow doctor to help you escort him out.

| 1 | 2 | 3 |
|---|---|---|
|  |  |  |

**Q45.** You are in the middle of your morning shift, when you notice that one of your colleagues appears very down and disconsolate. He doesn't seem to be interested in the patients, and when he returns from his break his face is streaked with tears. When you talk to him about the issue, he informs you that he lost big at the horse racing last night, but ran away before he could pay. He is worried that the people who he owes money to could show up at the hospital and take retribution.

**Take a look at the below answers, and then choose the three best options.**

A – Advise your colleague that if those people show up, you will tell them where to find him.

B – Sympathise with your colleague. Advise him to speak with the reception desk about these people.

C – Tell your colleague that he has your full support in this matter, but advise him that he should try to resolve this outside of work.

D – Tell your colleague that he should speak with a senior doctor about taking the rest of the day off, to go and deal with this matter.

E – Advise your colleague to call the police.

F – Ask your colleague not to involve you in a potentially lethal personal situation.

G – Tell your colleague that gambling is a serious problem.

H – Advise your colleague that his personal problems could put patients at risk.

| 1 | 2 | 3 |
|---|---|---|
|   |   |   |

**Q46.** You are discussing one of your patients with the ward consultant. The consultant believes that the patient in question should still be considered a serious risk, and will need to stay in the hospital for a good few weeks until they have sufficiently recovered. Yesterday, you informed the patient that they would likely be able to leave the hospital within the next few days.

**Take a look at the below answers, and then choose the three best options.**

A – Inform the consultant that you've made a big error, that will greatly upset the patient.

B – Go and find the patient, and apologise sincerely for the error. Explain the reasons why she will need to remain at the hospital.

C – Ignore the error. Hopefully the patient will just forget about what you said.

D – Apologise to the patient for your mistake. Inform her that her stay will need to be slightly extended.

E – Tell the patient that you believe the consultant is wrong.

F – Sit down with the patient and inform them that your consultant has made a major error in judgement.

G – Tell the patient that she will need to stay at the hospital for longer than anticipated.

H – Speak with the patient's relatives about the mistake you've made.

| 1 | 2 | 3 |
|---|---|---|
|   |   |   |

**Q47.** One of your patients is a member of a foreign royal family. The man is staying in the intensive care unit. On the evening that the man is admitted to the hospital, your consultant approaches you and informs you that he wants you to give special care to the patient, even if it means ignoring other patients who need your help. The consultant is from the same country as the patient.

**Take a look at the below answers, and then choose the three best options.**

A – Inform the consultant that you won't be giving the man any kind of special treatment.

B – Tell the consultant that whilst you will take the utmost care of the patient, he will be given the same level of treatment as any other patient on your list.

C – Tell the consultant that if he wants you to take special care of the man, he'd better make it worth your while…

D – Ask the consultant to come with you and explain this to another senior doctor.

E – Inform the consultant that all of your patients receive the same level of care, regardless of their position in society.

F – Assure the consultant that this patient will be given priority over all others.

G – Tell the consultant that if he wants the patient to have special treatment, he'd better treat the man himself.

H – Ask the consultant to clarify why he feels that this patient deserves better treatment than anyone else at the hospital.

| 1 | 2 | 3 |
|---|---|---|
|   |   |   |

**Q48.** When you enter the staff room on Wednesday, you find one of your colleagues sitting at the table crying. The colleague in question is new at the hospital, and was recently involved in treating a patient who passed away. She seems to have taken the incident extremely hard. She feels that she was responsible, even though both the consultant and your other colleagues disagree. When you talk to her about the issue, your colleague informs you that she doesn't know if she can continue working as a doctor, because this incident was so hard for her to deal with.

**Take a look at the below answers, and then choose the three best options.**

A – Reassure your colleague that she is a fantastic doctor, and that learning to deal with incidents like this is part of improving.

B – Tell your colleague that she needs to toughen up.

C – Advise your colleague that if she can't deal with incidents such as this, it might be better for her to resign.

D – Tell your colleague that she has your full support moving forward. Encourage her to see if counselling can be arranged.

E – Tell your colleague that there is nothing wrong with being a sensitive person, and that she will get used to dealing with incidents like this.

F – Blame your colleague for the incident. Tell her to resign.

G – Tell your colleague that she has your full support moving forward. Encourage her to consider a change of careers, if this is impacting her so heavily.

H – Tell your colleague to keep her pathetic problems to herself.

| 1 | 2 | 3 |
|---|---|---|
|   |   |   |

**Q49.** You are just about to start your shift at the hospital. As you walk through the main doors, you can't help but overhear one of your colleagues on his mobile phone, having a very animated conversation. The man's name is Gordon:

**Gordon:** *'No, I'm telling you, if Benny doesn't get back to school straight away, then he's in big trouble tonight.'*

*\*Pause\**

**Gordon:** *'Yes, yes I know that. Well let me tell you now, I'm going to punish him for this. Remember what happened last time he skipped school? Black and blue he was. Well it's going to be worse this time, ten times worse. I'll take my belt, and I'll wrap it round my hand, and then…'*

At this point someone interrupts you, so you don't hear the rest of the conversation.

**Take a look at the below answers, and then choose the three best options.**

A – Seek out Gordon as soon as possible. Accuse him of child abuse.

B – Endeavour to speak with Gordon as soon as you possibly can about what you heard.

C – Do nothing. You've probably misunderstood the situation.

D – Go straight to senior management. Tell them that Gordon is beating his son.

E – Call social services immediately.

F – Speak to a senior doctor about what you've heard. Ask them if they think you should report Gordon.

G – Inform Gordon that you are extremely concerned by what you heard, whilst eavesdropping on his phone call.

H – Ask Gordon to fill you in on how the conversation finished.

| 1 | 2 | 3 |
|---|---|---|
|   |   |   |

**Q50.** One of your fellow FY1s is an elderly man named Craig. Craig claims that he worked as a doctor over 40 years ago, but has been out of medicine ever since. You have noticed that Craig is extremely stubborn, and keeps trying to use outdated treatment methods. When you confront him about this, he claims that modern medicine is largely inferior to how it used to be, and refuses to change the way he's dealing with patients. He is also refusing to fill in any patient records, claiming that paperwork is a waste of time and trees.

You are concerned that Craig could be putting patients at risk. The ward consultant does not seem to have noticed that there is a problem.

**Take a look at the below answers, and then choose the three best options.**

A – Take Craig to one side and inform him that you are concerned he's using outdated clinical practices.

B – Inform Craig that if he doesn't make a sustained effort to improve, you'll make sure he's fired.

C – Try and speak to Craig again. If he won't listen to you, tell him that he needs to speak with the ward consultant.

D – Tell Craig that he can't keep getting away with these bad habits.

E – Ask the other FY1s working in the ward about whether they've noticed Craig's unusual methods.

F – Inform the ward consultant about your concerns.

G – Next time Craig makes a mistake, point it out to everyone working at the hospital.

H – From this point forward, document Craig's methods whenever you get the chance, before submitting this information to the ward consultant for review.

| 1 | 2 | 3 |
|---|---|---|
|   |   |   |

**Q51.** You have just arrived home after a hard day at work. In your spare time, you like to watch videos online, via a popular streaming website. Today, you are aware that one of your colleagues will be streaming on the website, as he plays video games. Your colleague is named Monty. In the middle of your colleague's stream, he starts to get quite angry. He starts naming hospital staff, and insulting them. After a tirade of racist and homophobic abuse, he claims that the head of your department is a pig, who doesn't deserve a job in the medical profession. The stream is being broadcast to hundreds of viewers around the world.

Not wanting to listen to any more, you turn the stream off and go to bed. You will be working at the hospital the next day, as will your colleague.

**Take a look at the below answers, and then choose the three best options.**

A – The next day, go straight to a senior doctor and inform them of what was said on the stream.

B – Speak to your colleague the next day. Tell him that you enjoyed watching his stream last night.

C – Speak to your colleague the next day. Ask him whether it was sensible to say what he said.

D – Speak to your colleague the next day. Advise him that it would be wise to tell a senior manager about the situation.

E – Speak to your colleague the next day. Inform him that what he said was unacceptable, and that you will need to report this to someone senior.

F – Speak to your colleague the next day. Advise him that he needs to be careful about how he behaves on the junior doctoret.

G – Show your fellow doctors what your colleague said about them.

H – Share a link to your colleague's stream on your own social media profile.

| 1 | 2 | 3 |
|---|---|---|
|   |   |   |

**Q52.** You are working during a busy Wednesday afternoon shift at the hospital. The hospital is currently understaffed, and your team in particular are working hard to save the life of a patient named Mrs Willmott. Mrs Willmott was admitted to the hospital yesterday, and her condition has deteriorated ever since. The team has still been unable to work out exactly what is wrong with Mrs Willmott, and the ward consultant has been pressing you and your colleagues to try and get to the bottom of the situation. Mrs Willmott's situation is listed as critical. The consultant believes that if she does not receive treatment by this evening, she is likely to die.

Halfway through your shift, your wife rings you. She claims that her car has broken down, and she can't pick up your son from school. She asks you to take a break from work, drive to the school and escort him home. The school is over an hour away from the hospital.

**Take a look at the below answers, and then choose the three best options.**

A – Immediately leave the hospital, and drive to pick up your son from school.

B – Speak to the consultant about whether you can go and pick your son up.

C – Tell your wife that she will need to ring the school herself, to inform them of the situation, as things are critical at the hospital.

D – Ring your son's school, informing them of the situation. Ask if it's possible for him to stay later, as both you and your wife are unavailable.

E – Ask the consultant whether it's possible for you to take a quick 5 minute break, whilst you arrange an alternative route home for your son.

F – Approach the consultant and demand that he allows you to leave immediately.

G – Ask Mrs Willmott whether it's okay for you to go and pick up your son.

H – Tell your wife that she needs to deal with this issue herself, because you are too busy.

| 1 | 2 | 3 |
|---|---|---|
|   |   |   |

---

**Q53.** You are currently treating a well-known politician. The politician in question is not particularly popular at the hospital, as he recently embarked on a long campaign to remove the NHS, and privatise all UK medical care.

The patient is currently sleeping. You have the following discussion with the ward consultant:

**Consultant:** *'I can't believe this guy has the audacity to use the NHS. Here we are, saving his life, and he wants to put us out of a job.'*

**You:** *'I know, it's pretty unbelievable.'*

**Consultant:** *'I've got a good idea. When he wakes up, slip a laxative into his tea. That'll make him uncomfortable!'*

**You:** *'That would be highly unprofessional, of course.'*

**Consultant:** *'No it wouldn't. I'm the consultant and I'm telling you to do it.'*

**Take a look at the below answers, and then choose the three best options.**

A – Inform the consultant that regardless of how you feel about the patient, you have an obligation to treat everyone who comes in with the utmost dignity and respect.

B – Agree to the consultant's demands. Place a laxative in the patient's tea.

C – Tell the consultant that you don't feel comfortable with being asked to do something like this.

D – Tell the consultant that if he wants to place a laxative in the patient's tea, he needs to do it himself.

E – Inform the consultant that doing this will only make the politician more determined to get rid of the NHS.

F – Tell the consultant that by the sounds of it, he deserves to be out of a job.

G – Try and reason with the consultant. Tell him that you should be aiming to improve people's view of the NHS, not harm it.

H – Ask the consultant what he thinks placing a laxative in the patient's tea will accomplish.

| 1 | 2 | 3 |
|---|---|---|
|   |   |   |

**Q54.** One of your patients has come to you to complain. She informs you that her previous doctor, whom you have just conducted handover with, was extremely unprofessional. The patient claims that whilst she was trying to talk to the doctor about her symptoms, he was playing on his phone. She feels that the doctor was uninterested in her condition. You can see from the patient notes that the doctor in question was distracted. Instead of writing down essential info, he has simply doodled in the corner of the sheet.

You will not see the doctor in question until tomorrow.

**Take a look at the below answers, and then choose the three best options.**

A – Tell the patient that because she has already been seen by a doctor, there's very little you can do about the issue now.

B – Tell the patient that if she was so bothered by the doctor's behaviour, she should have raised it to him, rather than whinging about it now.

C – Apologise to the patient. Inform her that the hospital will conduct a thorough review into your colleague's behaviour.

D – Call your colleague on his mobile, demanding that he comes back to the hospital and explains himself to the patient.

E – Wait until the next time you see the doctor, and then confront him over his unprofessional behaviour.

F – Apologise sincerely to the patient. Inform her that you will conduct a proper assessment of her symptoms yourself, right now.

G – Ask the patient why she feels that her condition deserves special treatment.

H – Apologise to the patient for your colleague's behaviour. Inform her that you'll ask him to be nicer next time.

| 1 | 2 | 3 |
|---|---|---|
|   |   |   |

**Q55.** One of your patients has come to you, claiming that the top floor women's toilets are absolutely filthy. She informs you that the floor is covered in water, and there is no wet floor sign.

**Take a look at the below answers, and then choose the three best options.**

A – Inform the patient that if she feels that strongly, she should go and find the domestic services manager.

B – Give the patient instructions on how to contact the domestic services manager.

C – Tell the patient to stop whinging.

D – Apologise to the patient. Inform her that you will contact the domestic services manager immediately.

E – Go and report this to a senior doctor.

F – Tell the patient to fetch a mop, so that she can clean up.

G – Ask one of the nurses to contact the domestic services manager about this incident.

H – Apologise to the patient. Show her where she can find another, cleaner bathroom.

| 1 | 2 | 3 |
|---|---|---|
|   |   |   |

**Q56.** One of your colleagues, named Gabriel, has recently resigned from being a doctor, as he found the stress of it too much. Instead, he has gained a position working in the hospital gift shop. Since he got a job working at the hospital shop, he appears to be much happier. Your colleagues have noted that he also seems to be making much more money. He is coming to work in a new flashy sports car every day, wears expensive Italian suits, and appears to have purchased several gold watches.

Several of your colleagues have speculated that Gabriel is stealing from the hospital gift shop, and that's why he's suddenly got so much more money. They have encouraged you to report Gabriel to hospital management.

**Take a look at the below answers, and then choose the three best options.**

A – Go straight to a senior member of staff and report Gabriel's behaviour.

B – Do nothing.

C – Encourage your colleagues to report Gabriel themselves.

D – Inform your colleagues that they shouldn't jump to silly conclusions.

E – Approach Gabriel and inform him that your colleagues are concerned over his newfound wealth.

F – Confront Gabriel. Demand to know why he's suddenly so rich.

G – Tell Gabriel that people think he's stealing from the hospital gift shop.

H – Ask your colleagues not to involve you in malicious gossip.

| 1 | 2 | 3 |
|---|---|---|
|   |   |   |

**Q57.** One of your patients has approached you to complain about a colleague. Your patient claims that every time this colleague walks through the ward, he whistles. The patient says that she can't stand whistling, and wants him to stop this behaviour immediately. She says that such behaviour should be a criminal offence.

To your knowledge, none of the other patients on the ward in question have complained about this issue.

**Take a look at the below answers, and then choose the three best options.**

A – Have a quiet word with your colleague, informing him about the patient's complaint.

B – Go straight to a senior doctor. Your colleague's behaviour has damaged the reputation of the hospital.

C – Approach your colleague, and inform him that his whistling is bothering the patients.

D – Ask the other patients on the ward about whether the whistling is bothering them.

E – Next time you see your colleague whistling, encourage him to try and keep the noise down.

F – Tell your colleague that although you don't mind his whistling, your patient is bothered by it.

G – Approach your colleague and inform him that if he doesn't stop whistling, you'll have no choice but to report him to senior management.

H – Encourage your colleague to try and find a better outlet for his musical inclinations.

| 1 | 2 | 3 |
|---|---|---|
|   |   |   |

**Q58.** The hospital has just had its yearly charity talent show. During the charity show, one of your colleagues, named Lizzie, got up on the stage and performed a number of classic songs. Unfortunately, Lizzie is not a good singer. In the days following the talent show, you have noticed a few of your colleagues teasing Lizzie over her performance at the show. Although she seems to be taking the teasing in good spirits, you suspect that Lizzie is feeling a little bit upset by this.

**Take a look at the below answers, and then choose the three best options.**

A – Take Lizzie to one side and inform her that you enjoyed her talent show performance, and that she did a great thing for charity.

B – Tell Lizzie that her performance at the talent show was quite frankly embarrassing. Inform her that she is the laughing stock of the hospital.

C – Encourage Lizzie to report the people who are teasing her to senior management.

D – Ask Lizzie whether she is feeling upset by the recent comments of your colleagues.

E – Tell Lizzie that you thought she was very brave to get up on stage and sing in front of everyone, and that this was admirable.

F – Inform a senior doctor that Lizzie is being bullied by your colleagues.

G – Speak to your educational supervisor about Lizzie's performance.

H – Tell Lizzie that it was pretty silly of her to get up on stage, when she can't sing.

| 1 | 2 | 3 |
|---|---|---|
|   |   |   |

**Q59.** Your consultant has asked you to complete a research project for him. At the start of the month, he informs you that the project will be due in 4 weeks' time – so you have the entire month to complete it.

A week later, your consultant approaches you and informs you that he wants the project completed one week earlier than you expected. When you ask him about the original deadline, he informs you that you've made a mistake, and the original deadline was always on this date.

You are confident that in this case, the consultant has made a mistake.

**Take a look at the below answers, and then choose the three best options.**

A – Reiterate to the consultant that he gave you 4 weeks, and not 3, so that's when he will receive the project.

B – Tell the consultant that you will do your very best to get the work in to him on time, but reiterate that the original deadline was for 4 weeks.

C – Apologise to the consultant for getting the deadline mixed up.

D – Ask the consultant to check his notes, because you are confident in the date of the original deadline.

E – Tell the consultant that you are happy to meet the new deadline, and will do your best to provide him with a fantastic project.

F – Inform the consultant that you will get him the work for the new deadline.

G – Tell the consultant that it's categorically impossible for you to get him the work in by the new deadline.

H – Angrily inform the consultant that he can't just change the goalposts whenever he feels like it.

| 1 | 2 | 3 |
|---|---|---|
|   |   |   |

**Q60.** There has been a recent spate of vandalism in the hospital toilets. It seems that somebody is using the anonymity provided by the toilets, to commit acts such as covering the stalls in urine, graffitiing the wall and throwing wet paper at the ceiling. Nobody has been able to work out who is doing this.

On Tuesday, you enter the toilet, and catch a group of boys in the act of vandalising the room. The boys are all patients in the paediatric ward. One of them is holding a can of graffiti. When you approach him, he threatens to give you a swirly if you tell anyone. He seems very angry and aggressive.

**Take a look at the below answers, and then choose the three best options.**

A – Attempt to physically restrain the boys yourself, then call security.

B – Leave the room and call security. They can deal with these individuals.

C – Ask another colleague to help you restrain the boys.

D – Tell the boys to leave the toilet immediately. Get in touch with the staff on the paediatric ward, to report their behaviour.

E – Call the police.

F – Tell the boys that if they leave the toilet immediately, you won't tell anyone.

G – Tell the boys that they are in serious trouble, and that you will be reporting this to the staff on the paediatric ward.

H – Ask the boys to explain why they are vandalising the toilets.

| 1 | 2 | 3 |
|---|---|---|
|   |   |   |

**Q61.** One of your patients is extremely unhappy. She claims that the TV in her private room is unable to show certain channels, which means that she can't tune in to her favourite daytime soap opera. After discussion with the nursing team, it emerges that the hospital are having some satellite problems right now, and a maintenance man is not scheduled to fix this until the end of next week.

**Take a look at the below answers, and then choose the three best options.**

A – Apologise to the patient. Inform her of what the nurses said, but tell her that the hospital has a wide range of other channels that will hopefully interest her.

B – Tell the patient that instead of watching TV, she should consider reading a book.

C – Apologise to the patient and explain that the hospital is having satellite issues. Try and arrange for her to be lent a laptop, on which she can watch her favourite show.

D – Ask the patient whether she would like to make a formal complaint.

E – Tell the patient that there are plenty of other channels she can watch.

F – Ask the patient's relatives to provide the woman with details on what happened in her favourite show.

G – Ask the nursing team whether it's possible for the maintenance man to come earlier.

H – Inform the patient that she can't watch her favourite tv show at this hospital right now. Apologise.

| 1 | 2 | 3 |
|---|---|---|
|   |   |   |

**Q62.** A patient in the maternity ward has come to speak with you. Although she is not one of your patients, she is being treated by a colleague, and you are familiar with her. Her name is Lucy. Lucy informs you that she feels quite uncomfortable when dealing with her doctor/ your colleague. She says that it feels as if your colleague is constantly trying to flirt with her, and maintains eye contact for too long. Lucy maintains that she has absolutely no interest in your colleague, but doesn't know how to tell him to stop. She admits that she isn't sure he knows what he's doing.

You are aware that your colleague is happily married, with two children.

**Take a look at the below answers, and then choose the three best options.**

A – Tell Lucy that you will have a quiet word with your colleague, to ask him what's going on.

B – Inform Lucy that she's probably just imagining things. Dismiss her concerns.

C – Ask Lucy to write down what she has said in the form of a formal letter, so that you can take it to senior management.

D – Ask Lucy if she would be interested in going out to dinner with you, once she's had her baby.

E – Apologise to Lucy for your colleague's behaviour.

F – Confront your colleague. Tell him that he is risking his marriage by engaging in such behaviour.

G – Tell Lucy that your colleague has a reputation for being a creep, and that you'll find her a new doctor.

H – Tell Lucy that you will ensure your colleague apologises sincerely to her, for this behaviour.

| 1 | 2 | 3 |
|---|---|---|
|   |   |   |

**Q63.** One of your colleagues has recently been promoted within the hospital. Several of the other junior doctors are very unhappy about this, and there has been lots of discussion amongst your group of doctors about how unfair this is. The colleague in question is seen by many people to be lazy, incompetent and not particularly bright. You do not have much experience in working with this person, and therefore don't have an opinion.

On Monday, you are all sitting in the break room, when the following conversation takes place:

**Katie:** *'I can't believe Jordan has been promoted, what an absolute joke!'*

**Jacob:** *'I know right, he's not even that great a doctor. I work so hard, but here I am in exactly the same position, and there's Jordan lording it over me now. It's not fair.'*

**Gemma:** *'I think we should say something to senior management about this. Just…you know…go to them and say that we don't think it's fair and that Jordan doesn't deserve that promotion.'*

**Katie:** *'Yeah, let's do it!'*

The three of them turn to you, and ask if you would also be willing to come and meet with senior management, to discuss the situation.

**Take a look at the below answers, and then choose the three best options.**

A – Tell your colleagues that Jordan was promoted for a reason, and that rather than complaining, they should try and improve their own methods of practice – if they want a promotion.

B – Agree to go with your colleagues to see senior management. Hopefully you can impress them and take Jordan's job.

C – Decline to go with them, on the grounds that you have very little experience of working with Jordan.

D – Inform your colleagues that on the few occasions where you've worked with Jordan, he has been extremely professional, and demonstrated excellent clinical skills.

E – Tell your colleagues to stop whinging, and start doing, if they want a promotion.

F – Inform your colleagues that their jealousy of Jordan's promotion is quite frankly pathetic.

G – Tell your colleagues that you are happy to go with them to see senior management, but that you won't have much to add.

H – Inform your colleagues that complaining to management will look extremely unprofessional.

| 1 | 2 | 3 |
|---|---|---|
|   |   |   |

**Q64.** You are working as a surgical FY1. You've been treating a patient named Mr Fenway for a week or so now, and have built up quite a good rapport with him. On Thursday, you have the following conversation with Mr Fenway:

**Mr Fenway:** *'So, what football team do you support, Doctor McCarthy?'*

**You:** *'Ah, I'm a fan of Carthroach FC. Sadly, we're not very good…'*

**Mr Fenway:** *'Excuse me?'*

**You:** *'Carthroach FC, sorry.'*

**Mr Fenway:** *'You what, mate?'*

**You:** *'I don't understand…'*

**Mr Fenway:** *'Shut it. You're scum. Scum. Get the hell away from me.'*

**You:** *'I beg your pard…'*

**Mr Fenway:** *'If you ever come near me again, I'll end you. Seriously, I will kill you.'*

Following this engagement, you feel threatened by Mr Fenway, and no longer feel comfortable treating him.

**Take a look at the below answers, and then choose the three best options.**

A – Go straight to a senior doctor and inform them of what has just happened. Tell them that you no longer feel comfortable treating Mr Fenway.

B – Tell Mr Fenway that you are his doctor, so he needs to try and get along with you.

C – Inform Mr Fenway that his behaviour is totally unacceptable. Demand an apology.

D – Tell Mr Fenway that you will find him a new doctor.

E – Go and consult the hospital legal team about Mr Fenway's behaviour.

F – Apologise to Mr Fenway.

G – Find a senior doctor and tell them that you no longer wish to work with Mr Fenway.

H – Tell Mr Fenway that as a result of his poor behaviour, his surgery will now be delayed.

| 1 | 2 | 3 |
|---|---|---|
|   |   |   |

**Q65.** One of your colleagues has confided in you that he is considering quitting medicine. He tells you that as a junior doctor he simply does not make enough money to sustain his new family, and is considering a new career – as a professional video gamer. He believes that with the significant growth in the industry, he can become far more successful than he would by pursuing a career as a doctor.

**Take a look at the below answers, and then choose the three best options.**

A – Encourage your colleague to pursue a career as a doctor. Tell him although he'll make less money, he can make a real difference to people's lives.

B – Tell your colleague that he should follow his passion, rather than what makes him the most money.

C – Advise your colleague that you will support him no matter what career path he chooses.

D – Tell your colleague that video games are for children.

E – Advise your colleague that the best path for him will be the one which makes him and his family happiest. Tell him that he has your full support, whichever decision he makes.

F – Inform your colleague that he would be better off discussing this with his educational supervisor.

G – Tell your colleague that he should discuss these issues with the Foundation Programme Director.

H – Tell your colleague that you appreciate his sharing with you, but you aren't in a position to give career advice.

| 1 | 2 | 3 |
|---|---|---|
|   |   |   |

**Q66.** In the middle of your shift today, one of the senior doctors approaches you. He seems fairly disgruntled, and informs you that he wants to see you in his office before you go home today. He then walks off. You have no idea what this meeting is about.

**Take a look at the below answers, and then choose the three best options.**

A – Wait until the end of your shift, and then go and see the doctor in his office.

B – Go and see the doctor during your break, to enquire about why he wants to meet with you.

C – Don't go and see the doctor. You don't need someone yelling at you before you go home.

D – Ask the nurses whether they can think of any reason for why the doctor wants to see you.

E – Have a look through your patient records and paperwork, to make sure you are up to date with everything before you see the doctor.

F – Ask one of your colleagues to go and see the doctor instead of you.

G – Chase after the doctor and inform him that you will not be meeting with him under any circumstances.

H – Call the doctor on his office phone during the day, to ask him if he wants you to bring anything to the meeting.

| 1 | 2 | 3 |
|---|---|---|
|   |   |   |

> **Q67.** One of your patients approaches you at the end of the day. He informs you that he does not know where the nearest bathroom is, and that when he asked one of your colleagues where to locate this, your colleague told him to go away. He is extremely unhappy.

**Take a look at the below answers, and then choose the three best options.**

A – Apologise profusely to the man on behalf of the hospital. Show him where the nearest bathroom is.

B – Show the man where the nearest bathroom is. Find your colleague and question him over his behaviour.

C – Tell the man to go away.

D – Show the man where the nearest bathroom is.

E – Tell the man to speak to another member of staff about this.

F – Ask the man to come with you to speak to senior management about this matter.

G – Tell the man that he needs to find the bathroom himself.

H – Ask the man why he needs your help to find the bathroom.

| 1 | 2 | 3 |
|---|---|---|
|   |   |   |

> **Q68.** One of your colleagues is sitting in the staff room. Although you are not on the same table as him, you can hear his conversation with his friends. Your colleague is being very controversial, and voicing opinions which could be seen as politically based, in a loud manner. The hospital has a strict policy of not allowing political discussion, because they believe it could impact staff-to-staff relationships.
>
> None of your other colleagues seem upset by this behaviour.

**Take a look at the below answers, and then choose the three best options.**

A – Inform your colleague that he is being very rude and obnoxious.

B – Ignore your colleague's behaviour and carry on with what you were doing.

C – Ask your fellow doctors about whether this is upsetting them.

D – Inform your colleague that the hospital has rules in place to prevent these kind of discussions.

E – Ask your colleague to keep his views to himself.

F – Tell your colleague that it would be better if he did not discuss political issues whilst at work.

G – Go straight to senior management. Your colleague has broken the rules.

H – Leave the room. You don't have to listen to this.

| 1 | 2 | 3 |
|---|---|---|
|   |   |   |

**Q69.** One of your colleagues – Fred, has recently had his car stolen. Fred is extremely angry about this, and is looking for someone to blame. On Friday, during your lunch break, the following conversation takes place between Fred and another one of your colleagues, named Janine:

**Janine:** *'I'm really sorry to hear about your car, Fred.'*

**Fred:** *'Oh are you now?'*

**Janine:** *'Yes, it's a terrible shame!'*

**Fred:** *'Shut up Janine, you haven't got a clue what you're talking about.'*

You notice that Janine is extremely upset by this.

**Take a look at the below answers, and then choose the three best options.**

A – Take Janine to one side and assure her that you will be reporting Fred to senior management.

B – Agree with Fred. Janine is being very ignorant.

C – Admonish Fred for his rude behaviour. Ask him to apologise to Janine.

D – Take Janine to one side and ask her whether she is feeling okay.

E – Take Fred to one side and inform him that you think he was quite rude towards Janine.

F – Do nothing.

G – Ask Janine whether she has ever had her car stolen.

H – Tell Fred that his rude behaviour is unacceptable, and that he is an unpleasant individual.

| 1 | 2 | 3 |
|---|---|---|
|   |   |   |

**Q70.** You are an FY1, treating a patient in the paediatric ward. The patient in a question is a young girl, of just 5 years old, named Melissa. She has come into the hospital with her mother. Whilst you are discussing Melissa's symptoms, her mother pulls you to one side and tells you that Melissa is being routinely sexually abused by her father – who is also extremely violent with the mother. She begs you for help.

**Take a look at the below answers, and then choose the three best options.**

A – Inform Melissa's mother that the hospital will contact social services on her behalf.

B – Tell Melissa's mother that there is very little you can do for her in this situation.

C – Inform Melissa's mother that you will need to ask both her and Melissa some questions about the situation, before reporting it.

D – Tell Melissa's mother that she needs to call social services as soon as possible.

E – Go and speak to a senior doctor about what the best course of action in this situation is.

F – Tell Melissa's mother that you do not believe her.

G – Call Melissa's father, to inform him about this troubling turn of events.

H – Ask Melissa's mother to step outside, whilst you ask Melissa some serious questions.

| 1 | 2 | 3 |
|---|---|---|
|   |   |   |

**Q71.** You are new to the hospital, having only just started this week, and still finding your feet. The third patient on your list for the day is a woman named Mrs Lechamps. She is a French patient, who speaks fairly poor English. When you arrive at Mrs Lechamps's bed, it becomes apparent that she is in quite significant pain. She is coughing, struggling to breathe, and her eyes appear to be bloodshot. The consultant is currently in another part of the hospital.

**Take a look at the below answers, and then choose the three best options.**

A – Tell Mrs Lechamps to try and explain to you how she's feeling.

B – Immediately ask one of the nurses to assist you in assessing Mrs Lechamps's condition.

C – Ask someone to get in touch with the consultant immediately, so that he can come and assess the situation.

D – Tell the nurses that they need to prepare to perform CPR.

E – Tell Mrs Lechamps that you'll come back and assess her situation later.

F – See if you can contact another doctor on the ward, who has previously dealt with Mrs Lechamps.

G – Ask one of the nurses whether Mrs Lechamps has any relatives visiting the hospital today.

H – Tell Mrs Lechamps that you don't know what's the matter with her.

| 1 | 2 | 3 |
|---|---|---|
|   |   |   |

**Q72.** You have been working as an FY1 in the Orthopaedic unit at your hospital, for a few months now. Recently, refurbishment to the ward has meant that there are fewer and fewer inpatients being admitted to the department, and some patients are being sent to alternative medical practices nearby, in order to be treated. You feel that with there being less patients on the ward, there are now less opportunities for you to learn, and as a result you aren't improving as fast as you'd like.

**Take a look at the below answers, and then choose the three best options.**

A – Speak to your educational supervisor about the possibility of you moving to a different ward.

B – Tell your educational supervisor that you are extremely unhappy with the impact this has had on your learning.

C – Get in touch with the Foundation Programme Director. Inform her that this situation is utterly unacceptable.

D – Arrange to speak with the Foundation Programme Director. Inform her that the orthopaedic unit, in its current state, is not conducive to a good learning environment.

E – Do nothing. The less patients, the less work for you.

F – Ask the registrar on the orthopaedic ward to try and admit more inpatients to the department, so that you can work on them.

G – Resign. This hospital clearly has low standards.

H – Offer to participate in the refurbishment work, to speed things along.

| 1 | 2 | 3 |
|---|---|---|
|   |   |   |

**Q73.** Your hospital has recently conducted a major health and safety overhaul, and now has new rules for all staff to follow. One of the key rules that staff must follow, is that they will need to wash their hands twice in quick succession. They must wash their hands as soon as they enter the hospital, and then they will need to do it again before entering the patient wards.

One of your colleagues, Mandy, is quite stubborn. On Tuesday you both arrive at the hospital at the same time. While you wash your hands, Mandy informs you that she won't be doing this, and will only wash them before she goes into the patient wards.

**Take a look at the below answers, and then choose the three best options.**

A – Try and explain to Mandy that the reason for double hand washing is to ensure the safety of both patients and staff. Urge her to comply with the rules.

B – Ask your registrar to try and explain the importance of this rule to Mandy.

C – Immediately go to senior management, and report Mandy. She is willingly flaunting the rules, and must be punished.

D – Allow Mandy to get away with it today, but make sure that she complies with the rule tomorrow.

E – Ask Mandy whether she wants to be held responsible for the deaths of patients and staff members.

F – Tell Mandy that you fully support her decision to not wash her hands, and will refuse to wash yours tomorrow too, as a show of solidarity.

G – Tell Mandy that if she doesn't wash her hands, you'll need to report her to someone senior.

H – Ask Mandy whether she'd like to go out to dinner with you.

| 1 | 2 | 3 |
|---|---|---|
|   |   |   |

**Q74.** You are a surgical FY1. The consultant has asked you to begin the process of prepping a patient for surgery. The patient in question is a 17 year old boy named Johnny, who requires a knee operation. Johnny is extremely nervous, as he believes that he has an exciting football career ahead of him, and is worried that the operation could derail this.

You are fairly new to the hospital, and quickly realise that you have no idea of the correct way to begin the pre-operational procedures on the patient. The consultant has gone home for the day.

**Take a look at the below answers, and then choose the three best options.**

A – Begin prepping Johnny for surgery. Inform him that you don't have any idea of what you are doing.

B – Seek out the registrar, and ask for his advice on what to do.

C – Tell Johnny that you will find someone else who can help him.

D – Call the consultant on his mobile and demand that he returns to the hospital at once.

E – Ask the available nurses for help on getting the patient ready.

F – Try and perform the surgical prep on your own. You might not get it right but at least you'll get points for trying.

G – Inform Johnny that you are going to find a senior doctor who can help you to perform this procedure.

H – Offer to bring Johnny to see your educational supervisor, who will be able to provide the two of you with advice.

| 1 | 2 | 3 |
|---|---|---|
|   |   |   |

**Q75.** Your hospital is currently conducting major refurbishment work on one of the wards. In order to complete this work, the hospital has hired an external company to complete the refurbishment process. The work has been going on for several weeks, and is scheduled to be finished next month.

One of your colleagues approaches you on Wednesday morning, and informs you that some of the refurbishment workers have been making inappropriate comments towards her, bordering on sexual harassment, and that she feels very uncomfortable whenever she is working in the same ward as them.

**Take a look at the below answers, and then choose the three best options.**

A – Tell your colleague that you will have a word with the refurbishment workers on her behalf. Angrily confront them.

B – Tell your colleague that she needs to stop being so sensitive to basic workplace banter.

C – Encourage your colleague to report the workers' behaviour to the ward sister.

D – Tell your colleague that she shouldn't have to put up with such bad behaviour, and you are happy to accompany her to discuss this issue with a senior member of staff.

E – Tell your colleague that this is unacceptable behaviour, and you will support her if she chooses to report it.

F – Encourage your colleague to have a quiet word with the workers, to try and get them to stop.

G – Encourage your colleague to think about whether she has simply misunderstood the nature of the comments.

H – Tell your colleague that she should be flattered by the attention she's receiving.

| 1 | 2 | 3 |
|---|---|---|
|   |   |   |

**Q76.** You are treating a patient who is a heavy smoker. The patient was treated for lung cancer several years ago. Although he made a full recovery, he has continued to smoke, and now has returned to the hospital. Your consultant informs you that the signs suggest that the cancer has returned, but the team will need to run extra tests to confirm this.

Whilst you are speaking with the patient, he informs you that he doesn't feel the staff are being honest with him, and asks you to give him a clear answer on whether his cancer has returned or not.

**Take a look at the below answers, and then choose the three best options.**

A – Tell the patient that unfortunately his cancer has returned.

B – Inform the patient that there is no way for the hospital to determine whether he has cancer or not.

C – Assure the patient that the staff will always be as honest as possible with him. Tell him that you cannot determine his condition until further tests have been done.

D – Tell the patient that you cannot give him a definitive response yet.

E – Inform the patient that he probably has cancer, but it's not definitive yet.

F – Encourage your patient to submit a formal complaint, if he feels the staff aren't being honest with him.

G – Ask the patient to explain to you why he feels the staff aren't being honest.

H – Tell the patient that the hospital staff will always be as honest as possible with him, and that you'll have a diagnosis for him soon.

| 1 | 2 | 3 |
|---|---|---|
|   |   |   |

**Q77.** One of your colleagues approaches you and informs you that she is in a difficult position. She is fairly new to the hospital. She claims that she had a conversation with the consultant earlier, but didn't agree with his assessment of a patient. She believes that the medicine prescribed by the consultant will harm the patient, but was too scared to argue with him. The consultant has now gone home.

**Take a look at the below answers, and then choose the three best options.**

A – Encourage your colleague to go and discuss her concerns with the registrar.

B – Tell your colleague that it would be foolish to disagree with the consultant.

C – Tell your colleague that she needs to speak with her clinical supervisor about this issue.

D – Inform your colleague that it's important for her to voice her opinions, especially if she believes there has been a mistake.

E – Tell your colleague that she should overrule the consultant's decision, if that's what she thinks is best.

F – Ask your colleague why she is talking to you about this, when she should be changing the patient's medicine.

G – Tell your colleague to stop being disrespectful to senior doctors. Accuse her of being arrogant.

H – Ask your colleague whether she feels that there were any factors specific to today, which could have impacted the consultant's performance.

| 1 | 2 | 3 |
|---|---|---|
|   |   |   |

---

**Q78.** You are working in the paediatric ward as an FY1, dealing with a patient named Adam. Adam is 7 years old, and has come into the hospital with his parents – complaining about constant nausea, and dizziness. Adam is behaving quite badly, and refuses to let you physically examine him. His father, Dale, is enraged at this:

**Dale: 'Adam, sit still now. The doctor needs to examine you.'**

**Adam:** *'No!'*

**Dale:** *'Do it, or else…'*

Adam still refuses to cooperate. In response, Dale raises his hand and strikes Adam across the temple, leaving a superficial wound on his son's head.

**Take a look at the below answers, and then choose the three best options.**

A – Do nothing. Adam was being a brat.

B – Continue treating Adam. Resolve to discuss this issue with a senior doctor later on.

C – Inform Dale that you not believe his behaviour was justified, and that the hospital will need to investigate this incident.

D – Tell Dale that as a result of his behaviour, you will be reporting him to social services.

E – Go and find a senior doctor. Inform them of what just happened, and that you don't feel it was acceptable.

F – Ask Adam whether he will now allow you to physically examine him.

G – Inform Dale that smacking is no way to treat a child.

H – Tell Dale that his behaviour constitutes a criminal offence, and that the hospital will be taking action.

| 1 | 2 | 3 |
|---|---|---|
|   |   |   |

**Q79.** A 52-year-old woman has come into the hospital, and requires a physical examination. The registrar has asked you to conduct this. Whilst conducting the examination, you quickly realise that the woman has a set of deeply offensive tattoos on her body – expressing controversial political views. Outwardly, the woman seems extremely polite.

**Take a look at the below answers, and then choose the three best options.**

A – Tell the woman that you are extremely offended by her tattoos. Refuse to finish the examination.

B – Question the woman over why she would put such ugly tattoos on her body.

C – Tell the registrar that this woman needs to be asked to leave.

D – Conduct the physical examination as planned.

E – Ask the registrar not to give you patients with such political views.

F – Once you've finished the examination, discuss your concerns with the registrar.

G – Inform the woman that while you are happy to finish the examination, her tattoos are quite offensive.

H – Finish the examination. Speak to your clinical supervisor about how you should approach such situations in the future.

| 1 | 2 | 3 |
|---|---|---|
|   |   |   |

**Q80.** The ward consultant has asked you to complete a research project for Friday. Although you have got the majority of the task done, in the past week the hospital has become extremely busy, and you've been working far beyond your expected end time. As a result, you realise that you won't be able to get the projected completed for the deadline, and will need the weekend to finish it in time for Monday.

Your colleague, who has already finished his project, tells you that the consultant is probably going to fire you if you don't get it in on time.

**Take a look at the below answers, and then choose the three best options.**

A – Make an appointment with the consultant. Accuse him of setting you an unreasonable deadline.

B – Do as much as you can by Friday, and then hand in the unfinished project. Half is better than nothing.

C – Email the consultant, informing him that you would rather jump before you are pushed, and resign.

D – Approach the consultant and ask him if you can have a small extension, because you haven't finished the project.

E – Wait until Friday, and then explain to the consultant that because of the extra work you've been doing, you have been unable to complete the project.

F – Explain to the consultant that because of the extra workload, you may need some extra time to finish the project.

G – Make an appointment with the consultant. Explain the situation, and ask him if you can have a small extension.

H – Tell the consultant you won't be able to make the deadline. Demand that he gives you a week-long extension.

| 1 | 2 | 3 |
|---|---|---|
|   |   |   |

**Q81.** One of your patients has come to you to complain. The patient in question is deeply religious. She claims that when she went to see the hospital chaplain, he was very disrespectful towards her religious views, and tried to convert her to Christianity. She claims that the chaplain urged her to confess her sins, and convert, or she would be going to hell. The woman has asked you to show her how she can go about making a formal complaint.

When you confront the chaplain about this issue, he informs you that if you allow the woman to make a formal complaint about him, then you too will be condemned to eternal damnation.

**Take a look at the below answers, and then choose the three best options.**

A – Show the patient how to make a formal complaint. Inform her that you are happy to add your perspective to the report if necessary.

B – Urge the woman to reconsider, before the pair of you are condemned in the eyes of the lord.

C – Tell the chaplain that he has acted extremely unprofessionally, and that you will be showing the woman how to complain about his behaviour.

D – Tell the chaplain that it is his responsibility to be welcoming to people of all religions.

E – Inform the woman that you cannot help her to make a formal complaint.

F – Ask the woman whether she would be willing to speak with your clinical supervisor about this issue.

G – Apologise to the woman on behalf of the hospital. Show her how to go about making a complaint.

H – Tell the chaplain that although you are religious, you don't believe in the idea of hell.

| 1 | 2 | 3 |
|---|---|---|
|   |   |   |

**Q82.** In the previous question, you chose option A. The hospital disciplinary team have launched a full investigation into the chaplain's behaviour, and now want to speak to you about the issue.

You are due to attend a meeting with the disciplinary team on Wednesday. On Tuesday, your consultant approaches you. He requests that you do not attend the meeting. The consultant claims that the chaplain has been extremely helpful for many of his patients in the past, and that his dismissal would have a negative impact on proceedings at the hospital. He finishes by saying:

*'Look, if the chaplain gets sacked…we're going to have a problem. Specifically, you are going to have a problem. I can make life pretty difficult for you at this hospital.'*

**Take a look at the below answers, and then choose the three best options.**

A – Inform the disciplinary team that the chaplain acted very unprofessionally.

B – Tell the disciplinary team that you would like to tell about the chaplain's behaviour, but you are under strict instructions not to.

C – Recommend to the disciplinary team that the chaplain is removed from his post with immediate effect.

D – Inform the disciplinary team that the chaplain was disrespectful, and that you witnessed him threatening the patient with religious retribution.

E – Tell the disciplinary team that your experience with the chaplain was extremely negative, and seems to correlate with what the patient was complaining about.

F – Tell the disciplinary team that the chaplain was acting in the best interests of both yourself and the patient.

G – Ask the disciplinary team whether your observations will have any impact on the chaplain keeping his job.

H – Tell the team that the chaplain has behaved very poorly, and further similar behaviour could upset future patients.

| 1 | 2 | 3 |
|---|---|---|
|   |   |   |

**Q83.** You are a surgical FY1. You are currently living with one of your colleagues, named Gemma. Unfortunately, Gemma has been underperforming at work recently, and the consultant has picked up on this. He has demanded that Gemma study hard in time for Friday's surgical ward rounds, or he will be considering her job position. Over the last week, you have noticed that Gemma has not been studying at all. Instead, during her free time, she's just been playing video games. When you confront her about this, she assures you that it will be fine. Although you've tried to persuade her to study, she fails to do so.

On Friday, during surgical ward rounds, the consultant asks Gemma a question. She does not know the answer.

**Take a look at the below answers, and then choose the three best options.**

A – Tell the consultant that Gemma doesn't know the answer, because she's been playing video games all week.

B – Try and answer the question before Gemma. Hopefully you can impress the consultant.

C – Let Gemma try and answer the question. She needs to deal with this herself.

D – Lie to the consultant, telling him that Gemma has been ill this week, so she hasn't been able to study.

E – Gently try and remind Gemma, giving her a clue to the answer.

F – Give Gemma the chance to answer. If she can't, then inform the consultant that you know the answer.

G – Inform the consultant that Gemma hasn't studied at all this week.

H – Wait until after rounds. Tell Gemma that she needs to get her act together.

| 1 | 2 | 3 |
|---|---|---|
|   |   |   |

---

**Q84.** You are working on the orthopaedic ward, as an FY1. A patient recently left the hospital, but before they left they claimed that they had lost their phone on the ward. Although staff conducted a thorough search, nothing could be found. You remember what the phone looks like, as you saw it when the patient first came in, and it has a very distinctive case.

Today you are treating a younger patient, named Martin. Whilst consulting with Martin and his parents, he pulls out a phone from his pocket. It has the exact same case as the phone which was lost. Martin's parents seem nonplussed as to where he got the phone from, but Martin claims that it is his. He cites the 'finder's keepers' rule.

**Take a look at the below answers, and then choose the three best options.**

A – Explain to Martin that if he doesn't hand over the phone to you, he will be prosecuted for theft.

B – Do nothing. In this case, Martin has found the phone, so it's his now.

C – Explain to Martin's parents that a phone matching this description was lost by a previous patient, and that you need Martin to give it back to you.

D – Tell Martin's parents that you would appreciate taking a look at the phone, to establish who it belongs to.

E – Challenge Martin to give you the name of first person in the mobile's contact list.

F – Contact the ward sister and ask her to have a word with Martin's parents.

G – Snatch the phone away from Martin.

H – Tell Martin's parents that they need to try and amend their son's reprehensible behaviour.

| 1 | 2 | 3 |
|---|---|---|
|   |   |   |

Q85. One of your patients has been admitted to the hospital. The patient in question is named Darius. Darius seems extremely distressed. He informs you that this is the first time he has ever had to visit a hospital, despite living in the UK for his entire life, and that he is extremely afraid of having to pay for a large hospital bill. He tells you that he simply can't afford treatment, but is worried that he'll die if not.

You need to conduct a physical examination of Darius, but his nervous behaviour is making this impossible.

Take a look at the below answers, and then choose the three best options.

A – Explain to Darius that if he doesn't stop worrying, you won't be able to treat him.

B – Explain to Darius that he is being treated at an NHS hospital, and therefore will not need to pay a hospital bill.

C – Assure Darius that the hospital staff will take the best possible care of him.

D – Tell Darius that if he can't afford to pay for NHS treatment, he cannot be seen.

E – Tell Darius that the only charge he'll have to pay is for outpatient prescriptions.

F – Try to assure Darius that if there are any charges, you'll let him know about them before treatment is done.

G – Tell Darius that the longer he whinges, the more expensive the treatment will be.

H – Inform Darius that this is an NHS establishment, so he is receiving excellent, and free, medical care.

| 1 | 2 | 3 |
|---|---|---|
|   |   |   |

Q86. Over the past week, several patients have approached you, complaining about one of your colleagues. They have claimed that your colleague's breath is always bad after lunch, and find it quite uncomfortable to deal with him.

You are aware that your colleague has a tuna sandwich every day during his break, and that this could be part of the problem.

Take a look at the below answers, and then choose the three best options.

A – Approach your colleague and suggest to him that maybe he should change the food he's eating whilst at the hospital, to make things easier for the patients.

B – Walk up to your colleague and demand that he stops eating smelly foods for lunch.

C – Talk to your colleague and inform him of what the patients said. Ask him if he could try to find a solution to this problem.

D – Approach your colleague and suggest that he brushes his teeth after lunch.

E – Tell your colleague that eating tuna whilst at work is totally unacceptable.

F – Inform the patients that they are complaining about a minor issue, whilst the doctor is working hard to save their lives. Tell them to get some perspective.

G – Tell your colleague to consider switching up his diet, for the sake of the patients.

H – Ask your colleague whether it would be possible for him to monitor his personal hygiene following lunch.

| 1 | 2 | 3 |
|---|---|---|
|   |   |   |

**Q87.** The colleague from the previous question has reacted extremely badly to you raising the issue of his breath. Although you were sensitive and polite about the issue, he has filed a complaint to senior management, accusing you of bullying him.

Your registrar has asked you to see him in his office this morning, to discuss the accusations, and explain your side of the story.

**Take a look at the below answers, and then choose the three best options.**

A – Tell the registrar that you were acting in the best interests of the patients by bullying your colleague.

B – Tell the registrar that you do not feel your behaviour amounted to bullying, and that you were acting in the best interests of the patients. Offer to apologise.

C – Inform the registrar that you believe your colleague is overreacting to a simple issue.

D – Tell the registrar that you didn't mean to upset your colleague. Offer to apologise but refuse all allegations of bullying.

E – Explain the situation to the registrar. Ask him what you should have done differently in this scenario.

F – Defend yourself against the bullying accusation. Tell the registrar that if anything, you are now the one who is being bullied.

G – Beg the registrar not to fire you.

H – Tell the registrar that your colleague needs to start taking some responsibility for his actions.

| 1 | 2 | 3 |
|---|---|---|
|   |   |   |

**Q88.** You are living with one of your work colleagues. Your colleague's name is James. On Thursday morning, before the two of you are due to start work, James informs you that he can't be bothered to go into the hospital that day, and asks you to tell the consultant that he is sick. Although you try to persuade him to go in, as he has patients that he needs to attend to, he refuses. When you leave the house, James is playing video games.

As soon as you get into work, the ward consultant approaches you, asking where James is.

**Take a look at the below answers, and then choose the three best options.**

A – Inform the ward consultant that it would be a good idea for him to contact James himself.

B – Tell the ward consultant that James has refused to come into work today, even though you tried to persuade him otherwise.

C – Tell the ward consultant that James is ill today. Apologise on James's behalf.

D – Tell the ward consultant that you haven't seen James today, so you don't know where he is.

E – Call James, and put him on the phone with the ward consultant.

F – Tell the ward consultant that you don't know where James is.

G – Tell the ward consultant that James isn't in today, but it would be better for James to explain the reasons himself.

H – Ask the ward consultant whether it's okay to inform on your friend.

| 1 | 2 | 3 |
|---|---|---|
|   |   |   |

**Q89.** One of your colleagues has been dating a fellow staff member from the hospital, but they have recently split up. Your colleague seems to have taken this extremely hard, and you have noticed that it has had a significant impact on his mood. He often spends time alone in the break room, and doesn't say much to any of your colleagues. A few of his patients have commented to you that their doctor doesn't seem as interested in engaging with them anymore. He also doesn't seem to be eating much. Your colleague's ex-partner is still working at the hospital, and seems very happy.

**Take a look at the below answers, and then choose the three best options.**

A – Sit down with your colleague and inform him that he needs to start engaging more with his patients. Encourage him to pretend to be happy, for the good of everyone else at the hospital.

B – Ask your colleague whether he truly cares about medicine anymore.

C – Contact your colleague's ex-partner, to discuss the possibility of her getting back together with him.

D – Sit down with your colleague and inform him that you've noticed a change in his mood recently. Ask him whether there's anything you can do to help.

E – Tell your colleague that you are concerned about his mood and behaviour.

F – Speak to your educational consultant about why your colleague is acting this way.

G – Do nothing. He'll cheer up eventually.

H – Tell your colleague that you have noticed a change in his mood recently. Inform him that you are always here if he needs someone to talk to.

| 1 | 2 | 3 |
|---|---|---|
|   |   |   |

**Q90.** The hospital at which you work has recently put a 'see and tell' policy into action. This policy essentially encourages all employees to come forward to report the very slightest wrongdoing, to senior members of staff. The policy was enforced after a string of serious incidents, which were ignored because staff members didn't want to inform on their colleagues. Now, the hospital has published a list of 'reportable offences' on the staff room wall. Alongside serious offences, this includes:

- Any kind of littering;
- Any form of swearing;
- Any form of inappropriate joke;
- Any form of error when dealing with patients, no matter how amendable.

You have noticed that this list is causing major problems amongst the staff. Nobody seems to trust each other anymore, and there is an undercurrent of resentment building in the workplace.

**Take a look at the below answers, and then choose the three best options.**

A – Pay close attention to the people who disagree with the list. Endeavour to report them to senior management.

B – Go and see your ward registrar. Try and explain the negative impact that these changes are having on the staff.

C – Try and gather some of your colleagues together, to discuss the negative feeling that these changes is creating.

D – Do nothing. Rules are in place for a reason.

E – Speak to one of the nurses about these changes.

F – Ask the staff to stop informing on each other. Only together can you overcome this system.

G – Arrange a meeting with the ward consultant. Try to suggest to him that the changes are a little too heavy-handed.

H – Arrange a hospital-wide forum, so that everyone working within the building can voice their concerns.

| 1 | 2 | 3 |
|---|---|---|
|   |   |   |

---

**Q91.** There is a new registrar on the ward in which you work. Her name is Dr Glynis. The pair of you dated several years ago, before either of you was involved in the medical profession, but it ended very badly.

Dr Glynis is by all accounts an extremely intelligent, capable and friendly member of staff, who seems to get along with everybody in the ward…with the exception of you. So far, Dr Glynis has refused to acknowledge you, introducing herself to everybody else on the ward apart from you, and whenever she needs to contact you about an issue, asks someone to speak on her behalf. You have spoken to your colleagues about this issue, but they don't know what to suggest.

**Take a look at the below answers, and then choose the three best options.**

A – Try and arrange a one to one meeting with Dr Glynis. Urge her to put professionalism over personal grievances.

B – Arrange a meeting with the ward consultant. Tell him that unfortunately, he'll need to decide between keeping you on as a member of staff, or sacking Dr Glynis.

C – Ask the ward consultant for advice on the best way to approach this situation. Explain that you want to work with Dr Glynis, not against her.

D – Ask your colleagues about what you should do.

E – See if you can get in contact with Dr Glynis. Ask her if she'd like to go on a date, for old time's sake.

F – See if you can be moved to a different ward in the hospital.

G – Speak to your clinical supervisor about how to navigate your differences with Dr Glynis.

H – Ignore the situation. You are working on the same ward, so Dr Glynis will have to talk to you at some point.

| 1 | 2 | 3 |
|---|---|---|
|   |   |   |

**Q92.** On Tuesday afternoon, the FY1s in your ward are scheduled to attend a research workshop. During this workshop, each of you will present the final version of the projects that you have been assigned, as part of a presentation to the whole group. The project and presentation count for a large percentage of your score for the year.

Following your presentation, one of your colleague's – named Pablo – stands up to give his own. During Pablo's presentation, you quickly notice that much of the material he has gathered comes from an junior doctoret page that you previously visited. It appears that Pablo has copied and pasted this information, even though the group were under strict instructions to deliver original material.

At the end of Pablo's presentation, the consultant informs him that he has done a wonderful job, and that this was the best one so far.

**Take a look at the below answers, and then choose the three best options.**

A – Go and speak to Pablo following the workshop. Inform him that you know he has plagiarised the content.

B – Immediately speak up, following Pablo's presentation. Loudly accuse him of plagiarising the content.

C – After the workshop, speak to Pablo and encourage him to be honest with the consultant about where he got the content from.

D – Say nothing. Pablo's presentation is nothing to do with you.

E – Find the consultant after the session, and inform him that Pablo's content was not original.

F – Show your colleagues the webpage. Ask them whether you should tell the consultant about Pablo's behaviour.

G – Following the workshop, show Pablo the webpage. Ask him to elaborate on how his content is different from this.

H – Congratulate Pablo on his excellent presentation.

| 1 | 2 | 3 |
|---|---|---|
|   |   |   |

**Q93.** As an FY1, part of your requirement for passing the year is that your clinical supervisor observes you performing a number of essential procedures, and is then able to sign off on you performing these procedures in a competent manner.

It is near the end of the year, and unfortunately your supervisor is very ill. He will not be able to come into the hospital for at least another month, and an alternative supervisor has still not been arranged.

The deadline for signing off on these procedures is just 2 weeks away.

**Take a look at the below answers, and then choose the three best options.**

A – Email the forms over to your supervisor, asking him to sign them from his sickbed. You are confident in your ability to perform every procedure on the list to a good level.

B – Ask the Foundation Programme Director whether it's possible to pass without getting these forms signed.

C – Ask the Foundation Programme Director if it's possible for you to get an extension on the forms.

D – Ask one of your FY1 colleagues to observe you, and then sign off on the forms.

E – Ask the ward registrar if she can observe you performing these procedures instead.

F – Sign the forms yourself.

G – Ask the consultant to arrange for someone who can observe you.

H – Call your supervisor at his home and tell him that he needs to come in, or else...

| 1 | 2 | 3 |
|---|---|---|
|   |   |   |

**Q94.** You are working in the A&E department, on a patient who has contracted HIV. The patient has come in asking you to look at an injury on his hand, which he picked up whilst building a shelf in his home. The patient is in severe pain. Whilst you and another colleague are treating the man, he begins crying, and some of his tears fall onto your colleague's arm. Your colleague immediately becomes hysterical, declaring that he is now at risk of contracting HIV, and blaming the patient.

**Take a look at the below answers, and then choose the three best options.**

A – Inform your colleague that he is incorrect, and HIV cannot be transmitted via tears.

B – Tell your colleague that he needs to go and speak to the nurses about getting a blood test done.

C – Apologise to the patient. Gently inform your colleague that HIV cannot be transmitted via tears. Ask him to try and calm down.

D – Ask your colleague to step outside and speak to one of the nurses about the issue, whilst you continue working on the patient.

E – Tell your colleague that it's highly likely that he's transmitted HIV.

F – Inform the patient that he has put your colleague at risk, and therefore you must ask him to leave.

G – Apologise to the patient. Inform your colleague that he cannot contract HIV from tears. Ask him to go outside and try to calm down, whilst you finish working on the patient.

H – Tell the patient that he has acted highly irresponsibly by coming to the A&E department for this type of injury.

| 1 | 2 | 3 |
|---|---|---|
|   |   |   |

---

**Q95.** You are dealing with a patient in the paediatric ward. The patient is an 8-year-old boy named Samuel, who has come into the ward with his mother. Samuel's mother seems very sceptical about your ability to treat her son. In order to diagnose Samuel properly, you need to conduct a physical examination. Samuel is being quite stubborn, and doesn't want to allow you to examine him.

Upon asking Samuel's mother about whether she could assist you with this, she responds with the following:

*'You're a doctor, and you want MY help?! That's disgraceful. What rank are you anyway, just a junior doctor? That's just not good enough, I'm afraid. You're just an amateur.'*

**Take a look at the below answers, and then choose the three best options.**

A – Assure Samuel's mother that although you are a junior doctor, you are more than capable of treating her son, and can provide him with an excellent level of care.

B – Tell Samuel's mother that her attitude is extremely poor, especially considering you have the power to make her son feel better…

C – Tell Samuel's mother that you asked her to assist with the examination, because this will be more comforting and less stressful for her son.

D – Tell Samuel that his mother is extremely rude.

E – Ask Samuel's mother whether she would prefer to speak to a senior doctor about this issue.

F – Ask Samuel's mother to leave the hospital immediately.

G – Inform Samuel that he will not be treated until his mother apologises to you.

H – Ask Samuel's mother to explain why she feels uncomfortable with junior doctors.

| 1 | 2 | 3 |
|---|---|---|
|   |   |   |

---

**Q96.** As you walk into the hospital on Monday morning, you notice that there are three youths sitting on the car park wall outside, drinking and smoking. The youths appear to be swearing at visitors and staff as they walk past, and at one point even flick cigarette ash at an elderly lady.

**Take a look at the below answers, and then choose the three best options.**

A – Go straight to the hospital security team, and inform them of this situation.

B – Approach the youths and tell them that they are behaving unacceptably. Ask them to leave.

C – Ignore the situation. As long as they don't come into the hospital, it's not a problem.

D – Ask the people walking outside the hospital about whether this behaviour is bothering them.

E – Tell the youths that they need to leave the premises at once. Threaten them with physical retribution.

F – Tell the youths that if they don't leave, you'll contact the police.

G – Ask the youths to sit down for a quiet chat with you, to discuss their poor behaviour.

H – Inform the youths that smoking and drinking are illegal on hospital premises.

| 1 | 2 | 3 |
|---|---|---|
|   |   |   |

**Q97.** Today is Thursday. You have just started working at a new hospital, and are scheduled to have your first meeting with your educational supervisor. After knocking on his door, and taking a seat, it quickly becomes apparent to you that your supervisor speaks extremely poor English. Although he is clearly a capable doctor, you have major doubts over whether he can manage your educational and learning needs appropriately.

**Take a look at the below answers, and then choose the three best options.**

A – Hire a translator, for the next time you need to speak with your supervisor.

B – Ask your translator whether he feels you would be better suited to working with someone else.

C – Following the meeting, arrange a call with the Foundation Programme Director, so that you can discuss your concerns.

D – Contact the Foundation Programme Director. Demand to be assigned a new supervisor.

E – Be honest with your supervisor. Tell him that although you can appreciate he is a great doctor, you feel as if there is a significant language barrier which could impact on your learning.

F – Tell your supervisor that if he wants to work with you, he needs to improve his spoken English.

G – Speak to any colleagues who share the same supervisor. Ask them how they are planning to bridge the language barrier.

H – Tell your supervisor that you don't want to work with him.

| 1 | 2 | 3 |
|---|---|---|
|   |   |   |

**Q98.** You are scheduled to take a week off from the hospital, to go on holiday. Your plane leaves on Friday evening. You plan to leave work an hour before the flight is due, go home, get changed and then head straight to the airport. Although you have discussed this plan with the ward registrar, who agreed to it, when the time comes he refuses to allow you to leave on time. He claims that there are too many jobs to be done right now. You disagree with this, as the hospital is not particularly busy, and you have completed all of your allocated tasks.

**Take a look at the below answers, and then choose the three best options.**

A – Tell the registrar that you are leaving, and there's nothing he can do about it.

B – Remind the registrar of your original agreement. Point out that you have completed all of your tasks for the day.

C – Ask the registrar to point out which jobs need to be completed, before you can go home.

D – Tell the registrar that if you do not leave on time today, you will miss your flight.

E – Agree to stay until whenever the registrar allows you to leave.

F – Call the airport, and cancel your booking. You won't be going on holiday this year.

G – Demand that the registrar allows you to leave, at once.

H – Speak to the consultant and ask him if you can go home, as the registrar is being unreasonable.

| 1 | 2 | 3 |
|---|---|---|
|   |   |   |

**Q99.** The consultant on your ward is a man named Dr King. Dr King is in relatively poor health. Not only is he significantly overweight, but he also takes several smoking breaks a day. Despite this, Dr King is an excellent consultant, and has excellent rapport with all of the patients.

On Tuesday, you enter the break room to find a number of your colleagues discussing Dr King:

**Kirsty:** 'How can Dr King sit there and treat patients when he is in such bad shape? He's fat, he smokes, it's so hypocritical.'

**Gary:** 'Yeh, I agree. It's a bad look for the hospital too, when you need assistance and this bloke comes waddling over.'

**Andrea:** 'I think we should complain to someone higher up about it. I never liked Dr King anyway, he's too smarmy. We could get him replaced with someone who's a bit easier on the eye.'

Upon spotting you, the three of them ask you if you would agree to be their spokesperson, when discussing these issues with a member of staff.

**Take a look at the below answers, and then choose the three best options.**

A – Agree to do it. Dr King needs to go.

B – Tell your colleagues that they are acting extremely unprofessionally.

C – Suggest to your colleagues that if they have an issue with Dr King's weight, they should discuss it with him directly.

D – Tell your colleagues that you will have a word with Dr King about his health issues.

E – Tell your colleagues that Dr King is a fantastic consultant, and that they should be more respectful.

F – Inform your colleagues that Dr King's clinical skills are what matters, and not what they think of his appearance.

G – Tell your colleagues that you will be reporting this conversation directly to Dr King.

H – Tell your colleagues to leave you out of such matters.

| 1 | 2 | 3 |
|---|---|---|
|   |   |   |

**Q100.** An outpatient approaches you in the hospital, and claims that the bike she drove to the hospital on has been stolen. She says that the padlock has been ripped off, and the bike is nowhere to be seen.

**Take a look at the below answers, and then choose the three best options.**

A – Tell the patient that she should have used a better padlock.

B – Apologise to the patient for any inconvenience this may have caused. Tell her that there is a bus stop across the road.

C – Take the patient to the hospital security office. Inform them of the situation.

D – Tell the patient that she needs to report this incident to hospital security.

E – Offer to buy the patient a new bicycle.

F – Sympathise with the patient. Give her instructions on where to find the hospital security office.

G – Tell the patient that you don't care about her bike.

H – Find a senior doctor, who can deal with this situation.

| 1 | 2 | 3 |
|---|---|---|
|   |   |   |

**Q101.** One of your outpatients approaches you at the end of your shift, and asks you if you would like to go and see the new Sci Fi movie with her. You have built up a good rapport with her over the past week.

Your hospital has an extremely strict policy, banning staff from socialising with patients outside of work.

**Take a look at the below answers, and then choose the three best options.**

A – Angrily inform the woman that you are not willing to risk your career for someone like her.

B – Tell the woman that you are happy to go and see a film with her, but she can't tell anyone.

C – Thank the woman for her kind offer, but explain that the hospital has strict rules in place, meaning that you can't.

D – Inform the woman that you would love to go and see the movie with her, but the hospital rules say that you can't date patients.

E – Explain to the woman that hospital rules forbid you from socialising with patients.

F – Tell the woman that you really appreciate the offer, but aren't interested in pursuing this activity.

G – Thank the woman for her kind offer. Tell her that you will pick her up at 7pm.

H – Tell the woman that she must be crazy to think you'd go out with her.

| 1 | 2 | 3 |
|---|---|---|
|   |   |   |

**Q102.** Today, one of your colleagues has returned from holiday in South East Asia. Just before the two of you are due to start your shift, your colleague informs you that he did not have any jabs prior to going on holiday, and nor has he been checked out since returning. Both of you are working on the Emergency Care Unit today.

Your colleague is not showing any signs of illness, and appears to be fit and healthy.

**Take a look at the below answers, and then choose the three best options.**

A – Inform your colleague that it's imperative for him to get checked out immediately. Ask him to speak to one of the nurses about arranging this.

B – Tell your colleague that he will not be able to work until he's checked out.

C – Do nothing. Your colleague appears fit and healthy, it's unlikely that he's picked up anything whilst abroad.

D – Ask your colleague to tell you about how his holiday went, whilst you assess the patients.

E – Inform the registrar immediately.

F – Advise your colleague that if he starts feeling unwell, he needs to speak to one of the nursing staff immediately, and get a full check-up.

G – Tell your colleague that he needs to fill in a form, declaring that he is fully competent to practice medicine after such an extended break.

H – Ask your colleague whether he came into contact with anyone who was seriously ill, whilst on holiday.

| 1 | 2 | 3 |
|---|---|---|
|   |   |   |

---

**Q103.** You are walking through the gynaecology ward. The ward is extremely busy today, and there are lots of people milling around, speaking with their relatives. Unfortunately, as you walk through the room, you bump into a woman standing by the door. Consequently the woman spills her tea, which splatters her shoes. She appears irate at this:

*'Oh my god, do you know how much these boots cost? They are real suede! You've ruined them, you've ruined my boots. I can't believe this, £800 down the drain.'*

Although you have tried to apologise, the woman is not having any of this, and demands to know what you are going to do about this issue.

**Take a look at the below answers, and then choose the three best options.**

A – Inform the woman that she took the risk by wearing suede boots in a busy canteen.

B – Apologise again to the woman. Tell her that the hospital will cover the cost of her shoes.

C – Tell the woman that you are happy to pay for a replacement pair of boots.

D – Escort the woman to the ward sister, who can deal with this complaint.

E – Assure the woman that this was an honest mistake. Inform her that if she wants to initiate a complaint against you, then you can show her how to do so.

F – Tell the woman that you feel she is overreacting to what was a simple accident.

G – Ask the woman whether she would like the hospital to pay for repairs to her shoes.

H – Inform the woman that the hospital will try and resolve this problem for her, and that you are sorry for the mistake.

| 1 | 2 | 3 |
|---|---|---|
|   |   |   |

**Q104.** One of your colleagues approaches you during your shift, and asks you if you can cover his patients for an hour, as he needs to leave the hospital to deal with an immediate personal situation. You are currently working well beyond the end of your shift, and feel tired and stressed. You do not feel as if you have the capacity to provide your colleague's patients with the appropriate level of care.

**Take a look at the below answers, and then choose the three best options.**

A – Tell your colleague that you absolutely will not cover his patients, and that he needs to stay and do it himself.

B – Inform your colleague that you are happy to cover his patients for an hour, but no longer.

C – Tell your colleague that you are feeling extremely tired, and were meant to finish work over an hour ago. Advise him to find someone else who can assist.

D – Ask your colleague why he feels the need to foist his problems onto others.

E – Tell your colleague that you do not feel as if you will be able to help him on this occasion.

F – Ask your colleague to speak to the registrar about this issue, as you cannot cover his patients at this time.

G – Tell your colleague that you will not bow to his selfish demands.

H – Tell your colleague that you will find someone else to cover his patients, whilst he deals with his problem.

| 1 | 2 | 3 |
|---|---|---|
|   |   |   |

**Q105.** You are working over the weekend at the hospital. On Saturday afternoon, the ward is extremely busy, and the consultant has expressed that all staff members will need to remain at the hospital during their lunch period – just in case they are bleeped to attend to a patient. Many of your FY1 colleagues are disgruntled by this, as they like to go out for lunch.

During your own break, as you make your way to the staff room, you notice that the registrar has just returned with a bag containing food from the local sandwich shop.

**Take a look at the below answers, and then choose the three best options.**

A – Go straight to the consultant and inform him that the registrar has broken the rules.

B – Politely enquire as to whether the registrar has been out of the hospital. Remind him of the rules.

C – Demand that the registrar explains where he got his sandwich from.

D – Ask the registrar whether he is aware of the consultant's request for staff not to leave the hospital.

E – Ask the registrar to confess his unacceptable conduct to the consultant.

F – Do nothing. The registrar is more senior than you, so you aren't in a position to question his behaviour.

G – Speak to the Foundation Programme Director about what you witnessed.

H – Go out and buy a sandwich. If the registrar can do it, then so can you.

| 1 | 2 | 3 |
|---|---|---|
|   |   |   |

**Q106.** One of your colleagues has arrived to work in an inebriated state. She is clearly not fit to deal with patients, and stinks of alcohol. Upon further assessment, you suspect that she may be suffering from alcohol poisoning. You are the first person to see her this morning.

**Take a look at the below answers, and then choose the three best options.**

A – Escort your colleague back to her home, before returning to work.

B – Bring your colleague to see one of the nurses. Inform them that you think she is suffering from alcohol poisoning, and needs to be checked out.

C – Do nothing. Your colleague will only get soberer as the day goes on.

D – Take your colleague to see the registrar. He needs to be informed about her condition.

E – Tell your colleague that she needs to go home and sober up before she can work today.

F – Ask one of the nurses to check over your colleague, whilst you inform the consultant about this situation.

G – Tell your colleague that she is likely to lose her job for this heinous behaviour.

H – Ask your colleague whether she'd like you to fetch her a glass of water.

| 1 | 2 | 3 |
|---|---|---|
|   |   |   |

**Q107.** One of your colleagues approaches you during your shift. He sits you down and informs you that he is in terrible financial trouble, after borrowing money from some questionable people, who now want three times the original debt back. He claims that his creditors have threatened him with violence if he doesn't make the payment within 2 days.

Your colleague asks you if he can borrow £2000, to cover his debts. You do not feel comfortable lending him this kind of money.

**Take a look at the below answers, and then choose the three best options.**

A – Advise your colleague that if he is being threatened with violence, then he should contact the police.

B – Tell your colleague that it's always a mistake to use money-lending companies. Advise him against this in future.

C – Sympathise with your colleague, but inform him that you don't feel happy to lend him this type of money.

D – Tell your colleague that, if he survives the next week, he will have learned a valuable lesson.

E – Tell your colleague that he would be better off speaking to his educational supervisor about this issue.

F – Ask your colleague whether he feels that this situation will impact upon his ability to treat patients.

G – Advise your colleague that he should speak to the ward sister about this serious issue.

H – Tell your colleague that you aren't willing to lend him £2000.

| 1 | 2 | 3 |
|---|---|---|
|   |   |   |

**Q108.** Your hospital has recently published a new set of rules, surrounding staff partaking in charity or sponsored events. Staff are now forbidden from participating in any events that could lead to a drastic change in their appearance – such as Movember, based on the board's belief that this makes doctors look unprofessional.

On Sunday, you are speaking with a patient's family. The patient is named Sonia. Sonia has been suffering from breast cancer. In a show of solidarity, the patient's family have shaved their heads. Whilst speaking to them, Sonia's sister encourages you to do the same, since Sonia is your patient. When you inform her that you can't do this, she becomes irate:

*'Okay then, well I guess that shows how much you care about your patients. Your hair is more valuable than my sister, is that it? Wow. You're so unprofessional.'*

**Take a look at the below answers, and then choose the three best options.**

A – Inform Sonia's sister that whilst you care deeply about the patient, you are under no obligation to shave your head.

B – Tell Sonia's sister that the hospital has a rule forbidding doctors from significantly changing their appearance.

C – Tell Sonia's sister that you do care about your patients. Ask her to fetch a set of hair clippers.

D – Tell Sonia's sister that you think she is being quite rude and unfair.

E – Tell Sonia's sister that she is right, and your hair is more valuable than the patient.

F – Tell Sonia's sister that she looks ugly now she's shaved her head.

G – Ask the registrar whether you can shave your head, to show solidarity with the patient.

H – Assure Sonia's sister that you will continue to treat her relative with the utmost care, regardless of whether you shave your head.

| 1 | 2 | 3 |
|---|---|---|
|   |   |   |

**Q109.** Today, one of your long-term patients approaches you and informs you that he has some serious concerns about an issue. He informs you that whilst he has been at the hospital, he has ended his relationship with his partner, but that this person continues to visit him every single day. Your patient tells you that he is deeply uncomfortable with these visits, and that he feels too scared to ask his ex-partner not to come anymore. He claims that his ex-partner is exhibiting sinister behaviour, and is worried about what this person will do once he is discharged from the hospital.

**Take a look at the below answers, and then choose the three best options.**

A – Inform your patient that if he wants this person to stop visiting, he needs to be straight with them.

B – Tell your patient that you are happy to speak with the hospital reception and security team, to ensure that this person isn't granted visitation privileges.

C – Tell your patient that you will discuss his concerns with a member of the hospital reception team, to see if this person can be blocked from visiting.

D – Advise the patient that it would be wise for him to discuss these issues with his ex-partner, before blocking them from visiting the hospital.

E – Tell the patient that the next time his ex-partner shows up at the hospital, you'll have them arrested.

F – Tell the patient that you cannot guarantee this person won't be allowed to visit them at the hospital.

G – Tell the patient that this person will be blocked from visiting. Advise him to speak to the hospital welfare team about what to do once he is discharged.

H – Take the patient to see your registrar, with whom he can discuss these issues.

| 1 | 2 | 3 |
|---|---|---|
|   |   |   |

**Q110.** One of your patient's relatives has approached you. Her daughter is suffering from a liver problem, and has been staying at the hospital for several weeks now. The woman informs you that she has had an argument with her daughter/your patient, who is no longer speaking to her, and won't give her any updates on how her treatment is progressing:

*'Please, doctor, can't you convince her to talk to me? I just want to know what's happening with the treatment.'*

**Take a look at the below answers, and then choose the three best options.**

A – Tell the woman that it not up to you to intervene in her personal issues with her daughter.

B – Tell the woman that you will speak with her daughter, but ideally she needs to resolve the issue herself.

C – Tell the woman that you will ask her daughter about whether it's okay for you to disclose treatment information.

D – Inform the woman that her personal relationship with her daughter is none of your concern.

E – Ask the woman to explain to you why her daughter won't speak to her.

F – Inform the woman that ultimately you cannot discuss information without the consent of her daughter, but you are happy to request this on her behalf.

G – Inform the woman about exactly what stage of treatment her daughter is at, and what will come next.

H – Tell the woman that her daughter needs to discuss any treatment information with her mother herself.

| 1 | 2 | 3 |
|---|---|---|
|   |   |   |

**Q111.** You are an FY1 working in the orthopaedic ward. One of your patients is staying in a private room. On Friday, when you come in to speak to him, you interrupt him whilst he is on his laptop. Although he shuts the screen off quickly, you notice that he was watching pornography. The hospital guidelines clearly state that no customer or employee is to use the hospital internet for inappropriate purposes. This includes the watching of pornography.

**Take a look at the below answers, and then choose the three best options.**

A – Immediately inform the registrar of what you saw.

B – Tell the man that you are going to call the police.

C – Question the man over what you saw. Inform him that the hospital will need to conduct an investigation in this incident.

D – Inform the man that the hospital has guidelines in place for the use of the internet, and that he cannot watch pornography here.

E – Ask your consultant for advice on what you should do if this incident happens again.

F – Tell the consultant that you caught your patient watching illicit material.

G – Apologise to the man. Inform him that you will come back later.

H – Tell the man that he has broken the hospital internet rules, and that his behaviour is utterly disgraceful.

| 1 | 2 | 3 |
|---|---|---|
|   |   |   |

**Q112.** One of the patients on your ward informs you that he has very specific dietary needs, that the hospital will need to address. When he informs you of what his diet consists of, you are unsure of whether the hospital can meet this requirement. The registrar has gone home for the night.

**Take a look at the below answers, and then choose the three best options.**

A – Write down a full list of the man's dietary requirements, and then speak to the ward sister about whether the hospital is able to fulfil these.

B – Tell the man that he will need to get by on hospital food, whilst he is staying here.

C – Enquire about the reasons for the man's dietary requirements. If they are not medical, then dismiss his concerns.

D – Inform the man that you will speak with the ward sister and see if this is possible.

E – Tell the man that although it's unlikely, the hospital will try their best to fulfil his needs.

F – Assure the man that the hospital will meet all of his dietary requirements.

G – Ask the man to go and speak to the canteen staff, if he wants special food.

H – Tell the man that you understand his dietary needs, and will do your best to assure that these needs are met.

| 1 | 2 | 3 |
|---|---|---|
|   |   |   |

**Q113.** The relatives of one of your patients have come to you with some very bad news. Unfortunately, last night, the patient's beloved dog died. The patient's relatives have asked you to break the news, because they feel too guilty.

As a new doctor, this is your very first experience of breaking bad news to a patient, and you are unsure of how you should proceed.

**Take a look at the below answers, and then choose the three best options.**

A – Tell the patient's relatives that you are unwilling to do this. Inform them that this is something that should be done by a family member.

B – Sit down with the patient and gently inform them that unfortunately their dog has died. Apologise for their loss, and tell them that there is a pet store nearby where they can purchase a replacement.

C – Agree to speak to the patient about the issue. Speak to your supervisor first about the best thing to say.

D – Encourage the patient's relatives to break the news themselves.

E – Go and tell the patient that their dog has died. Tell them you are very sorry for their loss.

F – Ask your supervisor whether you are the right person to break this news, given that you have no experience of doing so.

G – Ask your supervisor to break the news on your behalf.

H – Tell the patient that their dog has died. Encourage them to think positively.

| 1 | 2 | 3 |
|---|---|---|
|   |   |   |

**Q114.** The hospital has forbidden staff members from listening to music, or wearing headphones, whilst at work. The hospital believes that this makes staff look unprofessional.

On Monday, when you are walking through the ward, you notice a fellow junior doctor bending over the nurses' desk, whilst filling in paperwork. The doctor has a pair of headphones in his ears, and appears to be listening to music.

**Take a look at the below answers, and then choose the three best options.**

A – Immediately go and inform the consultant about this breach of the rules.

B – Politely tap your colleague on the shoulder, and remind him of the rules surrounding headphones.

C – Approach your colleague and yank the headphones out of his ears. Demand that he stops listening to music at once.

D – Do nothing. Hopefully he'll get caught and lose his job.

E – Tell your colleague that he is breaking hospital rules by listening to music, and that if he doesn't stop then you will need to report him.

F – Ask your colleague to stop listening to music, because it makes staff look unprofessional.

G – Ask the nurses to remind your colleague of the hospital rules. Get on with the rest of your day.

H – Take your colleague into a private room. Ask him to take a seat, make him comfortable, and then quietly and sensitively inform him that he needs to stop listening to music.

| 1 | 2 | 3 |
|---|---|---|
|   |   |   |

> **Q115.** One of your patients is just about to be discharged from the hospital. Just before she's going to leave, after signing the discharge forms, she tells you that she needs to stay at the hospital for at least another few hours. When you question her over this, she tells you that it's raining, and she doesn't want to damage her nice suede shoes on the walk to the bus stop.

**Take a look at the below answers, and then choose the three best options.**

A – Inform the woman that she can purchase an umbrella from the hospital gift shop.

B – Arrange for the woman to be given a bed at the hospital, until it stops raining.

C – Tell the woman that there is no medical reason for her to stay at the hospital now.

D – Inform the woman that she is more than welcome to spend time in the gift shop and hospital café, but you must get back to work.

E – Ask the woman whether she'd like to come and help you assess the rest of your patients.

F – Ask hospital security to escort the woman out of the building immediately.

G – Tell the woman that she should wear better footwear next time she comes into the hospital.

H – Tell the woman that if she speaks to the reception desk, they can arrange a taxi for her.

| 1 | 2 | 3 |
|---|---|---|
|   |   |   |

> **Q116.** Your hospital has recently opened a brand-new podiatry unit. One of the first patients in the unit is a 17-year-old boy, named Matthew. Matthew has been experiencing severe pain in his toes for the past few months, and his family believe that he needs to see a specialist about this issue. Whilst examining Matthew, it becomes apparent that the pain in his toes is a result of him wearing inappropriate footwear. However, you do notice that there is an unexplained swelling around the bottom of his ankle, which you are quite concerned about.
>
> Matthew is extremely worried about being seen at the hospital, and has a very nervous disposition. He admits that he suffers from health anxiety.

**Take a look at the below answers, and then choose the three best options.**

A – Explain to Matthew that you would like to conduct further examination of the swelling in his ankle. Assure him that this is just a precautionary step.

B – Tell Matthew that his ankle is swollen, and that he should prepare himself for the possibility of amputation.

C – Inform Matthew that you would like to run a few tests on his ankle, just to make sure the swelling isn't a sign of imminent death.

D – Tell Matthew that his ankle will need to be examined by hospital staff, just to make sure everything is okay.

E – Tell Matthew that he will need to remain at the hospital whilst his ankle is examined.

F – Tell Matthew that if the swelling in his ankle doesn't go down by next week, he should return to the hospital immediately.

G – Ask Matthew whether he would be happy for you to conduct further examination of his ankle.

H – Tell Matthew that he is free to leave, since the issues with his toes have been resolved.

| 1 | 2 | 3 |
|---|---|---|
|   |   |   |

Q117. One of your patients is a 4-year-old girl, named Belinda. Belinda needs to go in for surgery tonight. Her mother has informed you that she is out at a concert this evening, so won't be able to see Belinda before she goes in for treatment, but has asked you to call her following the surgery to let her know how it went.

Your surgical colleague believes that Belinda's mother is acting highly irresponsibly.

**Take a look at the below answers, and then choose the three best options.**

A – Agree to call Belinda's mother following the surgery, to let her know how it went.

B – Encourage Belinda's mother to be there when her daughter gets out of surgery.

C – Tell Belinda's mother that you cannot give her information about how the surgery went, without Belinda's consent.

D – Call social services. Belinda's mother is behaving unacceptably.

E – Ask Belinda's mother whether she can bring you back a souvenir from the concert.

F – Tell Belinda that her mother doesn't seem to care much about her.

G – Inform your colleague that although you agree with his opinion, unfortunately that's her prerogative.

H – Tell Belinda's mother that you cannot call her to give her news, and that she will need to be at the hospital to find out how the surgery went.

| 1 | 2 | 3 |
|---|---|---|
|   |   |   |

> **Q118.** You are working in the maternity ward. One of your patients is a young woman, named Mrs Edwards. Mrs Edwards has given birth prematurely, with her baby being born over 5 weeks before the expected date. As a result, the baby is in extremely unstable condition. As soon as the baby is born, it is taken to the neonatal ward to be cared for by the specialist nurses.
>
> Mrs Edwards is extremely distressed by this, and demands that you give her back her child.

**Take a look at the below answers, and then choose the three best options.**

A – Inform Mrs Edwards that her baby needs to be taken to the neonatal ward for immediate medical attention.

B – Try to reassure Mrs Edwards that you will take the best possible care of her child, who needs immediate medical attention.

C – Tell Mrs Edwards that her newborn baby is in immediate danger, and needs to be treated.

D – Assure Mrs Edwards that she will be reunited with her baby very soon.

E – Inform Mrs Edwards that it's highly unlikely that she'll ever see her baby again.

F – Ask Mrs Edwards to try and calm down. Assure her that everything will be fine.

G – Explain to Mrs Edwards that if she had given birth when expected, this would not have been an issue.

H – Ask Mrs Edwards to try and stand up, so that she can come with you to the neonatal ward.

| 1 | 2 | 3 |
|---|---|---|
|   |   |   |

> **Q119.** You are an FY1 working in the maternity ward. One of your patients is a woman named Jill. Jill has very recently had a baby boy. Upon consulting with Jill, she confesses to you that she is having extremely negative thoughts. She says that she feels as if her life is meaningless, and that having a son has brought her absolutely no joy whatsoever, even though she thought it would.

**Take a look at the below answers, and then choose the three best options.**

A – Tell Jill that you can't understand how she can be feeling this way, when she has just had a baby.

B – Tell Jill that she needs to try and cheer up, for the good of her son.

C – Screen Jill for signs of postnatal depression.

D – Following your conversation with Jill, express your concerns to the registrar.

E – Ask Jill whether she feels that she would be happier being treated on a different ward.

F – Sympathise with Jill. Inform her that you suspect she is suffering from postnatal depression.

G – Go to the consultant and inform him that you think Jill has postnatal depression.

H – Tell Jill that you appreciate her confiding in you. Ask her whether she would be happy to answer some more questions, because you'd like to explore her feelings in more depth.

| 1 | 2 | 3 |
|---|---|---|
|   |   |   |

**Q120.** The hospital at which you work has a very strict policy on socialising with patients and former patients. Doctors at the hospital are forbidden from doing so. On your night off from the hospital, you go out to dinner with your wife. Whilst sitting in the restaurant, you notice that one of your colleagues is at the same restaurant. He is out to dinner with a patient – who was only discharged this morning. You are aware that your colleague separated from his wife last year, and has been extremely unhappy ever since. This is the happiest you've seen him looking in a long time.

**Take a look at the below answers, and then choose the three best options.**

A – Ignore the situation. Your colleague is happy, and that's the important thing.

B – Immediately approach your colleague and the patient. Inform them that you will be reporting this deplorable meeting.

C – Ask your wife whether she thinks you should go over and say something.

D – Wait until the next time you see your colleague at work. Tell him that he is breaking hospital rules.

E – Ask your colleague about the incident next time you see him. Encourage him to think about what is best for his career.

F – Leave your wife at the dinner table, and go straight to the hospital to report your colleague.

G – Speak to the restaurant manager. Encourage him not to serve your colleague.

H – See if you can grab a quiet word with your colleague on the way to the bathroom. Ask him why he's breaking the hospital rules.

| 1 | 2 | 3 |
|---|---|---|
|   |   |   |

Q121. One of your patients, Patricia, is due to be discharged from the cardiology ward. She informs you that as soon as she gets out of the hospital, she is hopping on a plane to Los Angeles, where she will be attending the seminar of legendary junior doctoret marketing guru – Kenny Curdles. You wish her all the best.

Later on that day, your colleague informs you that Kenny Curdles is nothing more than a scammer, and has conned thousands of vulnerable people out of their money over the past few years. You are concerned about whether this will impact Patricia.

**Take a look at the below answers, and then choose the three best options.**

A – Do nothing. It's not your responsibility.

B – Try and get in contact with Patricia. Warn her that Kenny is not to be trusted.

C – Go and speak to your clinical supervisor. Ask him whether you could be held accountable.

D – Ask the reception desk to place a follow up call to Patricia, to check how she's getting on.

E – Tell your colleague that Kenny is one of the most respected junior doctoret salesmen in the world. This just can't be true.

F – Call the police.

G – Ask your colleague whether he thinks you are to blame for this.

H – Tell your colleague that you are not in a position to give patients advice on their personal life.

| 1 | 2 | 3 |
|---|---|---|
|   |   |   |

Q122. One of your colleagues, Jeremy, is colourblind. Although this colleague is an excellent doctor, he has been making some mistakes over the past few weeks, filling in certain prescription forms incorrectly, and making a few questionable calls over patients. There is no evidence that any of these errors are a result of him being colour blind.

Today, Jeremy has made another diagnostic error. One of your fellow FY1s has apparently had enough, and she lambasts him in the middle of the ward:

'For goodness sake, Jeremy. This is why we can't have colour blind doctors, it's so unsafe and so unprofessional. I don't think you are incompetent, but it's clearly a problem.'

**Take a look at the below answers, and then choose the three best options.**

A–Approach your colleague and inform her that you feel her criticism of Jeremy is unwarranted and unfair.

B – Tell your colleague that it's unfair to single out Jeremy, when she herself is a poor doctor.

C – Tell your colleague that she is wrong to bring up Jeremy being colour blind, when there is no evidence that this is the reason for his mistakes.

D – Agree with your colleague. Jeremy is clearly in over his head.

E – Inform your colleague that her behaviour is making both her and Jeremy look extremely unprofessional.

F – Politely ask Jeremy to explain why he has made another error.

G – Tell your colleague that she needs to try and be more polite when discussing staff errors.

H – Inform your colleague that she needs to deal with this issue in a private location.

| 1 | 2 | 3 |
|---|---|---|
|   |   |   |

---

**Q123.** Over the past few days, the hospital has received a number of complaints from patients, that their medical information has been published online via a private website – that claims to list the medical history of every single person in the UK. The hospital is unable to work out how this has happened.

On Tuesday, your colleague approaches you and confesses that he sold the information on to the website, as he has been in severe financial difficulty. He asks you what you think he should do. He informs you that he doesn't want to lose his job.

**Take a look at the below answers, and then choose the three best options.**

A – Tell your colleague that he has breached the doctor patient confidentiality agreement, and needs to confess this to a member of senior management.

B – Encourage your colleague to speak to a senior member of the nursing team about what he's done. Assure him that he won't get in trouble, because he's being honest.

C – Tell your colleague that he needs to hand himself in to senior management. Inform him that he is likely to lose his job over this.

D – Tell your colleague that you will go and speak to senior management on his behalf, to inform them about what he's done.

E – Tell your colleague that if he confesses to this action, he's likely to lose his job, so it's probably better not to admit it.

F – Tell your colleague that you won't tell anyone what he has done, as long as he shares some of the profits.

G – Ask your colleague not to discuss this issue with you.

H – Advise your colleague that you can't discuss his job security, but that he must confess this to senior management.

| 1 | 2 | 3 |
|---|---|---|
|   |   |   |

**Q124.** Several of your female colleagues have come to you, expressing concern that a male member of staff is being highly inappropriate over social media. Every single one of them informs you that they asked this person to stop, but he didn't, and as a result they have had to block his profile. To your horror, the same night, the male doctor begins messaging you too. You do not respond to him, but the messages only become more persistent.

**Take a look at the below answers, and then choose the three best options.**

A – Approach the doctor the next day and inform him that you would like him to stop messaging you, and your female colleagues.

B – Approach the doctor the next day. Tell him that his behaviour could be seen as sexual harassment, and that it needs to stop immediately.

C – Speak to a senior female colleague about how she would deal with something like this.

D – Inform the doctor that you do not intend on replying to any of his messages.

E – Block him, then do nothing. He'll move onto a new target very quickly.

F – Warn the doctor that if his behaviour doesn't improve, you'll report him to a manager.

G – Find a senior doctor and inform them that you are thinking of resigning.

H – Delete your social media profile.

| 1 | 2 | 3 |
|---|---|---|
|   |   |   |

**Q125.** As you are walking past the hospital gift shop on Tuesday, you notice a man sneaking an item under his arm, and then walking out of the door. Although he hasn't left the hospital yet, it is clear to you that he didn't pay for the item. In his right hand, the man is carrying an umbrella with a pointed end.

**Take a look at the below answers, and then choose the three best options.**

A – Confront the man about what you just saw. Accuse him of stealing.

B – Go straight to security and let them know about the incident.

C – Go into the gift shop and inform the person working behind the till that the man has just stolen.

D – Speak to your registrar about the incident.

E – Physically restrain the man.

F – Ask the man to return the item that he has just stolen.

G – Approach the man and ask him whether he paid for the item under his arm.

H – Do nothing. His umbrella is very sharp.

| 1 | 2 | 3 |
|---|---|---|
|   |   |   |

---

**Q126.** You are attending to Zelda, an 80-year-old patient who requires palliative care. Two weeks ago, Zelda signed a consent form, confirming that she was happy to be moved from hospital premises to a nursing home nearby. When the time comes for Zelda to be moved, she becomes very confused. She does not recall signing the form, and doesn't understand why the staff are attempting to move her. Her relatives are contactable via phone.

**Take a look at the below answers, and then choose the three best options.**

A – Tell Zelda that she's signed the form, and therefore she will be moved whether she likes it or not.

B – Ask the staff to halt the process of moving Zelda. Sit down with her and try to establish whether she is competent enough to make the decision.

C – Show Zelda the consent form. Ask her whether she would like to rescind her initial consent.

D – Ask Zelda whether she feels as if the staff misled her, before she signed the initial consent form.

E – Ask the staff to stop the move immediately. Sit down with Zelda and try to establish whether she understands the full implications of a move to a nursing home.

F – Tell Zelda that she could be held legally responsible for providing the staff with misleading information.

G – Call Zelda's relatives and ask them to come in, so that you can discuss the situation with the help of her family.

H – Ask Zelda whether her family have pressured her into moving to a nursing home.

| 1 | 2 | 3 |
|---|---|---|
|   |   |   |

---

**Q127.** You are working alongside an FY1 colleague, named Lori. Lori is struggling with her bedside manner. She claims that her people skills are not as good as yours. Today, she asked you whether you can observe her when dealing with a patient, to see if you can provide any tips on how to help her improve. The only time when you are available to do this is at the start of your lunch break, at half past 2.

**Take a look at the below answers, and then choose the three best options.**

A – Tell Lori that there's no available time for you to help her today.

B – Inform Lori that you are happy to watch her for a quick five minutes, at half past 2.

C – Inform Lori that if she wants advice, she should speak to the registrar or consultant.

D – Ask the consultant whether you can extend your lunch break, due to helping Lori.

E – Tell Lori that you will do your best to assist her, when you find time.

F – Advise Lori that a nurse would be much better placed to judge her bedside manner, since you are also an FY1.

G – Tell Lori to speak to her clinical supervisor, if she wants tips.

H – Inform Lori that you don't have any desire to help her improve.

| 1 | 2 | 3 |
|---|---|---|
|   |   |   |

**Q128.** One of your colleagues has approached you, asking for honest advice. She informs you that her clinical supervisor has told her that she needs to improve her teamworking skills, especially when it comes to working with other female staff. Her supervisor has informed her that she is rude and abrasive with other female colleagues, yet very courteous with male members of staff. She asks you what your opinion is.

You agree with her supervisor's assessment.

**Take a look at the below answers, and then choose the three best options.**

A – Tell your colleague that her attitude towards female members of staff is utterly unacceptable.

B – Advise your colleague that she could do with improving her communication skills with female members of staff.

C – Lie to your colleague. Inform her that her attitude is fine, and that you don't know what her supervisor is talking about.

D – Suggest to your colleague that her supervisor may have a point, and that you are happy to help her try and improve her communication skills if possible.

E – Tell your colleague that her attitude towards male members of staff is really good.

F – Ask your colleague whether she feels that her communication skills with female staff members are up to scratch.

G – Tell your colleague that yes, you do feel she could be a little more polite with other female colleagues, but that overall her communication skills are good.

H – Inform your colleague that she is a rude and ignorant person.

| 1 | 2 | 3 |
|---|---|---|
|   |   |   |

**Q129.** You are just finishing your shift, when you overhear a conversation between one of your colleagues, and the relatives of a patient. Your colleague is named Glenn.

**Glenn:** *'So yeh…it's bad news I'm afraid. Really bad actually. Your dad has bowel cancer.'*

**Patient's son:** *'Oh…wow. Okay, right…wow.'*

**Glenn:** *'Yep. Sorry. Anyway, I'm going to have lunch now, so see ya!'*

**Take a look at the below answers, and then choose the three best options.**

A – Immediately approach the patient's relatives and apologise for Glenn's insensitive behaviour.

B – Chase after Glenn and inform him that his behaviour is unacceptable.

C – Ignore the situation. It's Glenn's problem.

D – Apologise to the patient's relatives. Offer to sit down with them to discuss their relative's situation.

E – Make sure you are there next time Glenn speaks with a patient's family. Take notes if he is acting inappropriately.

F – Take the family to see the hospital chaplain, who will be able to talk them through this difficult issue.

G – Tell the registrar about what you have just witnessed.

H – Go and see Glenn. Ask him if he wants to grab a sandwich after work.

| 1 | 2 | 3 |
|---|---|---|
|   |   |   |

**Q130.** You have been working in the gynaecology ward for one year. Today you are due to have your yearly appraisal. The appraisal is being conducted by the ward consultant.

After sitting down, the ward consultant informs you that he is extremely disappointed in your overall performance, and that you have regressed as a doctor in the past 6 months. You are shocked by this.

**Take a look at the below answers, and then choose the three best options.**

A – Tell the consultant that you strongly disagree with his comments. Ask him to clarify why he feels so negatively about your performance.

B – Inform the consultant that you are really surprised by this feedback. Ask him to explain how you can improve your performance.

C – Tell the consultant that you think he is being really unprofessional.

D – Inform the consultant that you consider yourself to be one of the best doctors on the ward.

E – Ask the consultant to clarify why he is disappointed in your performance.

F – Agree wholeheartedly with the consultant. Tell him that you only took this job because it pays well.

G – Tell the consultant that you are very concerned to hear his comments, and would like feedback on how you can improve.

H – Tell the consultant that he is wrong.

| 1 | 2 | 3 |
|---|---|---|
|   |   |   |

**Q131.** A patient in your ward has come to you to complain. The woman is being treated by one of your colleagues. She claims that she specifically informed him that she was a vegetarian, but tonight has been brought a meat-based meal for dinner. The woman is incensed by this, and believes that your colleague did it on purpose. Your colleague has now gone home for the night.

**Take a look at the below answers, and then choose the three best options.**

A – Assure the woman that there has been an honest mistake, and that you will go and speak to the nursing staff to resolve this error.

B – Tell the woman that she needs to be grateful for what she's been given.

C – Assure the woman that the meat-based meal is one of the hospital's finest dishes.

D – Apologise on behalf of your colleague. Ask the woman if she would like to make a complaint.

E – Tell the woman that you are very sorry for the error.

F – Ask the woman whether she would be happy to wait, whilst you go and fetch a replacement meal.

G – Assure the woman that your colleague would never do something like this on purpose.

H – Tell the women that it serves her right for being picky.

| 1 | 2 | 3 |
|---|---|---|
|   |   |   |

**Q132.** One of the patients in your ward is a 13 year old boy named Martin. Today, Martin's friends have come to visit him. During their visit, a patient comes up to you to complain, claiming that Martin and his friends are being troublesome and disturbing the peace. He wants them thrown out.

The patient in question has a history of making what could be deemed unreasonable complaints. You have not noticed any behaviour from Martin and his friends that could be labelled as disruptive. You do not believe that the patient's complaint is accurate.

**Take a look at the below answers, and then choose the three best options.**

A – Ask the patient to calmly explain to you what exactly Martin and his friends are doing, that is causing disruption on the ward.

B – Assure the patient that you will deal with this as a matter of priority. Call security and have them remove Martin and his friends from the building.

C – Tell the patient that you will ask Martin and his friends to stop being disruptive.

D – Inform the patient that you have not noticed any disruptive behaviour, but if you do spot anything then you will definitely deal with it.

E – Tell the patient that you will keep an eye out for any disruptive behaviour, but you are not willing to have Martin and his friends thrown out.

F – Apologise to the patient for any inconvenience that Martin and his friends may have caused. Assure him that you will be instigating disciplinary procedures.

G – Inform the patient that Martin and his friends are not being disruptive, and that he needs to sit down and stop whinging.

H – Ask the man whether he would be happy to speak to a senior doctor about this, because you don't have time for silly complaints.

| 1 | 2 | 3 |
|---|---|---|
|   |   |   |

**Q133.** You are just about to start your shift for the day. When you walk into the ward, you notice that two of your colleagues are having an unusual squabble:

**David:** *'No, I'm telling you, ketchup goes in the fridge!'*

**Jarred:** *'No, it doesn't. You are just wrong. Ketchup goes in the cupboard, always.'*

**David:** *'And then it rots, and you get ill.'*

**Jarred:** *'Just shut up, you have no clue what you're talking about.'*

David and Jarred's argument is becoming more and more heated, and some of the patients are starting to stare.

**Take a look at the below answers, and then choose the three best options.**

A – Tell David that putting ketchup in the fridge would be a grave error in judgement.

B – Politely and sensitively ask David and Jarred to keep their voices down, because they are disturbing the patients.

C – Tell David and Jarred to stop having silly conversations, and get back to work.

D – Ask David and Jarred whether they would be happy to discuss this serious issue in the consultant's office.

E – Inform David and Jarred that they are being very unprofessional by yelling at each other in a busy ward.

F – Call security. This can only end in violence.

G – Tell David and Jarred that the only thing they should be discussing during work hours, is medical matters.

H – Point out to David and Jarred that this is a conversation which could be resolved in a private room, away from patients.

| 1 | 2 | 3 |
|---|---|---|
|   |   |   |

**Q134.** Your hospital has recently introduced strict new rules for all staff, on recycling. There are a list of recycling guidelines up on the wall of the staffroom, and everyone is expected to follow these. Upon seeing the list, one of your colleagues approaches you:

*'Pfff…I don't care about recycling, no way I'm doing that. We're humans, the dominant species. We can do whatever want to the planet, because it's OURS.'*

Just to emphasise his point, your colleague then takes a recyclable wrapper and throws it into the non-recycling bin.

**Take a look at the below answers, and then choose the three best options.**

A – Inform your colleague that the hospital has enforced these rules for a reason, and that he should stick to them.

B – Agree with your colleague. Recycling is a waste of time.

C – Encourage your colleague to respect the environment, and recycle whenever he can.

D – Immediately report your colleague to a member of senior management. Take a photo of the wrapper as evidence.

E – Ask your colleague to try and respect the hospital rules on recycling, because it's a very important issue.

F – Tell your colleague that he is being extremely disrespectful.

G – Ask your colleague whether he recycles at home.

H – Tell your colleague that by failing to recycle, he could be responsible for the deaths of thousands of people.

| 1 | 2 | 3 |
|---|---|---|
|   |   |   |

**Q135.** One of your fellow FY1s approaches you this morning. She is extremely distressed. When you question her about this, your colleague informs you that her mother passed away last night. She claims that she talked to the consultant about this, and asked for the day off, but the consultant refused this and informed her that she needed to work. She was so scared of losing her job that she came in today.

**Take a look at the below answers, and then choose the three best options.**

A – Tell your colleague that she should file a lawsuit against the consultant.

B – Offer your sincerest condolences to your colleague.

C – Tell your colleague to leave the hospital immediately.

D – Ask your colleague to come with you to see another senior member of staff about this issue. Assure her that she will be able to leave.

E – Offer your condolences to your colleague. Tell her that for now, she needs to try and focus on what her patients need.

F – Tell your colleague that, based on the circumstances, it seems extremely unprofessional for the consultant to ask her to come in. Offer your condolences.

G – Ask your colleague whether she would like you to drive her home.

H – Explain to your colleague that many people in this hospital will lose relatives today, so her problem isn't so special.

| 1 | 2 | 3 |
|---|---|---|
|   |   |   |

**Q136.** Your colleague, Stanley, approaches you and informs you that he is sick and tired of dealing with a particular patient. He tells you that Mr Milgrew, an elderly patient, keeps trying to chat with him. He is frustrated by this, claiming that he signed up to practice medicine, and not to make small talk.

**Take a look at the below answers, and then choose the three best options.**

A – Tell your colleague that he is under no obligation to speak with Mr Milgrew if he doesn't want to.

B – Encourage your colleague to tell Mr Milgrew how he feels.

C – Ask Mr Milgrew to stop trying to chat with Stanley.

D – Tell Stanley that it's very important for him to converse with patients, as this represents good bedside manner.

E – Inform Stanley that he needs to try and make an effort with Mr Milgrew, as he might be feeling lonely.

F – Ask Stanley why he feels that he should be exempt from talking to patients.

G – Encourage Stanley to try and make conversation with Mr Milgrew.

H – Tell Stanley that it's extremely important for him to be polite to patients.

| 1 | 2 | 3 |
|---|---|---|
|   |   |   |

**Q137.** As you walk through the ward the next day, you notice that Stanley is having a conversation with Mr Milgrew. He does not seem to be particularly happy:

**Stanley:** 'No thanks. Now, take your medicine.'

**Mr Milgrew:** 'But you haven't even told me what medicine I'm taking. What is this? What does it do?'

**Stanley:** 'It will make you better, for goodness sakes. Just stop asking questions, you stinky, stupid, old man. I don't want to talk to you anymore.'

Following this, Stanley storms off to deal with another patient.

**Take a look at the below answers, and then choose the three best options.**

A – Immediately approach Mr Milgrew and ask him whether he would like to file a complaint against Stanley.

B – Go and find Stanley. Inform him that his behaviour is totally unacceptable.

C – Tell Mr Milgrew that you are really sorry for your colleague's behaviour, and will launch a full investigation into this.

D – Ask Stanley whether he would consider partaking in extra communication training.

E – Tell Mr Milgrew that in future, he should refrain from asking silly questions.

F – Find the registrar and inform him about what you have just witnessed.

G – Approach Stanley when you get a free moment. Encourage him to apologise to Mr Milgrew.

H – Immediately apologise to Mr Milgrew for Stanley's rudeness. Offer to answer any questions that he has about the medication.

| 1 | 2 | 3 |
|---|---|---|
|   |   |   |

**Q138.** Several of your colleague's patients have approached you. They have informed you that your colleague, Kelly, keeps trying to read them her poetry. All of the patients have claimed that they feel uncomfortable when she does this, as her poetry is quite poor, and they don't know how to react. The patients have asked if you can have a word with her, as they feel too embarrassed to ask her to stop.

You do not know Kelly particularly well, and haven't spoken to her much in the past.

**Take a look at the below answers, and then choose the three best options.**

A – Tell the patients that they should feel honoured and privileged to listen to the work of such a talented poet.

B – Approach Kelly in private, and gently explain that her patients would prefer it if she stopped reading them her poetry.

C – Tell Kelly that she needs to stop reading patients her poetry.

D – Ask Kelly to consider whether reading her poetry to patients is an appropriate form of action.

E – Approach Kelly and tell her that her poetry is dreadful.

F – Inform Kelly that her patients are complaining about her reading poetry.

G – Ask a colleague who is friendlier with Kelly if they could break the news to her.

H – Ask your registrar if he could discuss this with Kelly.

| 1 | 2 | 3 |
|---|---|---|
|   |   |   |

**Q139.** You have noticed that one of your colleagues is sporting an extremely offensive, racist sticker in his car window. The colleague's car parking space is in full view of the patient entrance to the hospital. Although nobody has complained, you are concerned that this could damage the reputation of the hospital.

**Take a look at the below answers, and then choose the three best options.**

A – Immediately approach your colleague and inform him that he needs to move the sticker to somewhere less visible.

B – Try and arrange for your colleague to use an alternative car parking space.

C – Approach your colleague and demand that he removes the sticker from his car.

D – Break into your colleague's car and remove the sticker yourself.

E – Inform your colleague that his sticker is highly inappropriate. Ask him to remove it.

F – Tell your colleague that it is extremely important for him to remove this sticker, as it could harm the reputation of the hospital.

G – Go and discuss the situation with the hospital reception desk.

H – Call the police.

| 1 | 2 | 3 |
|---|---|---|
|   |   |   |

---

**Q140.** The ward consultant has arranged for some of the staff to go on an activity day. As a thank you for all of your hard work this year, he has paid for the staff to take part in a curling session, at a local ice rink. He believes that this will be team building.

Whilst in the staff room, you hear some of your colleagues complaining about this:

**Miranda:** *'Curling?! Curling? That's so lame.'*

**Brian:** *'I always knew the consultant was boring, but I didn't know he was this dull!'*

**Take a look at the below answers, and then choose the three best options.**

A – Tell your colleagues that they are being extremely ungrateful.

B – Go and ask the consultant whether an alternative activity can be arranged.

C – Tell the consultant that some of your colleagues are disgruntled about the exercise he has arranged.

D – Encourage your colleagues to give curling a chance, as they might like it.

E – Tell your colleagues that they are acting very unprofessionally, and that the consultant doesn't deserve to be spoken about in this manner.

F – Agree with your colleagues. The consultant is boring.

G – Tell your colleagues that you will be informing the consultant of exactly what they have said.

H – Explain to your colleagues that this is a team building exercise, and will be very important for ward morale.

| 1 | 2 | 3 |
|---|---|---|
|   |   |   |

---

**Q141.** One of your patients has asked you to take a look at the book that he's going to publish, when he gets out of hospital. In his book, he has included an account of his experiences at the hospital. He writes about the hospital in an extremely negative light, casting doubts over the professionalism of you and your colleagues, and has 'named and shamed' many staff members who he didn't like. You notice that the book is full of inconsistencies, and many of the scenarios written about have been edited to make them seem more dramatic.

The patient has asked you to provide him with your honest opinion of how the book reads.

**Take a look at the below answers, and then choose the three best options.**

A – Tell the patient that you think this is a great book, and will sell really well.

B – Inform the patient that you have major concerns over how he has spoken about the hospital in this book.

C – Go and speak to the consultant about this book, and the potential implications of publishing it.

D – Ask your patient whether there is anything you can do to try and improve his perspective of the hospital.

E – Ask your colleague to read the book, so that you can provide the patient with two opinions.

F – Tell the patient that you are very sorry he has been unhappy with the treatment provided. Inform him that there could be legal implications if he publishes this book as it is.

G – Encourage the patient to pass the book around to other staff members, and see what they think.

H – Tell the patient that his book is full of fabrications, and will never make it to print.

| 1 | 2 | 3 |
|---|---|---|
|   |   |   |

---

**Q142.** The patient from the previous question has published his book, and the hospital are taking legal action against him. The media are extremely interested in this story, and there are a group of reporters gathered around outside the entrance.

All staff are under strict instructions not to speak to any reporters. When you arrive at the hospital on Wednesday morning, you notice that one of your colleagues is having a conversation with a reporter:

'Yep, that's right. It's all a big pack of lies! I mean some of his allegations were true…sure, but not all of them! We are taking legal action against this man, and believe me, he won't get away with it. Any more questions? Who wants the latest scoop?'

**Take a look at the below answers, and then choose the three best options.**

A – Immediately approach your colleague and tell him that he is to stop talking with the reporters at once.

B – Grab your colleague by the arm and pull him away from the reporters.

C – Tell your colleague that he needs to go and see a senior member of staff straight away, to inform them of what he's done.

D – Go and find a senior doctor. Tell them about what your colleague just said.

E – Approach the reporter and tell him not to listen to a word of what your colleague said.

F – Inform the reporters that if they want a big scoop, they should come and speak to you instead.

G – Ask your colleague to stop giving false information to the reporters.

H – Tell the reporters that they need to leave immediately.

| 1 | 2 | 3 |
|---|---|---|
|   |   |   |

---

**Q143.** You are an FY1. One of your elderly patients has informed you that she would like to discharge herself from the hospital. Her daughter vehemently disagrees with this decision, claiming that her mother does not understand what she is doing. You do not believe that the patient has the capacity to make this decision by herself.

**Take a look at the below answers, and then choose the three best options.**

A – Sit down with the patient and assess the reasons for why she wants to discharge.

B – Discharge the patient. It's her choice, and one less problem for you to deal with.

C – Tell the patient that you don't believe she has the capacity to make this decision, and therefore must allow her daughter to decide.

D – Ask the registrar to assist you in assessing the patient, to check whether she has the capacity to make this decision.

E – Tell the patient that she cannot leave.

F – Inform the patient that if she wants to leave the hospital, she'll need to prove to you that she understands the implications of this.

G – Speak to the patient's daughter about her concerns. Ask her why she feels that her mother doesn't have the capacity.

H – Tell the patient that she is too ill to leave.

| 1 | 2 | 3 |
|---|---|---|
|   |   |   |

---

**Q144.** A woman has brought her elderly mother into the hospital, claiming that her mother took a fall at home. The patient has minor injuries. Whilst assessing the patient, you notice that she has a number of bruises on her arms and legs, that could not have been a result of her fall. You also notice that the woman seems quite snappy and abrupt when dealing with her mother.

**Take a look at the below answers, and then choose the three best options.**

A – Assess the patient for signs of physical abuse.

B – Question the patient over whether her daughter has ever struck her or physically harmed her.

C – Screen the patient for suicidal ideation.

D – Accuse the patient's daughter of physically abusing her.

E – Tell the patient that you are very concerned about the bruises on her body.

F – Question the patient over her relationship with her daughter.

G – Ask the patient whether her daughter pushed or tripped her, causing her to fall.

H – Speak to a senior doctor about your concerns.

| 1 | 2 | 3 |
|---|---|---|
|   |   |   |

**Q145.** One of your FY1 colleagues has received a complaint about the way he dealt with a patient. The patient is still on the ward, being treated by another doctor. Your colleague is extremely angry to hear about this. He storms into the ward, seizes the patient by the scruff of his neck, and demands that he rescind his complaint.

The patient does not seem intimidated by this, and tells the doctor that he is happy to have it out with him, right here right now.

**Take a look at the below answers, and then choose the three best options.**

A – Immediately intervene in the situation. Tell your colleague that he needs to go somewhere and calm down. Apologise to the patient.

B – Allow the two of them to fight it out. May the better man win.

C – Tell your colleague that he needs to come with you to see a senior member of staff. Ask the nurses to attend to the patient.

D – Call security to break the fight up.

E – Tell the patient that he needs to rescind his complaint immediately, or take a serious beating.

F – Apologise sincerely to the patient. Tell your colleague that he needs to go home at once.

G – Inform the patient that your colleague has a sustained background in martial arts training.

H – Tell your colleague that he is acting in an incredibly unprofessional manner.

| 1 | 2 | 3 |
|---|---|---|
|   |   |   |

Q146. You are working in the maternity ward. A patient approaches you, in an extremely distressed state. She tells you that she cannot find her eldest son, who was here visiting her at the ward. Her eldest son is 5 years old. The woman's husband, and the boy's father, is at the hospital canteen getting lunch.

One of the nurses informs you that she thinks she saw the boy, with his father, on the way to the canteen.

**Take a look at the below answers, and then choose the three best options.**

A – Accuse the woman of being irresponsible. Tell her that she alone is responsible for the loss of her son.

B – Try to calm the woman down, so that you can ask her some follow up questions on the last place she saw her son.

C – Assure the woman that you will locate her son. Immediately contact the ward sister, asking her to initiate a priority search for the missing boy.

D – Contact security and inform them that a child has been taken from the hospital.

E – Tell the woman that her son is likely with his father, but that you will go and check this is the case, before reporting back to her.

F – Inform the woman that the boy has gone for lunch with his father, at the hospital canteen.

G – Tell the woman that one of the nurses thinks they last saw the boy with his father, so you will go and check for her that this is still the case.

H – Ask the woman to keep a better track on her son's whereabouts, in the future.

| 1 | 2 | 3 |
|---|---|---|
|   |   |   |

Q147. One of your outpatients is a big fan of classic western movies. He frequently comes to the hospital wearing conspicuous clothing, including a large cowboy hat, boots with spurs, and bootcut jeans.

Today, your patient has arrived at the hospital requiring further treatment for his condition. There is a new doctor working on the ward this morning. His name is Joel. Joel approaches the patient and says the following:

*'You look like an absolute clown. Take that stupid hat off.'*

In response, the patient spits in Joel's face.

**Take a look at the below answers, and then choose the three best options.**

A – Immediately intervene. Tell the patient that his behaviour is utterly unacceptable, and that he will no longer be treated at this hospital.

B – Inform the patient that as a result of his behaviour, he could face criminal charges. Ask

Joel to speak with you in a private room about the situation.

C – Apologise to the patient for Joel's rude behaviour.

D – Tell both Joel and the patient that they are acting like fools. Make them apologise to each other.

E – Inform Joel that he needs to go and see a senior manager immediately. Tell the patient that he won't be seen today, but the hospital will arrange a follow up call to discuss the situation.

F – Tell Joel that he needs to clean himself up and get back to work. Advise him to make a full apology to the patient, whilst you contact the nurses about potential disciplinary measures.

G – Tell the patient that his behaviour is out of line. Ask Joel to chat with you in a private room.

H – Do nothing. They are both equally responsible for this situation.

| 1 | 2 | 3 |
|---|---|---|
|   |   |   |

**Q148.** The hospital disciplinary team has asked you to meet with them, as you witnessed the above incident. They want you to tell them about Joel's behaviour.

Before you go into the room, Joel urges you to cast him in a positive light.

**Take a look at the below answers, and then choose the three best options.**

A – Tell the disciplinary team that Joel was provoked by the patient.

B – Tell the disciplinary team that Joel's initial conduct was unacceptable, but the reaction from the patient was far worse.

C – Inform the disciplinary team that Joel issued an unprovoked verbal attack on the patient.

D – Tell the disciplinary team that Joel has attempted to influence what you tell them.

E – Inform the disciplinary team that you believe Joel was the catalyst for the situation, and that the patient reacted understandably.

F – Inform the disciplinary team that whilst you believe Joel is a good doctor, his behaviour in this incident was out of line.

G – Tell the disciplinary team that because Joel is new, you think it would be unfair to blame him for this.

H – Urge the disciplinary team to sack Joel.

| 1 | 2 | 3 |
|---|---|---|
|   |   |   |

**Q149.** You are set to take part in surgery tomorrow morning, and want to get an early night. Two of your other colleagues have their day off tomorrow, and are trying to persuade you to come out with them. You know that if you go out with your colleagues, you are likely to stay up late and have a drink, which could impact on your performance tomorrow.

**Take a look at the below answers, and then choose the three best options.**

A – Tell your colleagues that you don't want to go out with them tonight.

B – Inform your colleagues that you have an operation tomorrow morning, and therefore you want to stay sharp.

C – Go out with your colleagues. Do your best not to drink.

D – Go straight to your consultant. Inform him that your colleagues are trying to persuade you to act in an unacceptable manner.

E – Politely decline your colleagues' request. Tell them that you will go out with them on another night, when you aren't required at work the next morning.

F – Tell your colleagues that they are acting childishly.

G – Go out with your colleagues. You'll regret it, but at least you'll have a good time.

H – Tell your colleagues that you can't go out with them on this occasion.

| 1 | 2 | 3 |
|---|---|---|
|   |   |   |

**Q150.** The ward consultant has called you into his office. You aren't sure what the meeting is about. When you sit down, the consultant informs you that he is extremely pleased with your progress this year, and feels that you improved leaps and bounds in the last few months.

He wants to know your feelings about your first year in medicine. You have enjoyed working at this hospital, and would like to continue.

**Take a look at the below answers, and then choose the three best options.**

A – Thank the consultant for his kind words. Inform him that by this time next year, you will have taken his job.

B – Inform the consultant that you are extremely happy with how your first year has gone, and thank him for all the help he's given you.

C – Tell the consultant that it's been a good year, and you are pleased with how you've progressed.

D – Ask the consultant why he thinks you are superior to your other colleagues.

E – Thank the consultant for his help over the past year.

F – Encourage the consultant to try and improve his practice in the following year, as you feel he is lacking.

G – Tell the consultant that you have been really impressed by the hospital's standards over the past year.

H – Tell the consultant that you feel as if you are the best doctor in the entire hospital.

| 1 | 2 | 3 |
|---|---|---|
|   |   |   |

You have now finished the second section of practice questions. Make sure that you check your answers.

# ANSWERS TO PRACTICE QUESTIONS SECTION 2

## Q1. C, E, D

**Explanation:**

The best responses in this case would be to apologise to the patient, as shown in option C, and to inform the patient that you will take action to prevent this from happening in the future, as shown in option E. Following that, it would reasonable to try and give the patient a small explanation for what happened. There's nothing in the question that suggests Fran is a bad doctor, and her bad mood clearly indicates that she was having 'an off day'. This happens to everyone sometimes. Although it's not an excuse for her behaviour, it's okay to inform the patient of this, so that he doesn't feel as if he's done anything wrong.

## Q2. B, H, A

**Explanation:**

In this case, the best response would be for you to inform the family about the diagnosis yourself, as shown in options B and H. Following this, you need to speak to Andrew about why he didn't deliver the news, as shown in option A.

## Q3. C, E, D

**Explanation:**

The best thing to do in this case would be to try and get a full account from the patient about what he felt was below standard, as shown in option E. Ideally, you should do this in a quiet room, so that the patient has a space where he can fully express his concerns, as shown in option C. Feedback from patients is extremely important, and the hospital staff should always be looking to improve their own practice. If options C and E are not available, then the best thing to do would be to ask the patient to speak to someone else about these issues. They shouldn't just be ignored.

## Q4. A, F, H

**Explanation:**

In this instance, your primary concern needs to be with the other patients in the ward. The first thing you should do is ask Stuart and his family to lower their voices. You should take into account that he is a young patient, so be polite and considerate about this. Following making a polite request, your second course of action would be to tell the patient and his family that they need to keep the noise down – this is not a request, but an instruction. Finally, if the patient does not calm down, you may be in a position where asking them to leave the ward is the best course of action.

## Q5. A, F, C

**Explanation:**

When dealing with a situation like this, the best person to speak to would be your clinical supervisor. Your supervisor should be able to determine whether you are receiving a suitable amount of clinical practice, or whether there is an imbalance that needs to be addressed. This is shown in option A. Option F is also useful. If you feel that the senior doctors in the ward aren't giving you respect, then it would be a good idea to try and raise this issue with the group. Finally, if the above two options fail, then you could always contact the Foundation Programme Director, as shown in option C, but this isn't something you should do immediately.

## Q6. B, E, H

**Explanation:**

In a situation like this, you should use common sense. The patient needs to be treated first, before any admin issues (such as car parking) are dealt with. Following this, you should use common sense to tell the woman how she can resolve this situation. The reception desk should be well placed to help the woman, since she has a reasonable explanation for why she could not pay the fare. Ideally, you should just give the woman advice on where she can resolve this, as shown in option B. If this is not an option, then the next thing to do would be firstly treat her, and then find someone who can resolve the problem for her. Option H is okay, but at the same time it implies that the woman won't need to pay for parking – which is incorrect.

## Q7. C, H, E

**Explanation:**

In this situation, the best response is to be honest with the patient about his father's status. Option C is very honest but tactful at the same time. Option H is also acceptable, although it doesn't fully answer David's query. The question clearly states that there will be a long wait, not that there could be. This is the same for option E, although option E does not give any indication as to the waiting time.

## Q8. D, C, F

**Explanation:**

Regardless of whether the patient has a history of making false claims, you need to treat this issue with the utmost seriousness. Therefore, the first thing you should do is to contact security, and ask them to check the CCTV as a matter of priority – as shown in option D. If you don't feel confident in trusting the patient on this issue, then the next best course of action would be to question the patient further, to establish what she saw. Finally, if none of these options are viable, then you should speak to the nursing team. However, it's worth pointing out that if one of the nurses had seen this individual in the ward, they would have already taken action – so it's unlikely that you will get a useful response.

**Q9. G, C, A**

**Explanation:**

This is a very serious situation. The best thing to do here is to take the issue to a senior member of staff. You are an FY1, so although there are steps that you can take, the most sensible option is to refer the issue to another member of staff, as shown in option G. If this is not a viable option, then the next thing to do would be to show the woman how can she go about making a complaint, after which the relevant management team would deal with the issue, as shown in option C. Finally, if neither of these two things are available, the best option is to apologise sincerely to the patient and assure her that this will be taken very seriously.

**Q10. E, F, D**

**Explanation:**

In a situation like this, the best approach would be to ask the consultant to clarify his decision. You should not be afraid to question decisions if you believe that they are wrong, just as long as this is done in a polite and respectful way, as shown in option E. Following this, the next best response would be to inform the consultant about what doubts you have, and why you think there are better solutions. Again, you should make sure that this is done in a polite and respectful way, as shown in option F. The third option here is D. In a situation such as this, you need to compare the benefits of option D with those of option B. Option B is very rude, to the point and doesn't give any reasoning to the consultant about why you don't agree with him. In contrast, an MRI scan takes 90 minutes to complete, and there are no side effects to this. If the consultant has ordered this test then there's likely a good reason behind it.

**Q11. C, B, F**

**Explanation:**

In this scenario, your colleague absolutely cannot remain at the hospital. After just one hour of sleep, he needs to go home and rest, as he is clearly not in the right mental state to treat patients. Telling him to notify a senior doctor, who might also be able to advise him about the financial problems he is having, is the right call, as shown in option C. Your colleague's clinical supervisor will also be able to point him in the right direction, and will tell him that needs to go home, as shown in option B. Option F is similar to option C, but you aren't telling your colleague that he needs to go home.

**Q12. B, D, E**

**Explanation:**

The best response in this scenario would be to meet with the family of the patient as soon as possible. During this meeting, you can apologise for any confusion, and reassure them of your capability as a doctor, and that you are trustworthy, as shown in option B. Option D is also a good option, as you are offering to answer any questions that they have and clarify things from the previous day, however you aren't apologising. Option E gives the family a chance to clarify their confusion, but doesn't apologise and is quite blunt.

## Q13. C, D, F

**Explanation:**

In this case, Mrs Long's son is being very abusive. You do not have to put up with this as a doctor, and you should make it clear that his behaviour is unacceptable. You also need to fetch a senior doctor. It would be much more appropriate for you to ask for help from another doctor, than to try and tackle this situation without a full understanding of the patient's condition, as shown in option C. Option D is very similar to this, but doesn't explain to the family about the benefits of finding a senior doctor to help. Option F is also reasonable, as you are providing the family with assurance in the ability of hospital staff, but at the same time you need to make it clear that Mrs Long's son is behaving unacceptably.

## Q14. B, D, H

**Explanation:**

In an incident as serious as this, your first line of action should be to report the behaviour. It makes sense to ask Hector to come with you, as he is a witness to this. Option B is also accurate, in that Nathan has committed a criminal offence, and you would have grounds to file charges against him. Option D is also acceptable, provided you actually back it up by reporting the behaviour. Option H is a good response because it allows you to calm down and carefully assess the situation, although in all likelihood your educational supervisor is going to advise you to report Nathan. They are not in a position to give you legal advice about this matter.

## Q15. A, D, G

**Explanation:**

In a situation such as this, where it appears that the patient is mistaken, it's important for someone to speak to the patient and alleviate their concerns. In this case, it should be the consultant. He is a senior member of staff. Although he might be slightly offended to be accused of this, he will need to take responsibility for dealing with the issue. This is best shown in option A. Option D is very similar to A, but in this option you aren't elaborating on what the problem is. Option G takes a sensitive approach to the problem, but the question clearly indicates that you do not have any reason to believe the consultant is acting whilst under the influence of alcohol – only the patient's viewpoint.

## Q16. B, C, H

**Explanation:**

In this situation, where you are dealing with a very distressed young child, the first thing you should do is try to speak to the child. Option B sees the doctor using a gentle and reassuring tone, to try and persuade Emma that you can help her. Once you have gained Emma's trust, it would be a good idea to ask Emma's father to assist with examining her. This will be more comforting for the patient. Option C is similar to B, except here you are trying to clarify the reasons for her refusing treatment – which then naturally leads into B.

## Q17. . G, B, D

**Explanation:**

In this instance, the doctor's obligation is to deal with the patient as matter of immediate priority. Whether he has the rest of his break afterwards will be for him to discuss with a senior member of staff, but he needs to go and help Mr Wiggins right away. Option D is the third best response, because it takes a sensible approach, encouraging the doctor to think about how this would impact his career. However, it would be better to just point out that patient safety should be the number one priority.

## Q18. C, H, E

**Explanation:**

The best thing to do here would be to take the form away from the patient immediately. Following this, you need to go and find the doctor who made the error, to explain to him what has happened. It will then be his issue to deal with. If neither option C or H is available, then you should bring the matter to a senior member of staff, who will have the power to investigate further.

## Q19. E, A, G

**Explanation:**

In a situation like this, it is the responsibility of the hospital staff to respect the patient's wishes and try to find alternative solutions to the problem. E is more definitive than A, you are making it clear that without the patient's consent, such diagnostic measures cannot be performed. G is a respectful and sensitive option, although it does not give any mention to alternative forms of diagnosis, which needs to be considered.

## Q20. D, G, E

**Explanation:**

In this situation, it's important for you to recognise that as an FY1, it is unfair and incorrect for the consultant to put in this position. Option D does this in a clear and respectful manner, that still emphasises your willingness to work as part of the team, whilst being firm about the mistake. Option G is very similar to this. The reason that option E is better than option A, is because you shouldn't rule yourself out entirely from dealing with situations like this. You are currently an FY1, but that doesn't mean that you won't eventually progress to becoming a senior member of staff, in which case you would need to assist with issues such as patient complaints.

## Q21. D, B, F

### Explanation:

This is a very serious breach of conduct from James, and it needs to be dealt with straight away. You should take action here, as you are a doctor working on the ward, and you have a duty to protect the patients. Therefore, your first action should be demanding that the individuals in question turn off their cameras, and leave immediately, as shown in option D. Next, you need to deal with James, who has behaved in an unacceptable manner. Taking this issue to senior management is the best way to do this. This is especially important given the seriousness of the situation. The question states that the patient in question is world famous. If these pictures leak all over the internet then this could have serious ramifications for the hospital. This means that reporting the incident to a senior manager is imperative, as shown in option F.

## Q22. D, F, E

### Explanation:

The best solution in this case would be to ask a senior member of staff to deal with the situation. It's true that you should take responsibility, but as an FY1 you shouldn't have to worry about the poor behaviour of senior managers. This is something that needs to be resolved immediately, but a senior member of staff should be the one to do it. If there is no option for senior staff to deal with the situation, then the best response is for you to make an appointment and sit down with the consultant, one to one, and discuss his behaviour.

## Q23. A, H, C

### Explanation:

In this scenario, you should point out to the consultant that the senior doctor in question recommended a different course of action to the one you initially chose. This is a fair and reasonable thing to point out. As a new doctor, although it's good to stick with your convictions, it is hard to blame you for taking the advice of a senior colleague. Option C does come with some issues, mainly that you aren't telling the complete truth. The question does not give any indication that you were against running a CT scan.

## Q24. C, G, H

### Explanation:

This is a tricky situation. You should always try to be courteous towards a senior member of staff, and it might well be the case that your supervisor is just too busy to meet with you at that particular time. Even senior doctors procrastinate! So, it might just be that your supervisor is engaged in something serious that requires immediate attention, whilst having the game on as a distraction in the background. However, in this scenario you would be entitled to question him about the validity of this. Option C is the politest way to respond, with G and H being natural follow ups to this.

## Q25. A, F, E

### Explanation:

In this scenario, your main priority should be in self-preservation. If the invigilator sees Steve sitting next to you chatting, then they will automatically assume that the two of you are cheating. With this in mind, you need to get their attention immediately, to make it clear that you have not solicited this conversation in any way. Both A and F deal with this in an appropriate manner. Option E is not great, because the invigilator will see Steve sitting next to you and assume the worst, but at least you are not involving yourself in his misbehaviour.

## Q26. E, B, D

### Explanation:

Obviously, this is quite a strange situation. In this scenario you need to see the invigilator as soon as possible. However, he is dealing with a very distressed colleague, so you could argue that it would be sensitive to wait until he's finished with this. Option B is just as acceptable though, as your exam should be an immediate priority. Option D isn't great but at least you are bringing the matter to someone's attention.

## Q27. E, H, G

### Explanation:

This is a tough question. In this scenario, it's very important to consider the age of the patient. Given the patient is just 14 years old, it is very likely that he doesn't have a full understanding of what he is saying. Therefore, in this situation, the best approach would be to try and educate the patient yourself, explaining why the comments are wrong – as shown in option E. Following this, the next best response would be to inform the patient's parents about the behaviour, so that they can educate him themselves – as shown in option H. Finally, if the patient refuses to be treated by you then you should fetch a senior doctor who can do so instead, as shown in option G.

**Q28. E, H, D**

**Explanation:**

In a scenario such as this, where a very young person has expressed suicidal thoughts, your immediate priority should be to keep them at the hospital whilst this is looked into and addressed. Given the age of the patient, you will need to discuss the issue with her parents immediately, as shown in option E. Option H reassures the patient that her issue will be given full assessment by the hospital. Finally, option D presents a supportive and helpful solution, although you still need to keep the patient at the hospital whilst this is resolved.

**Q29. D, B, F**

**Explanation:**

In this situation, the most immediate and obvious thing to do would be to tell your colleague to stop reading the book. Both D and B cover this, although how you rank each option depends on which way you would prefer to tell him. Option F is very similar, but instead of informing your colleague that the book is on the ban list, it just gives the reasons for why it's banned.

**Q30. F, B, C**

**Explanation:**

In a situation where you are unsure as to how you should proceed, as an FY1, your first priority would be to find a senior doctor. In this case, it would be wise to conduct a physical examination of Mrs Matthews whilst the nurse finds a doctor, as shown in option F. This means that when the doctor arrives, you'll at least have some useful information that you can provide him. Second to that, is simply finding a senior doctor yourself, as shown in option B. Finally, Option C somewhat covers both of the above, but the patient just wants someone who can treat her – you don't need to ask for her permission.

**Q31. B, G, F**

**Explanation:**

In a situation like this, the first thing to do would be to try and speak with Dr Taylor directly. This is the most courteous option. You shouldn't just jump to conclusions, as there may be a medical or equipment based reason as to why there is disparity between the results. Option G is quite abrupt, but at least you are taking the time to assess the situation properly before marching downstairs with your results. Finally, option F puts the problem in the hands of someone who might be able to offer an explanation, or is better placed to deal with the issue.

**Q32. A, D, G**

**Explanation:**

This question tests your ability to deal with a colleague who has confided in you. Options A, D and G are very similar – all offer some degree of positivity and encourage your colleague in different ways, whilst still asserting that your colleague needs to inform her partner about the problem.

**Q33. A, B, E**

**Explanation:**

In this question, Hakim has committed a serious breach of conduct, and this needs to be addressed straight away. The best thing to do would be to inform Hakim that he has broken the rules. Following this, the situation needs to be dealt with by a senior doctor, as a matter of priority. Option E is not really enough. This isn't just 'unacceptable behaviour' but it's a violation of the medical code of ethics.

**Q34. C, F, H**

**Explanation:**

This question is pretty much just a matter of common courtesy. All doctors have the occasional bad day, and sometimes if you are in a bad mood this could transfer over to your bedside manner, even if you try to avoid that from happening. The best thing to do here is to apologise, and then explain to the patient that she just caught you in a bad moment.

**Q35. A, G, B**

**Explanation:**

In this situation, you should encourage your colleague to get in touch with the radiology department and resolve the situation. Yes, he has made a mistake, but the only way to make up for it is just to admit the error and try to improve for next time. Your colleague needs to take responsibility. Option G is the second best option, but it's not great, because it would be better for your colleague to just go down to the department and get a replacement scan. Option B, although correct, is fairly insensitive.

**Q36. C, H, G**

**Explanation:**

In this scenario, your first obligation is to be honest. The question clearly states that you have not witnessed any bullying taking place, so you need to inform the doctor of this, as shown in option C. Option H is the second-best response, because it shows your integrity and professionalism. Option G is the third best response. Unlike options E and F, you aren't giving the doctor irrelevant information or taking shots at Paul and Melissa.

## Q37. G, H, B

**Explanation:**

The best thing for Melinda to do here would be to consult with the nursing sister about the issue. The question states that the patient is becoming irate and is threatening violence, which means that going directly to him and admitting the error could have a negative response. Although someone will need to break the news to him, it is better to discuss how and who will inform the patient about what has happened, before it's done. This ensures that the issue is dealt with in a sensitive manner. This is shown in option G, and in option H. If neither of the above two options are available, then your next course of action should be to encourage Melinda to speak with a senior doctor.

## Q38. G, C, B

**Explanation:**

There are several things that need to be addressed in this situation. Firstly, the nurse is being disrespectful to the patient and his dog. You should apologise on behalf of the hospital for her poor behaviour. Secondly, you need to ensure that the nurse's mistake is corrected. The question clearly states that guide dogs are the exception to the hospital's policy, and should be allowed. Therefore, option G is the best response, and is closely followed by option C. Option B also ensures that the situation is amended, but doesn't offer an apology to the patient.

## Q39. C, E, A

**Explanation:**

This is a very serious situation. Sabotaging the new website could put people at risk. Imagine if sick members of the public need to get online on launch day, to get the details of the hospital, but can't because Matt has ruined the website. You can't allow him to go through with this, or even risk the chance that he will. With this in mind, you have an obligation to report this to Matt's boss, as shown in option C. Following this, you'd just have to try and reason with him. Both options E and A attempt this to some degree. Option D is unsuitable because Matt clearly doesn't care about what his boss thinks, so threatening him in this manner is not going to work.

## Q40. A, G, D

**Explanation:**

In this scenario, the first thing you should do is question your colleague. You should give him the benefit of the doubt, because in this situation we would all of course be hoping that a fellow professional would not act in such a manner. Both A and G cover this, in a reasonable fashion. Following this, your next course of action would be to take the situation to a senior member of staff. The question clearly states that Barry's behaviour has escalated, to the point where he is being racist and extremist. Before this point, it was probably not reportable, but such behaviour indicates a dramatic escalation and should be dealt with as a matter of priority. It is not acceptable for a hospital staff member to behave in this manner.

## Q41. A, D, F

**Explanation:**

In this scenario, the best thing to do would be to first of all explain why the situation is as bad as it is, and then reassure the patient that steps are being taken to fix this issue. Obviously, it's unacceptable, so it's imperative that the patient knows something is being done – as shown in option A. Options D and F are useful, but at the same time there is not much a senior member of staff can do to amend the patient's opinion now that he's discharging, nor is there much you can do apart from assuring him that this will be dealt with.

## Q42. C, D, F

**Explanation:**

Even if the patient is being rude, in this situation you need to consider that they are clearly distressed and worried. Patients can sometimes build up a relationship of trust with their doctor, and therefore it might be very upsetting for Kevin to learn that he is now being treated by a new doctor – and it might take him some time to get used to you. Therefore, the best approach here is to reassure the patient that you are fully capable of treating him, as shown in option C. Following this, the most reasonable approach would be to gently try and persuade Kevin that he cannot be treated by Dr Square at this time, and therefore must come round to the idea of being treated by someone else, as shown in option D, and option F.

## Q43. F, A, H

**Explanation:**

This is a pretty tricky situation. Obviously, your immediate priority is clear – you shouldn't accept the money under any circumstances. However, after this it becomes a little bit grey as to how you should behave. In this instance, you do not yet have definitive proof that the woman picked up asbestosis from her working environment, and it is up to the patient to decide whether she wants to pursue action or not. Option F is the strongest response here. Not only are you refusing the money, and prioritising your patient's safety, but you are taking steps to ensure that the employer's behaviour is on record. If the issue does eventually go to court, then this could be very important. In Option A you are emphasising that the patient's welfare is your immediate priority, and rejecting the inappropriate offer. Option H again takes the view that if this is an issue that will be addressed legally, assuming the patient does decide to press charges, then the patient has the right to be told how her boss (against whom she'd be taking action) is behaving.

**Q44. A, E, G**

**Explanation:**

This is a very serious scenario. You should have spotted that the main issue here is that the man is browsing patient records. Even if he was just a worker performing maintenance, this would be totally unacceptable, so it needs to be dealt with right away. The security team are the best placed people to resolve this. It might well be the case that the man will be subject to criminal charges, as he has committed a serious offence by browsing through patient records. Option E and G are problematic, and don't address the issue urgently enough, but at least they go some way to dealing with the problem.

**Q45. B, D, C**

**Explanation:**

In this scenario, there is not much you can really do for your colleague, apart from offering support. However, it's imperative that the safety of patients is taken into account. This is why option B is the best response. Based on the information you've been given, you have reason to suspect that individuals with negative intentions could come to the hospital. This means that patients could be placed at risk, and therefore both the reception desk and security should be notified. Following this, the next best response would be to advise your colleague to take the rest of the day off and resolve this problem. The question clearly emphasises that your colleague is not able to work to the best of his ability, and is unable to focus on patients, because of his problems. Therefore, he needs to resolve this issue before he can be given responsibility of sick patients, as shown in option D. Finally, option C gives your colleague your full support, but emphasises that this issue cannot be allowed to carry over onto hospital premises, or impact patients.

**Q46. B, D, A**

**Explanation:**

This situation requires you to be honest and admit that you made an error. The best way for you to do this would be to apologise to the patient, and then give her a detailed explanation of why she'll need to stay at the hospital. If you can reassure her of the medical reasons for her extended stay, and that this is being done so that the doctors can ensure her wellbeing, then you might be able to offset some of her initial anger at the mistake. Option D is similar to this, although it seemingly underplays the issue – you initially told the patient that she will only be at the hospital for a few more days, but now it has emerged that she'll need to stay for a few more weeks, which is quite a difference. Option A is good because you are being honest with the consultant, who will be able to advise you on how to deal with this problem.

**Q47. B, E, A**

**Explanation:**

This question is essentially challenging your medical principles, and your ability to stand up to a senior figure if you believe that they are in the wrong. The best response here, option B, reassures the consultant about the level of care the patient will receive, whilst still emphasising that all patients should be given the same, excellent level of treatment. Option E is very similar to this, with the only difference being that in A you reassure the consultant over how you will treat the patient. Option A is okay, but it's quite blunt, and likely won't fill the consultant with confidence.

## Q48. A, D, E

**Explanation:**

This question tests how sensitively and appropriately you can deal with a distressed colleague. Working in a hospital is extremely difficult, and can take a severe emotional toll on staff. In this case, the best thing to do would be to state your confidence in your colleague's ability, and reassure her that feeling upset is not a barrier to working in the medical profession. This is shown in option A. Option D is similarly helpful, in that it suggests a useful avenue for your colleague to pursue if she's feeling distressed. Option E is also good, although informing your colleague that she'll get used to incidents like this paints a rather morbid picture moving forward.

## Q49. B, F, G

**Explanation:**

This is a very serious situation. However, the best thing to do would not to instantly jump to conclusions about your colleague, despite what you heard. You need to speak to your colleague first, before you take any other action. Once you've spoken to your colleague, you can make a decision on whether his version of events makes sense, or whether you should report the issue. This is why option B is the best response. Option F is also useful, but at the same time it would still be better to speak to Gordon yourself, rather than sharing the details of his phone conversation with another member of staff. Finally, option G will probably annoy him – as you've admitted to eavesdropping, but at least it confronts the issue.

## Q50. F, H, C

**Explanation:**

In a scenario such as this, where a fellow medical professional is behaving unacceptably, and won't listen to reason, your best option is to take the issue to the ward consultant. The question clearly states that you have attempted to speak to Craig about this issue. The fact that he is not completing any patient paperwork is very concerning, and the question also states that you are concerned for the safety of Craig's patients' welfare. You should see the consultant immediately about this issue. Option H is the next best thing to do. This will provide clear evidence to the consultant that Craig is acting contrary to GMC and hospital expectations. Finally, option C attempts to reason with Craig, but the question already states that you tried this and it was unsuccessful. Furthermore, given the doctor in question is so stubborn, it seems unlikely that he will be willing to speak to the consultant himself – especially if he hasn't acknowledged any wrongdoing.

## Q51. E, A, D

### Explanation:

In this scenario, your colleague's behaviour directly risks the reputation of the hospital, especially since he is broadcasting to hundreds of viewers worldwide. This type of behaviour would not be acceptable in any kind of organisation, let alone the medical profession, where patients must be able to trust their doctors to treat them with respect and dignity. The best way to deal with this would be to inform a senior doctor about the situation, so that they can instigate disciplinary measures against your colleague. However, it is courteous to inform your colleague of what action you are taking, before you do it, as shown in option E. Following this, option A would be the best choice. Either way, it needs to be reported. Finally, Option D is somewhat helpful, but doesn't really reflect the seriousness of the situation.

## Q52. C, E, D

### Explanation:

This question requires you to balance medical principles and dedication to patients with your own personal problems. In a situation like this, you would be expected to balance the seriousness of the scenario against how critically you are needed at the hospital. In this case, it could be argued that the needs of the hospital and your patient exceed those of your personal life. Your son does need a lift home from school, but this is something that can be arranged by your wife, who is not dealing with a life and death situation. Therefore, the most reasonable response in this situation would be to inform your partner that this isn't something you can deal with right now. If this option is not available, then asking your consultant for a quick five minute break, whilst you try and sort things out, would be reasonable.

## Q53. A, G, C

### Explanation:

In this situation, the best approach is to tell the consultant in no uncertain terms that you won't obey this instruction, and that you have a duty of care to protect all patients – regardless of how unpleasant they might be, or their political circumstances, as shown in option A. Option G is also a reasonable response, and points out just one of the flaws in the consultant's unprofessional plan, but it would better to just firmly tell the consultant that you won't do it. Finally, option C is similar to G, but not really assertive enough.

## Q54. F, C, E

### Explanation:

Your immediate priority here should be to deal with the patient at hand. The patient is understandably very upset at your colleague's behaviour, so the first thing you should do is to reassure her that you will now conduct a proper assessment of her condition, and apologise for the previous incident. Following this, we have option C. Option C is good, because it apologises to the patient for the incident and assures her that action will be taken, but it fails to mention anything about re-assessing the woman in a proper fashion. Finally, option E is useful because it deals with your colleague directly (something that will need to be done regardless of which option is picked) but gives priority to this over assessing the patient yourself.

## Q55. D, G, E

**Explanation:**

Naturally, hospitals place enormous importance on sanitation, and therefore it's very important that all facilities within the hospital are kept up to standard. The best thing to do here would be to apologise to the patient, and then inform the domestic services manager about the situation, as shown in option D. If you are unable to do this, then you should ask another member of staff to do this, as shown in option G. Finally, if neither of these two options is available, then the next best course of action would be to bring the issue to the attention of a senior doctor. It's important that this is resolved, and that other patients aren't impacted by it.

## Q56. D, H, G

**Explanation:**

This question is testing your ability to understand when a situation needs to be reported, when it needs to be dealt with by you, and when it can be left alone. In this scenario, the question gives no indication that your colleague is stealing. Therefore, the best response here would be to inform your other colleagues, who are seemingly spreading lies and malicious speculation, to (D) stop jumping to conclusions and (H) not to involve you in their gossip. Option G is not great, because it's very blunt and will offend Gabriel, but at least he will be able to address these rumours directly and put a stop to them.

## Q57. A, F, C

**Explanation:**

There's nothing too complicated about this question. You should be sensitive to your colleague's feelings – so don't march up and demand that he stops, and also acknowledge that this is a minor issue, so there's no need to overreact and take it to senior management. The best approach here is just to speak to your colleague in private and ask him to refrain from this behaviour, before explaining why.

## Q58. A, E, D

**Explanation:**

In this question you need to assess the seriousness of the situation. The question clearly indicates that this situation hasn't reached a point where it could be considered high priority or bullying. Although you have an inclination that your colleague is feeling a bit upset, you aren't sure of this, and the question indicates that she is taking the teasing in good spirits. Therefore, the best approach here is to encourage Lizzie and give her some positive feedback on her performance, as shown in options A and E. Option D is okay too, as you are being direct about the issue, but it might be a little unnecessary.

## Q59. B, E, D

**Explanation:**

In this scenario, if the consultant genuinely has made a mistake, then it's best not to be rude about it. You should stand your ground about when the original deadline was set, whilst at the same time attempting to be flexible and acknowledging that sometimes priorities change – and therefore you should do your best work in time for the new deadline. Both option B and E cover this succinctly. Option D comes across as argumentative, but it's still the next best option available, as it doesn't involve falsely admitting you were wrong or being rude to the consultant.

## Q60. D, G, B

**Explanation:**

The question here clearly states that the boys are patients at the hospital. Therefore, your first response should be to inform the staff on the relevant ward about their poor behaviour. The reason that this is the best response is twofold: firstly it might be the case that the boys have particular behavioural problems – which would account for their actions, and secondly it is likely that the staff's initial reaction will be to contact the boys' parents. Options D and G clearly cover this. Option B is very severe, and should only be done if you feel that the boys in question present a serious risk to either yourself or patients.

## Q61. C, A, H

**Explanation:**

This question wants you to consider a) how you would react to a patient complaint, and b) how you would factor the seriousness of this complaint. In this case, it's understandable that the patient would be annoyed, but at the same time it's a minor issue in the grand scheme of things. Option C is really good, as you are going out of your way to ensure that the patient is happy whilst at the hospital. However, if this is not possible, then the best response is be polite and honest with the woman, and explain the situation in full – hoping that she will understand, as shown in option A and option H.

## Q62. A, H, E

**Explanation:**

In a scenario such as this, it's entirely possible that your colleague is unaware of how he's behaving. Therefore, the best approach would be to give him the benefit of the doubt, but also ensure that a) his behaviour stops, and b) he offers a full apology to the patient. Option A covers the first option, and options H and E cover the second.

## Q63. A, C, H

### Explanation:

The best thing to do in this scenario, is to refuse to go. Not only do you not have experience of working with this person, but option H is correct – complaining to management about a promotion will make you look extremely unprofessional. Option A is the best response. You are encouraging your colleagues to try and better their practice, instead of undermining someone else. C is also acceptable. As the question states, you have little experience of dealing with Jordan and therefore it would be unfair for you to pass negative comment on him.

## Q64. A, G, E

### Explanation:

In a situation like this, where a patient has directly threatened you, you are certainly within your rights to inform the hospital that you no longer wish to treat them. Both options A and G cover this. Following that, things get a bit trickier. The patient has made a threat to your life. It's really up to you about how you deal with this. You would be perfectly entitled to seek legal advice, and even contact the police about the threat, if you felt truly threatened by this individual's behaviour.

## Q65. E, C, B

### Explanation:

This is more of an ethical question than medical. The best response here is to encourage your colleague to pursue a career which makes him happiest. Although you could try and persuade your colleague to continue working as a doctor, at the end of the day it's not your place to interfere in his career plans, so you should just encourage him to do whatever he thinks is best.

## Q66. E, A, H

### Explanation:

In this scenario, the doctor in question has acted a little unfairly by putting you on the spot like this, without telling you why. However, since he is a senior member of staff, you will need to attend the meeting regardless. Option E is the best response here, as it means that you are fully prepared and ready to attend the meeting, whether the results are positive or negative. In option A you are simply attending the meeting. In this case, this is a fair response, but it's good to try and prepare beforehand if at all possible. Finally option H is helpful but a little unnecessary, since you can assume that the doctor would have told you if you needed to bring anything.

## Q67. A, B, D

**Explanation:**

In this scenario, the first thing you should do is to apologise to the patient, and show him where he can find the nearest bathroom. Following this, you need to confront your colleague about their poor behaviour. It is unacceptable for them to treat patients in this manner.

## Q68. D, F, E

**Explanation:**

In this scenario, the best thing to do would be to approach your colleague and remind him about the rules and why they are in place. It's possible that your colleague has forgotten about this particular rule, which is an easy mistake to make. Therefore, it's much better to approach him in a polite fashion than to report him, especially since his behaviour is not upsetting anyone. You should still make sure that he keeps to the rules though.

## Q69. C, E, D

**Explanation**

In this scenario, the first thing to do would be to ask Fred to apologise to Janine. Disagreements between colleagues can happen, but it's important that this doesn't get out of hand. The question clearly states that you notice Janine has been upset by Fred's behaviour, and therefore the best solution would be to quickly raise this and get him to apologise, before moving on, as shown in option C. Following this, option E deals with the problem in a similar manner. Option D is okay because it considers the feelings of Janine, but the question already states that you can see she's upset.

## Q70. E, A, C

**Explanation:**

This is a really difficult situation, but the best thing to do here would be to go and find a senior doctor, who will have a reasonable idea of a) how to discuss the implications of the mother's accusation, and b) what the next steps would be. As an FY1, you would not be expected to deal directly with this situation. Following this, the next steps would be for the hospital to report this issue directly to social services, as you have a duty of care to the patient, and to further question both Melissa and her mother – to establish the full details of this issue.

## Q71. B, F, C

**Explanation:**

In this scenario, the first thing you need to do is ask the nurses to help you perform an immediate assessment of Mrs Lechamps condition. She is clearly in a very bad way, and needs immediate medical attention. The next option would be to consult with another doctor on the ward. If there is anyone on the ward who has dealt with Mrs Lechamps previously, they might be able to give you some indication of what the next steps should be. Finally, and as a last resort, you should contact the consultant.

## Q72. A, D, B

**Explanation:**

In this scenario, the best course of action would be to try and see if you can move to an alternative department within the hospital. This is a more than reasonable request, especially if you feel that your learning is being impacted. At the end of the day, as an FY1, you need to improve and grow as a doctor and therefore it's imperative that the hospital can provide you with an environment where this is possible. Therefore, option A would be the best response. Option D is also useful, in that you are explaining the issue clearly to someone very senior, who will then deal with this matter internally. Finally, option B is quite blunt and forthright – you could definitely be much more polite about this issue, but at the same time you are entitled to speak out if you don't feel that the standard of learning is high enough.

## Q73. A, B, G

**Explanation:**

In this situation, where you have a stubborn colleague who is refusing to adjust to the new rules, then the most reasonable primary approach would be to try and convince her otherwise. Realistically, showing Mandy that her refusal to cooperate could risk the lives of patients and staff, should get her to change her mind. Failing this, the next option would be to ask someone more qualified to explain the rule to her, as shown in option B. Finally, if Mandy still refuses, you would need to report her to a senior member of staff.

## Q74. B, E, G

**Explanation:**

In this scenario, the best thing to do would be to try and contact someone who can help you. Ideally, this should be the registrar, as shown in option B. However, if this person is not available then your next point of contact should be the nurses on the ward, who will likely have a good idea of how to proceed. Finally, if neither of those two options are available, then you should be honest with the patient and inform him that you need a senior doctor to assist you with this. The worst thing to do here would be to try and perform a procedure that you are unfamiliar with on your own. If you make a mistake then you could end up risking the patient's welfare.

**Q75. D, C, E**

**Explanation:**

No person should have to put up with sexual harassment. In this case, the workers have clearly behaved unacceptably and your colleague's first response should be to report this behaviour to a senior member of staff. Offering to accompany your colleague to report this is a good move. It can often be difficult or uncomfortable for someone to either discuss this issue or take action against it, and therefore it might be the case that your presence is reassuring and comforting. Option C is good because you are giving your colleague a suggestion as to whom is the best person that can she report this. Finally, Option E offers your colleague your full support, which hopefully will be comforting and reassuring for her at this difficult time.

**Q76. C, H, D**

**Explanation:**

In a scenario such as this, your first priority should be to reassure the patient in the integrity and honesty of the hospital staff. You should take into account that the patient will likely be feeling quite distressed about his condition. In this case, option C is the best response. Not only are you showing the patient that the staff operate with integrity and honesty, but you are also giving him an accurate assessment of the situation. Next, you have Option H, which is highly similar, but the question does not state the timeframe in which you'll receive the results – so you could be misinforming him here. Option D is honest, but not very comforting.

**Q77. A, C, D**

**Explanation:**

In this scenario, the best course of action would be for your colleague to go and speak to the registrar about the issue. In the absence of the consultant, and in a situation where the consultant's decision may need to be overruled, then the registrar is the most suitable person to decide on what course of action to take. Therefore, A is the best response. Following this, if the registrar isn't available, then the next thing to do would be for your colleague to speak with someone else who can assist or give her advice. In this question, option C provides the next best option. Finally, option D is helpful for the future, but doesn't resolve the situation at hand.

**Q78. H, C, E**

**Explanation:**

This situation is tricky, but the bottom line is that Dale has broken the law. Hitting a child in such a way that you would inflict injury is illegal, and the question clearly states that Dave has left a superficial wound upon his son's head. This is an extremely serious incident, and therefore your first action would be to inform Dale that a) he's broken the law and b) that the hospital will be investigating this. So, option H is the best response. Option C is also good. As the doctor who has witnessed the incident, you are justified in informing Dale that his behaviour was unacceptable, and that the hospital will investigate this. Finally, as an FY1, it would be a good idea to speak to a senior doctor and allow them to instigate the necessary next steps – with the aim of protecting the welfare of Adam, making option E the third best response.

## Q79. D, H, F

**Explanation:**

In a situation like this, unfortunately you just need to try and be as neutral as possible and deal with the situation as best as you can. It would be irresponsible for you to berate or criticise the woman for her tattoos, they are her personal business and she has come into the hospital for treatment – so you need to treat her in the same way that you would any other person, as shown in option D. If this is still an issue for you, then the best person to discuss this with would be your clinical supervisor, who can perhaps give you some advice on how to look at situations such as these, and if this isn't an option then you should speak to the registrar.

## Q80. G, F, D

**Explanation:**

This is a pretty simple issue. The best thing to do here is to take a polite and honest response to the situation, explaining to the consultant exactly why you are delayed. If he is reasonable, then he should understand, and will hopefully grant you the extension. In this situation, you shouldn't pay any attention to your colleague, who is making unprofessional speculation based on little evidence. Option G is clearly the most polite resolution, and this is followed by Option F. Option D doesn't really explain why you won't be able to make the deadline.

## Q81. A, G, C

**Explanation:**

In this situation, the hospital chaplain has behaved extremely poorly, and the patient is quite rightly upset. Before a patient makes a formal complaint, it's always best to try and see if matters can be resolved first. In this case, you have attempted to speak with the chaplain and he has continued to be disrespectful, so the best course of action would be to show the patient how she can make the complaint. Since you have also experienced the chaplain's unprofessional behaviour, it would not be a bad idea for you to add your thoughts to the complaint, and this will also help the patient to see that the hospital and its staff don't support such poor behaviour. Option G is similar to this, in that you are offering a full apology and granting the woman's request. Finally, option C is good, because it tells the chaplain in no uncertain terms that his behaviour is unacceptable, and that the complaint will go through.

## Q82. E, H, A

**Explanation:**

In this scenario, you have a responsibility to be honest with the disciplinary team. Ideally, you should also inform them of what the consultant has said to you, but this isn't mentioned in any of the answers so you need to work with what you've been given. The best approach here, as always, is to be honest and tell the team exactly what you experienced. Option E clearly explains that you believe the patient to be telling the truth, based on your own experiences with the chaplain. Option H is also good, in that it explains the detrimental impact that the chaplain's behaviour could have on future patients, and consequently on the reputation of the hospital. Finally, option A is acceptable, but doesn't really go into much detail. This is still better than option E, where you are lying, or option C, where you are recommending a course of action to the disciplinary panel – who are much better placed to make this decision than you.

## Q83. C, F, H

### Explanation:

In a situation like this, your colleague just needs to deal with the problem herself. The question clearly states that you have tried to persuade her to study. Even if Gemma is a good friend of yours, ultimately it is up to her to take charge of her own medical career, and you cannot do this for her. Therefore, she needs to try and answer this question herself, or suffer the consequences for her poor behaviour, as shown in option C. Option F is an okay response, as you are making yourself look good, but this option might cause a rift between yourself and your colleague. Finally, option H is useful, but the question clearly states that you have already tried to persuade Gemma to change her attitude, so you are just repeating this behaviour.

## Q84. C, D, F

### Explanation:

This isn't too tricky. In this situation, the first thing you should do is speak to the patient's parents and explain exactly what the issue is and why you need their son to give you the phone, as shown in options C and D. Hopefully this should resolve the situation. If this doesn't work, then your next step would be to contact the ward sister, who is better placed to ensure that the mobile phone is confiscated from Martin and passed on to its original owner.

## Q85. H, B, E

### Explanation:

In this scenario, the first thing you should do is to ally the patient's worries about the costs involved. This should be easy enough to do. The patient is clearly misinformed or doesn't know that the NHS is free, and therefore you should reassure him that there won't be an expensive treatment charge, as shown in options H and B. Finally, option E reassures the patient about the costs involved.

## Q86. C, H, D

### Explanation:

This is a minor issue, with a pretty simple solution. Obviously you should try to approach your colleague sensitively about the issue, there's no need to be rude – and he might well be embarrassed, but you should be honest with him here. Option C is quite to the point, but it's courteous and deals with the issue directly. Option H is similar to this, and puts the problem across in an understated fashion. Finally, Option D is providing a solution, but doesn't clearly explain the problem to your colleague.

## Q87. B, E, D

### Explanation:

In this scenario, your colleague has reacted very badly to what should have been a simple and polite request. However, what you need to remember here is that this doesn't put him in the wrong. It is possible that he has just misunderstood the situation and reacted badly because of this. You still need to ensure that your colleague's feelings are respected. Option B not only apologises, but also makes it clear that you were acting in the best interests of the patients, without meaning to upset your colleague. Option E is reasonable too, as it is difficult to imagine that any other doctor would behave differently than you did in this situation. Option D is also good, as it's important for you to defend yourself against these accusations, whilst being sensitive to the fact that you may have accidentally offended your colleague. Bullying is a serious issue though, so you have a right to argue.

## Q88. B, G, A

### Explanation:

In this situation, you are placed in a difficult position. At the end of the day, nobody wants to inform on their friends, but it's important to recognise that James is behaving unacceptably here. He is a doctor, so he needs to be held accountable to a higher standard of ethics and responsibility. You would be well within your rights to inform the doctor of why James isn't in today. Following this, options G and A are very similar, but at least in option G you are actually telling the consultant that James isn't at the hospital today, instead of giving him a vague response.

## Q89. D, E, H

### Explanation:

In this scenario, your immediate concern should be for your colleague's welfare. Your colleague is displaying symptoms of depression, and therefore your first course of action should be to sit down with him in a sensitive manner, and ask him about how he's feeling, and whether there's anything you can do. Option E is also useful. Option H is similar to option D, but is less proactive.

## Q90. G, B, C

### Explanation:

In this question, you are being tested on your ability to stand up against rules and regulations that you believe are actually having a negative impact. Of course, a hospital is a serious work environment, and patient safety and professionalism should be the number one priorities, but at the same time it's not a prison! Hospital staff should be allowed to enjoy their work, just as long as they are still behaving with integrity and decency. The best response in this scenario is to speak to someone senior, who can then raise the issue with the relevant hospital authority. Options G and B cover this succinctly. Finally, option C takes a more direct approach, trying to tackle the problem by actually speaking to members of staff and encouraging them to interpret the list in a less literal manner. Ultimately, it is for the benefit of the patients if staff can work in a harmonious, trusting and team friendly environment.

## Q91. A, C, G

### Explanation:

This is an unfortunate situation, but the best and most professional thing that you can do here is to try and meet with the registrar yourself, to discuss the situation. At the end of the day, you need to be able to work in conjunction with Dr Glynis, to ensure the wellbeing of patients. You don't have to be friends, or even get along, but you do need to try and maintain a professional working relationship. Following an attempt to speak to Dr Glynis yourself, your next course of action would be to speak to other senior members of staff, such as the consultant or your clinical supervisor.

## Q92. C, G, A

### Explanation:

In this scenario, the best approach would be to speak to Pablo directly about the issue. You should encourage him to be honest with the consultant, and do so in a way that makes it clear that plagiarism is wrong. Both options C and G cover this, with G actually asking Pablo to explain what the differences are between the original content and his own. If Pablo still refuses to acknowledge that he has cheated, then you should go and see the consultant by yourself.

## Q93. E, G, C

### Explanation:

In a situation like this, the best case solution would simply be to find an alternative, qualified, person, who could observe and then sign off on the forms. Your registrar would be the most reasonable person, but if they aren't available then you should ask the consultant whether they can arrange for someone, be that a senior doctor or another qualified professional, to observe. Your final course of action would be to ask for an extension, but it really shouldn't have to come to that.

## Q94. G, D, C

### Explanation:

This situation has a couple of layers to it. Firstly, you need to consider how the patient will be feeling here. The question states that your colleague has become hysterical, and is blaming the patient. This is simply not acceptable, especially given your colleague is incorrectly blaming the patient, for something which he – as a doctor – should be aware of. Therefore, your first course of action should be to apologise to the patient. Next, given your colleague is acting hysterically, it would be wise to ask him to leave the room. You do need to be sensitive to your colleague's feelings here. Although he has made a mistake, if he actually believes that he is at serious risk of contracting HIV then his reaction would naturally be one of distress, so you should try to reassure him that he's made an error. Finally, option C attempts to apologise to the patient and calm your colleague down, however it doesn't ask him to leave the room. Given his behaviour, it would be quite unwise for him to continue working with this patient.

## Q95. E, A, C

### Explanation:

In this situation, you need to remember that unfortunately not all patients or their relatives will be particularly pleasant to you, and that dealing with these individuals is a part and parcel of working in public healthcare. In this instance, the woman is being extremely rude, uncooperative and demeaning. As an FY1, you don't have to accept this behaviour, and would be more than entitled to find a senior doctor to deal with this situation if you believed this necessary. Alternatively, you could try and persuade the woman that you are more than capable of treating her son, as shown in option A, or explaining exactly why you asked for her assistance, as shown in option C. If the woman is still uncooperative though, then it would be better to fetch a senior doctor.

## Q96. A, B, F

### Explanation:

This one isn't too tricky. The youths are clearly behaving in an unacceptable manner, they need to be dealt with immediately. The best thing to do here would be to contact hospital security, who will take action to escort the youths from the premises. Ideally you shouldn't try to deal with the youths by yourself, but if you are going to do this then you should a) emphasise that their behaviour is unacceptable, and b) inform them of the consequences if they don't. In this case, they are swearing at/abusing members of the public, which could easily see them cautioned by the police.

## Q97. C, E, G

### Explanation:

In this scenario, you need to act in the way that you think will be the most beneficial for your learning and education. Therefore, the best course of action would be to speak to the

Foundation Programme Director, and see if you can be reassigned a new supervisor, as shown in option C. It's extremely important that you can maintain a good level of communication from your supervisor, who will provide you with support and essential advice during your training period. The next best option would be E. As long as you address the problem in a sensitive and courteous fashion, without insulting the consultant, then this is reasonable. Finally, option G involves asking others for tips on how they've dealt with the same issue – which could give you some insight into how you yourself can resolve it.

## Q98. B, C, D

**Explanation:**

This situation is tricky. On the one hand it is very normal for doctors to stay beyond the end of their shift. However, in this scenario you have extenuating circumstances, and a verbal agreement in place with the registrar. If you feel that he is being unreasonable then the best thing to do would be to question over this behaviour, and remind him of what was agreed earlier in the week. If the registrar continues to keep you at the hospital, you would go and speak to the consultant and seek his permission to leave, but hopefully it wouldn't come to that.

## Q99. E, F, B

**Explanation:**

There is a pretty simple solution to this, which is tell your colleagues that no you won't be their spokesperson, and to reaffirm your confidence in Dr King's clinical skills. Your colleagues are clearly acting maliciously here, you can see by their conversation that their concern isn't even for Dr King's health, so you need make it clear that they are in the wrong. Both options E and F emphasise this strongly, whereas option B points out their unprofessionalism in discussing a senior doctor in such a derogatory manner.

## Q100. C, F, D

**Explanation:**

In this scenario, the best suited people to assist the patient would be the security office, who can use tools such as CCTV to establish what has happened, and advise her on what her next course of action should be. Options C and F are the best responses here, because they give the patient clear instructions or guidance on how to find the security office, and in C you actually take her there yourself. In Option D you are being helpful, but leaving the patient to find the office on her own.

## Q101. C, E, F

**Explanation:**

In this scenario, you can be honest with the patient, and inform her that unfortunately the hospital rules prevent you from accepting her offer. This is shown in options C and E. If these options aren't available, then your next course of action would be option F. Although this isn't completely true, it's still better than accepting and breaking the rules.

## Q102. A, B, E

### Explanation:

In a scenario such as this, your primary concern needs to be for the patients at the hospital. If your colleague has not had jabs prior to going abroad, then this could present a serious safety risk to both patients and staff at the hospital. Therefore, he needs to be checked out immediately. This can likely be done by a member of the hospital team, as shown in option A, but if not then your colleague will not be able to work today, and will need to be seen by his GP, as shown in option B. Finally, Option E gives you the opportunity to inform the registrar. You could do this, but it would be better to advise your colleague to get checked out beforehand. The registrar will need to be informed if your colleague is unable to work, or if he will be delayed at the start of his shift.

## Q103. D, H, E

### Explanation:

This is a very unfortunate scenario. Accidents do happen though, and it would be the responsibility of the hospital to try and fix this issue for the woman. In this case, the first thing that should be done is to offer an apology. The question states that you've done this already. Given that this incident has happened in the ward, the best course of action would be to take the woman directly to see the ward sister, who can try and provide a solution for her. Following this, assuring the woman that the hospital will resolve this problem is the next best thing to do, as at least you are making an effort to try and calm her down. Finally, option E isn't great, but could be a last resort if no other options are available.

## Q104. C, F, E

### Explanation:

The question here clearly states that you do not feel you have the capacity to deal with your colleague's patients, therefore it is imperative that you do not attempt to do so. Although it's always good to try and help out your colleagues, you are not obligated to cover another doctor's patients, especially if you have worked past the end of your shift or don't feel as if you are in a condition to do so. Therefore, the best response here is to tell your colleague about why you can't help him, in an honest and polite manner. Following this, your colleague would need to speak to the registrar to arrange cover whilst he deals with his problem.

## Q105. B, D, C

### Explanation:

This scenario challenges your ability to question a senior member of staff, if you believe that they are acting in a way that is contrary to the hospital code of conduct. In this case, it's very important that you approach the situation in a reasonable and polite manner. It might well be the case that the consultant has granted the registrar permission to leave the hospital premises, or even that the registrar has had the food delivered to the hospital directly. Therefore, option B is the most sensible and reasonable response, and is closely followed by option D in this respect. Option C is not great, it's quite rude and abrupt, but it's still the third best option available – as at least you are enquiring with the registrar about his behaviour.

## Q106. F, B, D

### Explanation:

In this scenario, your immediate priority needs to be your colleague's safety. The question clearly states that you believe your colleague to be suffering from alcohol poisoning. This is a very serious condition, which requires immediate medical condition. Therefore, the best thing to do would be to escort your colleague to the nursing staff, as shown in option F. Following this, it's important that you discuss the situation with the consultant. Not only does he need to arrange cover for your colleague, but he also needs to be informed that one of the staff has turned up to work drunk – a situation which will need to be investigated. Option F covers both of these avenues, whereas option B ensures that your colleague is being checked over by the nursing staff, although it doesn't make any mention of informing the consultant. Finally, in option D you are still bringing your colleague to a senior member of staff, but it would be better for you to just bring her to the nurses directly – especially if you believe that she has a serious medical problem.

## Q107. C, A, H

### Explanation:

In this situation, although you should sympathise with your colleague, it's important that you don't put yourself into a position where you are uncomfortable. Therefore, it would be a huge mistake to lend your colleague the money, even if he is in rough spot. Both options C and H assert this, although at least C does this in a sympathetic way. Advising your colleague to go to the police is also useful, since he is being threatened with violence, and therefore the legal authorities would be best placed to deal with this.

## Q108. A, B, H

### Explanation:

In this question, the patient's relative is being very unreasonable and rude. You don't actually have to justify yourself to her in this position, so option A is the best response. Options B and H are also reasonable. Option B points out the hospital rule, but at the same time it shouldn't matter whether the hospital has a rule in place or not – if you don't want to shave your head then you don't have to. Finally, option H reassures the relative, and will hopefully calm the situation.

## Q109. G, B, C

### Explanation:

In this situation, you have a duty of care to the patient, and although he has not expressed it directly – it seems quite obvious that he would prefer it if this person didn't visit him. Therefore, the first priority should be ensuring that this action is taken. Given the patient has expressed concerns over 'sinister behaviour', it is even more important that the hospital takes step to prevent this from happening inside the premises, and furthermore that the duty of care to the patient once he has been discharged, is fulfilled. Although the hospital cannot take care of the patient's personal issues, they can offer advice on what his next steps should be.

## Q110. F, C, B

### Explanation:

In this scenario, it is not up to you to interfere in the relationship between the patient and her mother. However, it would be perfectly legitimate for you to request information from the patient, on her mother's behalf. You should take a sympathetic approach, whilst still standing firm on the fact that doctor-patient confidentiality comes first.

## Q111. D, H, E

### Explanation:

Obviously this is a highly embarrassing situation. The patient is participating in a behaviour that would be considered contrary to the rules, and therefore you should emphasise to him that his actions are unacceptable. Therefore, option D is the best response. Option H also accomplishes this, but is quite harsh. Remember that the patient is likely to be embarrassed, and may not be aware of the rules, so it would be better not to berate him like this. Finally, if you are really struggling with what to do, then you should speak to a senior member of staff for advice.

## Q112. A, D, H

### Explanation:

In this situation, the best thing to do would be to a) assess the reasons for the man's dietary requirements and b) assess whether these requirements are realistic. For example, if the man just wanted to eat one apple a day, for the entire time that he's in hospital, then this would clearly not be a realistic expectation – as it wouldn't be conducive to good physical recovery. Likewise, if the man's dietary requirements are down to a medical reason then it's more likely that the hospital will go out of their way to provide this for him. However, the hospital should still strive to make the patient as comfortable as possible, and therefore it's important to assess whether these requirements can be met – regardless of the reasons. In this situation, the ideal response would be to speak to the ward sister, who would be able to discuss the man's requirements with the hospital care team. Both options D and H are similar to this, and reassure the patient that his request will be considered.

## Q113. C, E, F

**Explanation:**

In this scenario, since the question states that you aren't confident in the right thing to say, then your first course of action should be to speak to your supervisor – who will be able to offer you sensible advice on how to go about doing this. It's an unfortunate truth that most doctors will need to learn how to go about breaking bad news, whether it's to patients or relatives, so this will be an important part of your training. In Option E you just get on with it, which is reasonable because at least you are making an attempt, but this feels a little bit robotic and forced. There isn't any genuine sympathy or people skills depicted in this response. Finally, option F will lead to the same resolution as C – with your supervisor giving you tips on how to go about breaking the news.

## Q114. B, F, G

**Explanation:**

This is a minor issue. All you need to do here is remind your colleague of the hospital rules. There's no need to be rude about it, as he has just committed a small error, and it should be brought to his attention. Both options B and F cover this succinctly. Finally, option G is the third best option, because it takes a reasonable approach. Option C is pretty rude and will serve to upset your colleague, whereas option H and E constitute a big overreaction.

## Q115. H, A, D

**Explanation:**

Again this is a fairly minor issue. Your best response in this case would be to give the woman advice on a) where can find alternative transport so that she doesn't have to walk and get wet, or b) where she can obtain an umbrella. Following this, if the woman still doesn't want to leave, then you should wish her a good day and get back to work.

## Q116. A, D, G

**Explanation:**

Regardless of a patient's disposition, you should always endeavour to be polite, respectful and take their needs into account. However, when a patient is particularly sensitive or nervous, it's important to ensure you deliver news in a way that won't alarm or upset them. In this case, the best response would be option A. In this response, you are gently informing the patient of what needs to be done and why. Options D and G are almost equally as good, because both take a sensitive and professional approach to dealing with a problem that could otherwise upset the patient.

## Q117. B, A, G

**Explanation:**

In this situation, while Belinda's mother is probably acting in a manner that could be deemed insensitive and irresponsible, there is nothing she can do for her daughter whilst she is in surgery. Yes, it would be better for her to be there when her daughter gets out, but that is her prerogative, even if you deem it to be poor parenting. So, while you should encourage her to be there for her daughter, as shown in option B, both options A and G are also correct.

## Q118. B, A, C

**Explanation:**

In this scenario, it's very important to recognise that you are dealing with a distressed mother. Not only has Mrs Edwards just been through the stress of having a baby, but having it taken away from her immediately will be particularly devastating. Therefore, you need to do your best to explain the seriousness of the situation to her, and comfort her at this difficult time. Option B is the most comforting approach here, whereas A and C are quite frank and honest about the situation at hand. None of the other approaches listed are particularly good or helpful.

## Q119. H, C, D

**Explanation:**

The feelings that Jill has expressed in this question are classic symptoms of postnatal depression, and therefore it's imperative that you conduct further questioning of the patient. Option H is essentially a more sensitive and longer explanation of option C. Option D is the third best response. As an FY1, although you can screen the patient for such serious symptoms, it would also be a good idea to speak to a senior doctor about what the next steps are, and to confirm your diagnosis.

## Q120. E, D, H

**Explanation:**

This is a tricky situation, especially given the personal circumstances of your colleague. However, hospital rules are there for a reason. With this in mind, the best thing to do would be to speak to your colleague and urge him to think about what's best for his career and future. This is the politest and most respectful way to show your colleague that breaking the rules will only harm him in the long term. Following this, option D would be the best choice, as again you are speaking to your colleague in a professional environment, and reminding him of the rules. Option H isn't ideal. It's unwise to try and interrupt your colleague or disturb him whilst he is out at dinner, although this is still better than any of the other options.


## Q121. C, H, A

**Explanation:**

There aren't really any great answers to this response, because at the end of the day there is nothing much you can do here. Along with this, the fact that your colleague believes the internet marketer is a scammer does not mean that he is one, your colleague could be wrong. Your consultant is likely to tell you that you aren't accountable and that it is not your responsibility to tell patients how they should live their lives, which is correct, and that's why C is the best option, as it will hopefully give you some peace of mind. Option H is similar to this, except it doesn't show much thought or care for the patient, even if it's not your responsibility. Option A is reasonable too, this just isn't your problem to deal with.


## Q122. C, H, E

**Explanation:**

In this scenario, your colleague is behaving in an extremely unprofessional manner, and you need to address this. There are two issues at hand here. Firstly, there is the fact that your colleague is calling Jeremy out in front of the entire ward – this is extremely uncalled for and will only damage the patient's faith in staff. This should be done in a private location. Secondly, there is the fact that your colleague is bringing up Jeremy being colour blind, when there is no evidence to suggest that this is the reason for the mistake. Your colleague is picking on a minor defect, that is not a barrier to becoming a doctor, and using it to illustrate her wider point – this behaviour is unfair and unprofessional. So, the first thing you should do, is to point this out to your colleague, as shown in option C. Option H is good because you are encouraging your colleague to have the conversation in private, but it doesn't point out to your colleague that her assumptions are wrong. Finally, option E is good because it points out how bad your colleague's behaviour is making both her and Jeremy look, but again it doesn't deal with the other issues listed here.


## Q123. A, H, C

**Explanation:**

In this scenario, the best thing you can do is to inform your colleague that he must confess his actions to a senior member of staff. You need to be firm and sensible here, your colleague has committed a major breach of conduct, and management needs to be notified about who is responsible. If possible, you should avoid speculating over your colleague's job security. Yes, he is likely to lose his job and there could be further consequences too, but this is for the disciplinary committee to decide. For this reason, option A and H are the best responses, with option C in third.

### Q124. C, B, A

**Explanation:**

In this scenario you need to take a hard stance against this individual. He is clearly behaving in an unacceptable manner, and the question even states that your colleagues have asked him to stop – to no avail. This behaviour is absolutely reportable. However, the question doesn't give you the option to do this, so the closest thing here would be option C – where you are at least informing a senior colleague about the issue. Following this, B would be the best option, as you are being direct and firm about your colleague's unacceptable actions. Option A is not direct enough, and doesn't tell your colleague, unequivocally, about how serious his behaviour is.

### Q125. B, C, G

**Explanation:**

In this situation, the worst things that you could do be to a) do nothing, and b) try and physically restrain the man. The best options here are to speak to security, who will be able to deal with the thief, or notify the shop staff – who will quickly be able to establish what to do next. If neither of these options are available then you should try to speak to the man yourself, without putting yourself at risk.

### Q126. G, E, B

**Explanation:**

In this scenario, the first thing you should do is to stop the move immediately. It's extremely important that the patient fully understands what is happening to her, and therefore you should not proceed with this until you are confident that you have the full consent of either the patient or her family (depending on if the patient is competent enough to make the decision) regardless of whether she signed the initial consent form. Option G focuses on bringing the patient's family into the decision, whereas option E focuses on dealing with the patient's individual view, before any other action is taken. Both responses are acceptable. Option B is similar, but jumps to the conclusion of testing the patient's competency, when it's possible that she simply misunderstood the situation on an initial basis.

### Q127. B, E, F

**Explanation:**

This scenario tests your teamwork skills and ability to prioritise. The question is essentially asking you to give up just a few minutes of your free time, to help your colleague out – so you should do it! B is the best response here, closely followed by E. Option F is useful too, since a nurse would be able to offer good tips, but there's no reason that you can't attempt to help out yourself.

## Q128. D, G, B

### Explanation:

In this scenario, your colleague has asked you to be honest with her. That doesn't mean you need to be nasty or blunt about it, as you can offer her constructive criticism and tips on how to improve. Option D is the most helpful, as it shows that you are considering the feelings of your colleague, and that you are also a team player. Option G is also useful, in that it gives your colleague a positive as well as a negative. Option B is quite blunt and to the point, and probably won't make your colleague feel particularly great – but at least you are being honest.

## Q129. D, A, G

### Explanation:

Obviously, in this scenario, Glenn's behaviour is just not okay. However, your first priority should be to deal with the patient's family, who have not been treated acceptably in the wake of devastating news. You need to apologise to the family, and make sure that they understand there is support available to them. Therefore, options D and A are the strongest responses here. Following this, the next best thing to do would be to report this behaviour. Glenn has been extremely insensitive, and it's imperative that this behaviour is amended for dealing with future patients.

## Q130. B, G, E

### Explanation:

In this situation, the best approach is to be polite and reasonable about the situation. Yes, the question states that you are shocked by these comments – so the consultant's feedback has clearly come as a surprise – but at the same time the consultant wouldn't be bringing this up without reason. If he feels that your performance has been poor, then it's likely that you have some serious improvements to make, and therefore it would be wise to take an open minded approach here. Showing the consultant that you have a desire to improve and take his feedback on board is the best way forward, and both B and G cover this extensively. Option E is okay, but it doesn't really show the consultant that you are interested in improving.

## Q131. A, F, G

### Explanation:

In this scenario, the first thing you should do is to apologise sincerely to the patient, who has every right to be disgruntled at the error. You should also make it clear that this is a result of error, and not down to any malicious intent from staff. Following this, you need to try and resolve the situation for the woman. Resolving this would involve speaking to the nursing staff, who could then take the proper steps for fetching a replacement meal.

## Q132. A, D, E

**Explanation:**

In this question, you need to demonstrate a) that you can deal sympathetically with any patient's complaint (regardless of how irritating that patient might be) and b) that you can use common sense to deal with problems. With this in mind, the best approach here is to make sure that you treat the patient with respect and dignity, by listening to his complaint, but also making sure that you don't act irrationally by doing something foolish – such as having Martin and his friends thrown out. For this reason, the best response is A. Here you are clearly listening to what the patient has to say, and following this can act accordingly. Option D and E are highly similar, both are okay responses, which acknowledge the patient's concern – but also take into account the patient's history of making unreasonable complaints, and your own observations of Martin and his friends.

## Q133. E, H, B

**Explanation:**

There is a pretty simple solution here, and that's to tell your colleagues to stop behaving badly in the ward. Not only are they having a pretty pointless conversation, but they are disturbing patients. Option E is the best response here, they need to stop shouting immediately. This is closely followed by H, where you make it clear that this isn't acceptable, and that the issue should be resolved elsewhere, and not in front of the patients. Finally, Option B is similar to E, but you should take a firmer approach here than just requesting that they stop shouting.

## Q134. A, C, E

**Explanation:**

In this scenario, your colleague is behaving in a very ignorant manner, and seems to be quite deliberately breaching the hospital's rules. Therefore, the best response is to tell him in no uncertain terms that he needs to follow these rules, as shown in option A. Options C and E take a gentler and politer approach, trying to persuade your colleague in the value of the recycling and why the hospital has enforced these rules. This is admirable, but based on your colleague's dialogue, just encouraging or asking him to follow the rules is probably not going to be sufficient.

## Q135. D, B, F

**Explanation:**

This is a tricky situation, but ultimately your colleague shouldn't be in work at this time. The best solution here is to take the issue to another staff member, who will assure your colleague that she can leave, and that her job won't be at risk as a result. Option D is the most straight-forward, best response. After this it gets a bit more difficult. Almost all of the options listed here have flaws. Option B is a very simple act of courtesy, that you would immediately offer anyway upon hearing the news. Option F is okay but at the same time it speculates on the consultant's behaviour, without having any understanding of the situation from his end. It would be better to focus on your colleague and how her needs can be met.


## Q136. D, E, G

**Explanation:**

Bedside manner is a key skill for doctors. In this case, your colleague needs to try and make an effort to speak with his patient, even if he feels uncomfortable with this. Explaining to him why this is important is the best approach, as shown in option D and in option E. Option G is similar, but doesn't explain why this type of approach is necessary.


## Q137. H, C, F

**Explanation:**

In this scenario your colleague has been extremely rude to the patient, who is likely to be very upset by this. The first thing you should do is to apologise sincerely to the patient. Based on the dialogue in the question, the next thing you need to do is to clearly explain to the patient about the medication he has been given, as it is imperative that he understands what he's taking and why. Therefore, option H is the best response. Option C is the next best response, as it assures the patient that this behaviour will be dealt with, but it doesn't explain about the medication issue. Finally, this poor behaviour is definitely something that should be reported to a senior doctor, as shown in option F.


## Q138. B, G, D

**Explanation:**

In this question, the only great response offered here is option B. The rest of the options all contain serious flaws. The reason that option B is good, is that it takes a polite and considered approach to the problem, gently informing your colleague of what the patients have said, in a way that is not likely to upset her. Following this, the options get significantly worse. Option G is the next best response, because you can (hopefully) assume that her friend will break the news in a way that isn't rude or upsetting. Finally, option D is the third best response, because it doesn't alienate the patients or come across as really rude, although it could still be put to Kelly in a much more courteous manner.


## Q139. C, F, E

**Explanation:**

In this scenario, the best thing to do is to immediately approach your colleague and tell him to remove the sticker. You don't need to justify this. It's a racist sticker, so it needs to go. Therefore, option C is the best response. Following this, option F is the best option. Although you don't need to justify why your colleague must do this, it might be helpful if you can provide him with a reason for why (other than just the fact that it's racist). Option E isn't stern enough, as you are simply asking your colleague to remove it, when you should be telling him that he must take action.

## Q140. E, H, D

**Explanation:**

In this scenario, your colleagues are being extremely rude and quite ungrateful. Therefore, the best response here would be to call them out over this behaviour, and speak up for the consultant, as shown in option E. Following this, there are a number of approaches you can take, depending on how much you want to encourage your colleagues to try and get on board with the task, or show them that their behaviour is wrong. H is the second-best option, as you are explaining the benefits of this exercise to your colleagues, who will hopefully come round to the idea. Option D is equally valid, because you are encouraging your colleagues to embrace the idea, by being positive.

## Q141. F, C, B

**Explanation:**

This is a pretty difficult situation. The patient has asked for your honest opinion on the book. In this case, given you believe that the patient has fabricated a lot of his material to cast the hospital and your colleagues in a negative light, it would be reasonable for you to be honest here. Option F is the politest but also the sternest response, which gives the patient a realistic view of what will happen if he publishes this book. Following this, it would be wise to contact the ward consultant, as it's important that the hospital is informed about this potentially serious situation before the book goes to print. Finally, option B is mostly just a lighter and less in-depth version of option F, and doesn't do enough to elaborate on your concerns.

## Q142. C, D, A

**Explanation:**

This is a pretty simple scenario, you need to inform a member of senior management about what has happened, immediately. Whether you do this or your colleague does it doesn't really matter, although it would be better coming from him. Option A isn't enough really. Your colleague has already done the damage, and potentially harmed the hospital in the process.

## Q143. D, A, G

**Explanation:**

In this scenario, you need to understand your limitations as an FY1. The best thing to do here would to be ask the registrar or another senior doctor to assist you in speaking to the patient, with the aim of assessing whether she has the mental capacity to make this decision for herself. Option A is essentially a lesser version of this, and doesn't cover everything listed in D, although it still covers an essential part of the assessment process. Finally, Option G is the third best response. It's very important to involve the patient's family in the decision, especially since the patient's daughter is opposed to her mother leaving the hospital.


## Q144. A, H, E

Explanation:

In this situation, the first thing you should do is to check for signs of physical abuse. There is not enough evidence in the question to suggest that the woman is being physically abused by her daughter, but the wording at the end clearly implies that you have a slight suspicion, so the natural move would be to assess the patient for further clues, as shown in option A. If you are still suspicious following this, then your next move would be to consult with a senior doctor, to get their opinion, as shown in option H. Finally, Option E isn't great – it doesn't really achieve anything and it would be better to just question the patient over where the bruises came from, but it's still the third best response.


## Q145. C, A, F

Explanation:

In this scenario, your first priority should be to ensure that this situation doesn't escalate any further. It's already extremely serious, with the doctor putting his hands on the patient, and therefore it needs to be dealt with by a senior manager immediately. With this in mind, C is the best option. A is also reasonable, but just telling your colleague to 'go and calm down' isn't enough. Your colleague has physically accosted a patient, and is in serious trouble. Option F is similar to A – in that sending the doctor home won't really help the situation in the long term, although it will get him away from the scene.


## Q146. G, E, B

Explanation:

In this situation, it's important that you try to take a calm and measured approach to resolving the problem. The mother is extremely distressed, and understandably so if she cannot find her son. The best thing to do here would be to inform her of the (somewhat) reassuring message from the nurse, and then take steps to establish that this report was accurate and that the son is with his father. Options G and E are more suitable than F, because F is definitive, which could lead to major problems if the nurse was mistaken. If neither of these options is available then the next best thing to do would be to try and calm the woman down, and ask her some routine questions to help locate her son, before initiating security protocols.


## Q147. E, B, G

Explanation:

This is a very serious incident. The question here is testing your ability to weigh up how each party has acted and how you believe they should be dealt with. In this case, your colleague has acted extremely inappropriately, and rudely, but this does not justify the response from the patient. Spitting is considered to be assault, and therefore he has broken the law. The best thing to do in this case would be to send Joel to a senior manager, where both his conduct and his feelings towards the patient's behaviour can be assessed, and send the patient home – after an incident like this it would be incorrect for the hospital to continue treating him today, and the police will need to be contacted. Therefore, option E is the best response. Option B is okay, but doesn't escalate the situation to a senior member of staff, although the information that you are giving the patient is factually correct. Option G isn't an accurate reflection on how serious this situation is.

## Q148. C, F, B

**Explanation:**

In this scenario, your best course of action is to be completely honest with the panel about what you saw. Option C is the most accurate reflection of what happened. Option F is also good, but there isn't any indication in either this question or the previous question about Joel's qualities as a doctor. Option B is the third best response, but it makes it seem as if you are trying to offset the impact of Joel's behaviour, by pointing out that the patient behaved worse. This is irrelevant, since Joel's behaviour was still unacceptable.

## Q149. E, B, H

**Explanation:**

This is a pretty simple scenario. Obviously, your best course of action is to decline the request. Ideally you should do this in a polite manner, that doesn't risk offending your colleagues. It's important to build good relationships with other staff at the hospital. In this case, E would be the best response, as it doesn't rule out the possibility of socialising with your colleagues in future, and is closely followed by B. Option H is better than A, because telling them that you can't is preferential to telling them that you don't want to.

## Q150. B, C, E

**Explanation:**

This is a very simple one. All you have to do here is be polite and appreciative to the consultant, and thank him for all of the help he's given you over the last year! Option B is the best response, because it fully answers the question he has asked you, in a courteous and appreciative manner. Option C is little more self-centred, but it still answers the question. Finally, option E is appreciative, but doesn't quite answer the consultant.

# Get Access To

# FREE

## Situational
## Judgement
## Test Questions

www.MyPsychometricTests.co.uk

Printed in Great Britain
by Amazon